# ARABLE CULTIVATION
# IN ROMAN ITALY

# ARABLE CULTIVATION IN ROMAN ITALY

## *c.*200 B.C.–*c.*A.D. 100

M. S. SPURR

SOCIETY FOR THE PROMOTION OF ROMAN STUDIES
JOURNAL OF ROMAN STUDIES MONOGRAPHS NO. 3
1986

First published in 1986 by
The Society for the Promotion of Roman Studies
31–34 Gordon Square, London WC1H 0PP

ISBN 0-907764-06-1

Typeset by Amaranthus, 36 Vicarage Street, Warminster, Wilts.
Printed in Great Britain

# CONTENTS

*MAGISTRIS OPTIMIS*

# PREFACE

This book owes most to the unfailing advice of Peter Brunt, who supervised the doctoral thesis of which it is a part, and to Martin Frederiksen, whose inspiration survives his death. Of both teachers I hope it is worthy. Peter Garnsey and Graeme Barker, who examined the thesis, made valuable comments.

I should like to thank many others who read sections of the work in earlier drafts, including Ewen Bowie, Michael Crawford, Doug Kelly, Frank Lepper, Fergus Millar, Nicholas Purcell, Elizabeth Rawson, Geoffrey Rickman, K. D. White and David Whitehouse. Among those archaeologists who tolerated my inexperience are Andrea Carandini, Lorenzo Costantini, Barri Jones, John Lloyd, Alastair Small, Bryan Ward-Perkins, and the members of the Albegna valley survey. To the Italian landowners and farmers who have shown me hospitality and taught me about agriculture, Maria Teresa Occhionero and family, Biagio Pepe and family, Gerardo Salinardi, Stefano Zezza, and the inhabitants of Giogalto village, are due my warmest thanks.

I acknowledge with gratitude all the financial help towards my research from Corpus Christi College, Oxford, from Oxford University, and from the British School at Rome. While I was teaching at the Australian National University, the Classics Department generously put its excellent typing facilities at my disposal. I should also like to thank the Roman Society for accepting this book for publication as a JRS Monograph, and the Central Photographic Unit of University College London for preparing the photographic plates. I owe a great deal also to Helen Cockle, whose practised eye has made many improvements to the text.

It is a pleasure finally to record my thanks to Luciana Valentini and her library staff and to Amanda Claridge for all their assistance during my time as Rome Scholar. Maria Cristina Gaja, from the Istituto Italiano per il Medio ed Estremo Oriente, kindly helped in numerous ways. My wife, Susanna Armani, took the photographs and shared the preparation of the bibliography and so much more.

*Eton College, November 1985*                                                    M. S. S.

# ILLUSTRATIONS

(The figures are after H. J. Hopfen and E. Biesalski, *Small Farm Implements* (1953); P. Scheuermeier, *Il lavoro dei contadini* (1980); K. D. White, *Agricultural Implements of the Roman World* (1967).)

*Plates*

   I: 1. Eared plough, Alba Fucens, Abruzzo, 20 March 1982.
      2. Ploughing oxen used for transport, Alba Fucens, Abruzzo, 20 March 1982.

  II: 1. Neck yoke, Alba Fucens, Abruzzo, 20 March 1982.
      2. Toothed harrow, nr. Francolise, Campania, 21 April 1981.

 III: 1. Reaping by hand, nr. Ruoti, Basilicata, 28 July 1981.
      2. Threshing and winnowing tools, nr. Ruoti, Basilicata, 2 August 1981.

 IV: 1. Leaves as forage, nr. Poppi, Tuscany, 22 December 1982.
      2. Sledge, nr. Poppi, Tuscany, 22 December 1982.

# ABBREVIATIONS

The following are the only non-standard abbreviations used in this work:

      Cato    Cato, *de Agri Cultura*
      V.       Varro, *Res Rusticae*
      Col.    Columella, *de Re Rustica*
      P.      Pliny the Elder, *Naturalis Historia*

# INTRODUCTION: THEORIES AND THE EVIDENCE

## THEORIES

'Grain was to antiquity what oil is to the world of today.'[1] The juxtaposition startles and thus serves its purpose, even though under scrutiny it ceases to satisfy on several counts. Yet a review of major works will show that the importance of grain in the history of the Roman world has rarely been underestimated. All the more surprising then that the cultivation of cereals in Roman Italy has never been properly examined.

Instead, generalized discussions of the subject have been allowed to stand, which reveal scant knowledge of agriculture and only superficial acquaintance with the Roman agricultural treatises or any other useful evidence. Vague in themselves, these arguments become dangerous when they propose full-scale reconstructions of the rural economy. While they might differ in the prominence given to the various aspects of the process, all deduce a decline in cereal cultivation after the Hannibalic War. This is not acceptable, as the following chapters will demonstrate. Since my views diverge so widely from that conclusion, and from every contributing factor to it, it will suffice here to summarize the better known traditional arguments, so that later refutation, often implicit rather than explicit, will be more easily recognizable when it occurs.

After the Hannibalic War wealth and slaves poured into Italy as a result of imperial expansion. Increased investment in Italian land was supposedly characterized by the growth of agricultural villas, which specialized in olives and vines, or by sheep ranches. Both concerns were staffed by slaves and both were profit-oriented. Grain, it is asserted, neither profitable, nor suited to slave labour, was relegated to poor soils and allocated minimum attention. If there was any progress in agricultural 'technology', it was confined to olive and vine cultivation.

Long absence or death abroad on campaign, combined with their expropriation by the rich at home, drastically reduced the peasantry. Since, as subsistence farmers, their main crop had been cereals, this was another major reason for the supposed decline of cereal cultivation. Expropriated peasants drifted to Rome where they were fed on grain—but grain imported from the provinces of the empire, not from Italy.

This process continued into the early imperial period. Then, from the end of the first century A.D., growing provincial competition in wine and oil, and a reduction in the slave supply, gradually forced arboriculture to cede to extensive pastoralism and cereal cultivation on *latifundia* run mainly by tenants.[2]

Instead, in contradiction of this traditional picture, the evidence presented in the following pages leads to the conclusion that cereal cultivation was ubiquitous in Italy during the period under discussion. Moreover, among the various modes

---

[1] L. Casson, 'The Role of the State in Rome's Grain Trade', in *The Seaborne Commerce of Ancient Rome. Studies in Archaeology and History*, ed. J. H. D'Arms, E. C. Kopff, Memoirs of the American Academy in Rome 36 (1980), 21–34.

[2] The main lines of this traditional interpretation can be found in A. J. Toynbee, *Hannibal's Legacy. The Hannibalic War's Effect on Roman Life* (1965), II, 247 ff. and *passim*; M. Rostovtzeff, *The Social and Economic History of the Roman Empire*, ed. P. M. Fraser (2nd ed. 1957), II, 17 ff. and 98 ff.

of arable farming it is possible to identify intensive production of cereals and legumes for the market by slave-staffed estates. For various reasons this form of production increased, and techniques of cultivation improved, during the late Republic and early Empire.

Yet full-scale examination of the various orthodox hypotheses is not within the scope of this book. Instead the principal aim has been to avoid generalizations about cereal cultivation, in order to discover the agricultural reality of Roman Italy. This involves a detailed exposition of the considerable quantity of relevant literary evidence in the Roman agricultural writers. The exposition is based on direct practical knowledge of Italian agriculture gained from field work in various parts of the country. The increasing evidence from archaeological investigation has also been assessed in order to test the literary evidence. This study seeks, therefore, to provide much firm detail and to lay securer foundations for future work on Italian agriculture and the Roman economy as a whole.[3]

One of the results has been to reveal a hitherto unimagined complexity and diversity in the practice and techniques of Roman arable cultivation. Such diversity, which is clearly reflected in the agricultural writers—for cereals and for the rural economy as a whole—and which is being increasingly demonstrated by archaeological survey, must in turn lead to a fundamental reconsideration of the development of agriculture in Roman Italy.

## THE EVIDENCE

### The Agricultural Writers

Field work consisting of close observation and experience of 'pre-industrial' agriculture still practised in Italy, acquaintance with the rural environment of the country as a whole, and the reading of Italian agricultural manuals, have led to the conviction that the Roman agricultural writers (often referred to hereafter simply as 'the agronomists') present reliable information about an Italy they knew well. It has also become clear that such knowledge of Italian agriculture and the countryside is what the agricultural writers took for granted in their audience and easily explains parts of their texts which might otherwise appear lacunose, obscure or even confused.

That statement of credence apart, it is essential to dispose of some misplaced traditional objections to the agronomists' reliability before proceeding. Firstly, it perhaps needs to be pointed out that the fact that Columella treats arable cultivation in one book but viticulture in two and a half books cannot be taken to reflect the relative extent of cultivation of cereals and vines on the ground.[4] Any handbook which purports to provide a full account of Italian agriculture will necessarily treat the complexities of arboriculture at greater length than the comparatively straightforward practice of arable cultivation.

---

[3] Despite the existence of the technically oriented books of K. D. White, *Roman Farming* (1970); *Agricultural Implements of the Roman World* (1967); *Farm Equipment of the Roman World* (1975), most of the technical discussion of this study is new. References to White occur mainly on matters of disagree-ment. Both White and (to a greater extent) J. Kolendo, *L'agricoltura nell'Italia Romana* (1980), rely only on literary sources and fail often to consider the reality and diversity of agricultural practice.

[4] As does J. Toutain, *The Economy of the Ancient World* (1930), 233 ff.

Secondly, and more importantly, Gummerus,[5] whose thesis is widely accepted, thought Cato wrote from first-hand experience and that, while Columella wrote stylishly and cited Greek and Roman sources and referred to what appeared to be an ideal estate, he demonstrated sufficient personal knowledge of Italy and practical agriculture, and was critical enough of earlier works, to be taken seriously. Varro, however, was stigmatized as an armchair theorist (*Stubengelehrter*), reliant on Greek sources and with no practical knowledge of agriculture. Two recent studies have helped to correct this view and the following observations are meant to complement their accounts.[6]

First of all there is the reassuring Italian emphasis. Varro makes clear at the outset that Italy is the country under discussion: 'You have all travelled through many lands; have you seen any country more fully cultivated than Italy?' (V. 1. 2. 3). He continues by reference to specific areas and products: Campanian emmer wheat, Apulian hard wheat, Falernian wine, oil from Venafrum (1. 2. 6). The technique of composition is to be noted: the general statement is backed up by specific examples.

To bear out a discussion on the profitability of pasture land, the upland plain of Rosea is cited (1. 7. 10), and the reliability of this evidence is assured by Varro's own association with Reate and his ownership of horses there (2 *pr.* 6). *En route* to Reate along the Via Salaria it is possible to observe how farms in the Tiber valley near Crustumerium built banks to protect their fields from flooding (1. 14. 3). In addition to his praise of the wine and emmer of Campania, specific details are provided about local climate, land measurement, and ploughing in the region (1. 6. 3; 1. 10. 1; 1. 20. 4). Credibility is reinforced not only by the information, casually introduced, that Varro owned an estate on the slopes of Vesuvius (1. 15), but also by his membership of the board of commissioners to distribute land in the Ager Campanus in 59 B.C. (1. 2. 10). Other examples of this first-hand knowledge are the varied references to Apulia and the reasonable supposition that Varro owned a base farm there for his transhumant flocks (1. 6. 3; 1. 29. 2; 1. 57. 3; 2 *pr.* 6).

As regards supposed reliance on Greek theory, it should be enough to cite Varro's own criticism of Theophrastus: too much theory, too little practicality (1. 5. 2). Varro, whenever necessary, transfers discussion from the level of theory to that of practice. Theoretically, soils can be divided up into numerous categories, but for the farmer such knowledge is not of practical use: he needs to be aware only of the three main distinctions of rich, medium, and thin (1. 9. 5). This is necessary, for example, when estimating sowing amounts (1. 44. 1). Empirical

[5] *Der römische Gutsbetrieb als wirtschaftlicher Organismus nach den Werken des Cato, Varro und Columella*, Klio Beiheft 5 (1906, repr. 1979).

[6] J. E. Skydsgaard, *Varro the Scholar, Studies in the First Book of Varro's* de re rustica (1968); K. D. White, 'Roman Agricultural Writers I: Varro and his Predecessors', in *Aufstieg und Niedergang der römischen Welt* I. 4, ed. H. Temporini (1973), 440–97. Previously Varro's treatise had only been considered as an exercise in *Quellenkritik* (Skydsgaard, 62 ff.). Thus as a source on technical aspects of Roman agriculture Varro could be dismissed as 'really pretty ignorant': M. W. Frederiksen, 'The Contribution of Archaeology to the Agrarian Problem in the Gracchan Period', *Dialoghi di Archeologia* 4–5 (1970–1), 351. Cato's supposed dependence on Greek sources is disposed of by A. E. Astin, *Cato the Censor* (1978), 165, 199 f. Columella is sometimes thought of as a *laudator temporis acti* out of touch with the supposed agricultural decline of his age, reliant on the written tradition: R. Martin, *Recherches sur les agronomes latins* (1971), 289 ff.; cf. P. D. Caroll, 'Columella the Reformer', *Latomus* 36 (1976), 783–90. But this view has little substance.

methods of distinguishing the three main types of soil are suggested and Italian geographical *exempla* given (1. 9. 5–6).[7]

Even though at a superficial level Varro's schematization of his material (perhaps due to the influence of Greek prose style) appears to give a rigid aspect to his work, a very realistic flexibility occurs within the various sections of the schema. For example, whereas farm equipment is classified under three theoretical sub-headings, 'equipment which is articulate, inarticulate, and mute' (slaves, animals, and wagons respectively; 1. 17. 1), the actual discussion gives attention to the differences in type and amount of equipment caused by local conditions, and urges a more flexible approach than Cato and the Sasernae (see especially 1. 18. 6–7; 1. 20. 4–5).

Furthermore, Varro was no passive copier. His comments on Cato range from disagreement (1. 7. 10), to criticism (1. 2. 28; 1. 18; 1. 19. 1), to interpretation (1. 22. 4), to confirmation (1. 7. 1; 1. 24), and to confirmation combined with up-dated example (1. 2. 7). In one of the few places where it can be shown that Varro made use of Theophrastus (his main Greek source), namely the highly technical discussion of plant reproduction, Varro clearly attempts to reduce the botanical theory of his source to a practical level and to fit it into an Italian context. Whereas Theophrastus discusses the various methods of reproduction in an abstract way, without giving preferences to any particular method, Varro comments that in the case of slow-growing plants it is more practical to propagate from quick-sets rather than from seed (1. 41. 4—advice which appears in modern Italian agricultural manuals[8]). This recommendation is backed up by examples which surely derive from Varro's own knowledge and experience: figs and olives are grown from cuttings not seeds; cultivation from seed is only practised when figs are exported or imported, as in the case of African or eastern Mediterranean figs. (He adds that before transportation figs are dried and then tied together by passing a thread through them (1. 14. 5)—a practice still employed throughout the Mediterranean today.) The practical application of theoretical information borne out by examples rich in incidental reference to contemporary practice (invaluable for the historian) is not untypical of Varro's *modus operandi*.

'The literary aspirations [sc. in Varro's *Res Rusticae*] make it a little misleading to treat it in a work called *Das systematische Lehrbuch*'.[9] If this type of argument is to be maintained it must be demonstrated that the 'literary aspirations' (which include the dialogue format, introductory dedications and prefaces, invocation of the gods, anecdotes, and etymological references) detract from the serious agricultural content of the treatise.

In fact it is not possible to show this. Etymology was a feature of Stoic thought characteristic of all Varro's writings and should not be understood as mere embellishment. Nor can it be proven that etymological examples were deliberately worked into the text instead of simply arising at appropriate points from the agricultural discussion. Invocation to the gods, although a poetical

[7] E. Rawson, 'The Introduction of Logical Organization in Roman Prose Literature', *PBSR* 46 (1978), 15, misleads with the comment, 'having established at least 99 kinds of soil, Varro takes fright and reduces his *discrimina* to only three'.

[8] Cf. G. Tassinari, *Manuale dell'agronomo* (5th ed. 1980), 751.

[9] Rawson, 'Logical Organization', 14.

device, is purposely limited to rural deities and the choice of each is explained (1. 1. 4-7). Anecdotal material adds valuable information.

The dialogue form is not cosmetic or prejudicial to the serious content; it is rather used to raise new points or as a link to move from one area of discussion to another. The occasions on which it is difficult to discern which character is speaking (e.g. 1. 8 ff.; 2. 2. 9) show that the dialogue's utility value is paramount. The dialogue form enabled Varro to introduce various opinions on certain subjects, for example the important definitions of *agricultura* (1. 2. 12-28) and *villa* (3. 2. 3-16).

Moreover, studies of the prose style of the *Res Rusticae* demonstrate that Varro did not strive after literary or rhetorical effect but employed the language of everyday speech, with ideas and thoughts and new items of information 'tacked on' to the main sentence without careful arrangement.[10]

Combined with the discussion in the following chapters, the above comments should serve to dispel doubts about the value of the Roman agricultural writers. There are two further important points:

(1) The agricultural writers do not describe only one type of farming and estate management. This means not only that they describe polyculture of vines, olives, and cereals, but that within a discussion of any given crop a variety of methods and modes of cultivation is either described or referred to. Recognition of this diversity is a fundamental key to the understanding of the agricultural texts.

(2) Nor do they consider only some ideal type of farm. Even when they appear to *prescribe* ideal conditions rather than *describe* real conditions there is an awareness of the practical problem involved with meeting the prescription. This, then, is another key to their use: one must always look for the 'tension' between prescription and description, between the ideal and the real, the theoretical and the practical. This will be brought out throughout the study that follows. Pliny the Elder differs from the other writers in that his work is almost entirely descriptive.[11]

It is in fact an aim of this study to demonstrate once and for all that the agronomists had and used an empirical familiarity with diverse agricultural practices in different parts of Roman Italy.

*Archaeology, Ethnoarchaeology, and the Comparative Method*

This multiple heading includes the use of:
(1) rural archaeology
(2) field work
(3) medieval and early modern 'pre-industrial' studies
(4) modern Italian agricultural manuals.
'Ideally you now have to be an agronomist, an historian and an archaeologist all

[10] J. Heurgon, 'L'effort de style de Varron dans les *Res Rusticae*', *Revue de Philologie* 24 (1950), 57-71; E. Laughton, 'Observations on the Style of Varro', *CQ* 10 (1960), 1-28.

[11] For recent comments on Pliny: M. W. Frederiksen, 'Plinio il Vecchio e l'agricoltura in età imperiale romana: gli aspetti tecnici ed economici', in *Tecnologia, economia e società nel mondo romano*, Atti del Convegno di Como (1980), 81-97. I have occasionally cited Virgil (*Georgics*) who, in my view, provides an accurate, although selective, treatment of the agriculture of his period: M. S. Spurr, 'Agriculture and the Georgics', *G&R* 33 (1986), 49-72.

rolled into one.'[12] It is with this ideal in mind that I undertook research into Roman agriculture.

Ethnoarchaeology or 'living archaeology' comprised field work in the remoter areas throughout the country, where traditional agriculture is still practised, in all seasons of the year. The main periods were: August 1980 to February 1981; June and July 1981; March and April 1982. The main areas of concentration were: (1) the Casentino district in Tuscany, especially near Poppi and Bibbiena; (2) the region between Campobasso and Larino in Molise, especially in the village of Montorio nei Frentani; (3) inland from the gulf of Policastro near Sapri on the Campania-Basilicata border, especially in the village of Torre Orsaia; (4) the region of Potenza in Basilicata, especially the village of Ruoti. In all these areas the method has been close observation and interviews with farmers. In areas (1)-(3) it has included living and working on small farms. In the present study I have not allowed this experience to intrude obviously (apart from occasional citations of sources of information and the inclusion of photographs), but its effect and use for understanding the ancient evidence are implicit throughout.

This experience, combined with consultation of modern Italian agricultural manuals and reading of medieval and early modern studies of agriculture and rural society, has resulted above all in awareness of an unsuspected variety of agricultural practice in any given area and not just from region to region. It has also made it possible to identify certain general principles of agriculture and the rural economy which may reasonably be applied over an extensive chronological period.

These results have in turn allowed an approach to the available archaeological material which asks more questions (and suggests more possible answers) than would have been possible only from knowledge of the Roman literary texts.

The ideas generated by this process are then tested against that literary evidence, which Roman historians (unlike prehistorians) are fortunate to possess. In short, I hope to present a study which will be of use for the present and the future in a field of research which is developing rapidly.

---

[12] G. W. Barker, Review of J. M. Frayn, *Subsistence Farming in Roman Italy* (1979); E. Gabba and M. Pasquinucci, *Strutture agrarie e allevamento transumante nell'Italia· romana (III-I sec. a.C.)* (1979); and J. Kolendo, *L'agricoltura nell'Italia romana* (1980), *JRS* 72 (1982), 192.

# CHAPTER I: ENVIRONMENT AND VARIETY

## INTRODUCTION

The agricultural writers, far from relegating cereals to the poorer soils in favour of vines and olives, stressed that cereals should be cultivated in rich soils capable of producing the highest yields. This would have been especially the case on estates which produced cereals for the market. However, the agronomists were at the same time well aware of the rarity of such ideal conditions in Italy, and it is clear from their evidence that cereals were grown everywhere, in valleys, plains, hills, and mountains, in every type of soil, and in every climatic region. It is also clear that a considerable variety of cereals was cultivated throughout the country.

## SOIL CHOICE

> In the first place it is not only an art but a necessary and important art. It is also a science, which explains what crops are to be sown and what cultivations are to be carried out in each kind of soil, in order that the land may always render the highest yields. (V. 1. 3)

Thus Tremellius Scrofa, one of the foremost agriculturalists of his time, a colleague of Varro on the commission set up by Caesar in 59 B.C. in order to allocate land to veterans in the Ager Campanus (V. 1. 2. 10), defines agriculture.[1] The latter part of the definition is important here: the aim of agriculture is to achieve the greatest possible return and for this it is necessary to select soil carefully according to crop. It is of fundamental importance to know what type of soil is best suited to each given crop so that the highest yields can be obtained.

The emphasis on achieving the highest yields is an unmistakable indication of the intensive form of agriculture advocated by Cato, Varro, and Columella. Doubt must remain as to how diffuse such an approach to agriculture was in Roman Italy.

Definitions are needed. 'Intensive' is taken to mean considerable expenditure in labour and capital to achieve the maximum yield from any given area of land. 'Extensive' agriculture, on the other hand, is still profit-motivated but in accordance with a different set of values. A large landowner, unwilling to pay high labour costs to farm intensively, is content with low yields over a considerable acreage. What he loses in reduced yields he gains in low labour costs and thus still finishes with a profit. Columella cites Celsus' advice that capital outlay can be lessened by the purchase of small oxen and light ploughs (2. 2. 24), and that labour can be reduced by not weeding legumes (2. 11. 6). Celsus, therefore, could be an exponent of extensive agriculture, although there are some doubts (see pp. 34 and 41 below). On the other hand, Columella criticises certain unidentified large landowners, who abandon extensive tracts of land to long-fallow (1. 3. 10, 12). That seems to imply *laissez-faire* rather than extensive agriculture.

---

[1] *Ars* ('art') and *scientia* ('science') appear to mean something like 'theory' and 'practice', in the sense that the approach to agriculture should be a combination of both intelligent discussion and empirical experience. See *Varron, Économie rurale I*, ed. J. Heurgon (1978), 119 and Skydsgaard, *Varro the Scholar*, 89 ff.

As in all periods the picture was surely complex. Just as there were depressed and impoverished small farmers unable or unwilling to improve their conditions, there were rich landowners who were uninterested in deriving maximum profits from their estates, either because they had other sources of income, or because they were content to farm on an extensive basis. Equally, however, there can be no denying that an intensive mode of agriculture was practised by certain farmers belonging to all levels of society. What follows are a few examples to bear this out.

The impoverished market gardener, described by Apuleius, grew vegetables to sell at the local centre (*Metam.* 9. 32). This, of course, was an enterprise on a completely different scale from that described by the agricultural writers, but nevertheless is an example of the same profit- and market-oriented approach. It is not an example of mixed farming for subsistence purposes. Two brothers who had served as ordinary soldiers under Varro ran a profitable honey-producing concern on one *iugerum* of land (V. 3. 16. 10). Again, they presumably purchased their staple foods with the proceeds. Pliny the Elder records stories of industrious freedmen farmers who made large profits from small estates (14. 48; 18. 41). At a higher financial and social level stood the *praefectus fabrum* of Varro, Marcus Libo, whose vineyards at Faventia produced yields worthy of comment (V.1.2.7). We hear also of L. Tarius Rufus who, after his elevation to the consulship by Augustus, retired and invested all his money in land, which he farmed superlatively well, in Picenum (P. 18. 37). Of course, the fact that such examples were chosen for comment could imply that there was something unusual about them (although equally they might typify certain modes of agriculture), and therefore it cannot be securely argued that such intensive agriculture was common. Indeed, one of the freedmen praised by Pliny (18. 41) was envied by his neighbours who were evidently neither as well-equipped nor as diligent as he; and the story of the retired Tarius Rufus finishes by observing that his heir refused to take over the properties.[2]

Yet the participants of the dialogues which make up Varro's treatise on agriculture were all either senators or equites, and there can be no doubt about

[2] On Tarius Rufus: P-W 4 A. 2. 2320-3 (and perhaps *CIL* 5. 8112, 78; 3. 12010, 30). The reason for refusal will remain conjectural. Perhaps the heir considered continual personal supervision of estates in Picenum not to be consistent with an elevated social position. His benefactor, like Sextus Roscius who was 'a country type, unknown at Rome' (*Pro Roscio Amerino* 20), might have been atypical. Certainly, while the Roman agricultural writers advocate close personal surveillance, they do not for a moment suggest *permanent* residence in the country. On the other hand, municipal aristocrats 'who think of nothing except their fields and bits of farms and investments' (*ad Att.* 8. 13. 2) would have been less bound by Roman upper-class 'ideology'. Note that Pliny's freedman story (18. 41) shows that diligence and intensive farming were admired. Permanent residence in rural areas, combined with intensive farming, might not have been so unusual for wealthy veterans and freedmen. Such men might well have been among the avider readers of the agricultural treatises. Thus the retired tribune C. Castricius from Forum Livii, himself a distinguished agriculturalist, commemorated faithful freedmen who farmed industriously (*CIL* 11. 600). There has been only incidental research in this area. Cf. S. Treggiari, *Roman Freedmen during the Late Republic* (1969), 109; E. Rawson, 'The Ciceronian Aristocracy and its Properties', in *Studies in Roman Property*, ed. M. I. Finley (1976), 93 f.; D. B. Nagle, 'Toward a Sociology of South-eastern Etruria', *Athenaeum* 59 (1979), 411–41. References to an (undefined) class of medium-size property holders occur in the discussions of E. Gabba, 'The Perusine War and Triumviral Italy', *HSCPh* 75 (1971), 140 f. and A. Aymard, 'Les Capitalistes romains et la viticulture italienne', *Annales ESC* 2 (1947), 257–65. For some epigraphic evidence of settled veterans who became members of local curial classes, supposedly after investment in profitable agriculture: P. Castren, *Ordo Populusque Pompeianus. Polity and Society in Roman Pompeii*, Acta Instituti Romani Finlandiae 8 (1975), 87 ff. On the successes and failure of veterans as agriculturalists, see now L. Keppie, *Colonisation and Veteran Settlement in Italy 47–14 B.C.* (1983).

their agreement with Scrofa's concern for maximum yields. (Even if the occasions of the three dialogues were fictional, the ideas expressed must surely have remained within the bounds of contemporary credibility.) The eques Gaberius, who sought to achieve rapid profits from large-scale goat breeding, was ridiculed not because he sought profit but because of his patent lack of agricultural knowledge (V. 2. 3. 10). The thrust of Varro's treatise, perhaps more immediately apparent than in either Cato's or Columella's, is that whether arboriculture, crop-husbandry, pastoralism or specialized animal breeding (*pastio villatica*) are being practised, the highest profits can and should be sought by those with a thorough knowledge of agriculture.

All Italians, according to Varro, sought a return from their agricultural enterprises which would cover their expense and labour-time.[3] While this observation cannot be taken to mean that all Italians sought *maximum* yields, it at least shows that Varro thought that there was a general awareness of the fundamental equation that profit equals yield minus input in expense and labour, and it cannot be lightly dismissed. Moreover, as this study attempts to show, the agricultural writers, representative of a group however large or small which sought to achieve a high level of agricultural productivity, were aware of a more complex matrix of factors in the profit equation; factors which include the available soil, topographical situation, type of crop, prevailing climatic conditions, available tools and labour, and the possibilities of transport and marketing.

> Secondly the type of soil of which the farm is composed must be considered. It is chiefly in respect of this that a farm is considered good or bad; for it determines what variety of crop, and in what measure, can be sown and cultivated; for not all crops can be grown with equal success on the same land. As one type is suited to the vine and another to grain, so of others—one is suited to one crop, another to another.
>
> (V. 1. 7. 5)

The above passage is indicative of another important facet of intensive agriculture: specialization. This will require brief comment here, since there has been some debate on whether the slave-run estates as described by the agricultural writers specialized in one crop or instead practised mixed farming. The latter view is normally held: it is argued that mixed farming was the general rule because of the need not only to provide subsistence for the workforce, but also to keep it busy all the year round, since idle slaves represent economic loss.[4]

---

[3] 'spectasse videntur Italici homines colendo, possentne fructus pro impensa ac labore redire' (V. 1. 2. 8).

[4] Busy slaves: Cato 39. 2, cf. 2. 3, 37. 3; V. 1. 18, 1. 36; Col. 1. 8–9, 11. 2. 90. Reference to mixed farming: Cato 10–11; V. 1. 13; Col. 1. 2. 4–5; *Dig.* 33. 7. 8. For intercultivation, see n. 15 below. P. A. Brunt, Review of K. D. White, *Roman Farming, JRS* 62 (1972), 153–8: 'mixed farming was the rule'. Yet in *Italian Manpower*, 369, Brunt carefully qualifies this: 'There is abundant evidence that the owners of great estates raised grain, and produced wine, oil, vegetables, fruits, usually in a mixed husbandry, whose precise character was determined by the quality of the soil and the accessibility of markets'. The idea expressed in the last clause, outside the scope of his book, is not developed. Duncan-Jones, *Economy of the Roman Empire*, 34–8, while he collects most references which appear to relate to profitability and specialization, argues that autosufficiency was almost 'an unassailable moral precept' which therefore dictated mixed farming. This would also keep slaves continually busy, protect the estate from paying high prices for any staple food in times of shortage, and allow occasional profits from the sale of surplus produce. See also P. Veyne, 'Mythe et réalité de l'autarcie à Rome', *REA* 81 (1979), 261–80. I do not doubt it is a true generalization that mixed farming

Another passage of Varro usually overlooked as regards this debate makes it clear that specialization did exist.[5] The limiting factor was the possibility of access to a supply of subsistence necessities not produced on the estate: proximity to a market centre or to other estates which specialized in other crops or practised mixed farming was required. More isolated estates would have to be self-sufficient and would thus have to carry out mixed farming. Again, this is clear from Varro.[6]

The argument that the economics of slavery required crop diversification is only relatively compelling. As will be demonstrated later, a specialized arable farm producing a variety of cereals and legumes for the market could keep its skeleton workforce busy almost all year round.[7] Moreover, we have too little evidence to be dogmatic, and rival hypotheses could be proposed. For example, since it was not unusual for a rich landowner to possess several estates in the same region, it is possible that some or all specialized in different crops and that there existed a mobile slave workforce, which could be moved from one estate to another according to the seasonal labour requirements of the various crops.[8]

However, there is another type of agricultural specialization which was perhaps more usual in the context of Roman intensive agriculture, mainly because it is more consonant with the extremely varied topographical conditions in Italy. On any one farm there is likely to be some sloping, some flat and some dissected areas; some locations will receive more sun or be more sheltered than others; and the soil will vary in quality. Thus a variety of crops are cultivated in order to utilize fully the diverse potential of the farm. To state the idea paradoxically: intensive agriculture often results in mixed farming. A profit will usually be sought from all crops. The Tuscan estate of Pliny the Younger is a good example: the land comprised the Tiber valley floor, the river terraces, and the hills behind. Cereals, vines and woodland were cultivated in the appropriate places and all surplus crops were sent down river to the market at Rome (*Ep.* 5. 6).

In general, the best crops grow in rich (*pinguis*) soil (V. 1. 9. 5-6). The best soil, according to Columella, is both rich and friable and thus requires the minimum in labour and expense to produce the highest yields.[9] The next best soil is that which is rich and heavy (ibid., n. 9): the high yields still allow a profit to be

---

was prevalent in Italy (as in the modern and, sup-posedly, pre-Roman eras: G. W. Barker, *Landscape and Society: Prehistoric Central Italy* (1981), 23, and see below n. 15), but it is one which obscures the variety and diversity of agricultural concerns, especially within the *territoria* of towns.

[5] 'Many landowners have among their estates some which have to import the grain or wine or other products which they lack. There are also many who produce a surplus for export' (V. 1. 16. 2). A similar specialization seems referred to by Columella 1. 7. 6.

[6] See his remarks on the owners of large estates distant from 'towns or villages' (1. 16. 4).

[7] Chapter VIII, pp. 137–40. 'Skeleton workforce' is the permanent staff as opposed to the seasonally hired hands.

[8] There is no good evidence for this. The agronomists rather stress that slaves should remain on the one farm (cf. Col. 11. 1. 23; Cato 5. 2, 5). Yet Pliny the Younger discussed the question of utilizing the

same staff on neighbouring estates (*Ep.* 3. 19). There is a suggestion that some slaves could be imported to supervise a new tenant-farming system, but this reference cannot be pressed (ibid. 9. 37). An ideal situation for this type of internal mobile labour force would have been that of Sextus Roscius with thirteen farms almost all near each other in the Tiber valley (*Pro Roscio Amerino* 18–20). Heitland, *Agricola*, 170, interpreted Cato's 'if you are popular in the neighbourhood . . . it will be easier to hire extra hands' (4), as the hiring out of slaves between neigh-bouring farms for tasks beyond the capabilities of the permanent workforce. Cf. *Dig.* 33. 7. 12. 8: agri-cultural slaves can be hired out in that part of the year when there is nothing to do on the estate.

[9] 'Land which is both rich and friable (*pinguis ac putris*) yields the greatest returns, because in pro-ducing most it demands least, and what it does require is supplied with only slight labour and expense' (Col. 2. 2. 5).

made, even though more labour has to be expended in working the soil. It is precisely these rich soils which are recommended for grain. Cato advises thick, fertile soil without any arboreal intercultivation as long as such land is not subject to fogs (6. 1), and Varro agrees (1. 24. 1).[10] The importance of establishing what soil on the farm is best for grain is revealed by the several recommended tests (and by the debate as to the utility of the different tests) to ensure that the soil is not only rich but also of a certain required taste (Col. 2. 2. 14–20).[11] Spontaneous vegetation is also a good guide (Col. 2. 2. 20; V. 1. 9. 7). Yet examination should not be limited to the superficial; it should also include the subsoil to a depth in proportion to the root-size of the crop. The fertile soil suitable for grain should be consistent to a depth of at least two feet (Col. 2. 2. 21).[12]

Colour, taste, texture and appearance all reveal a simple empirical method. Yet, of course, laboratory soil analyses are a modern development and, although they exist in Italy, farmers continue to use with success the tried and tested empirical techniques and terminology which do not differ from the recommendations of the agricultural writers. One farmer and his neighbours with whom I worked (see Introduction) on the Campania-Basilicata border continued to speak of local soils as 'soft' (*soffice*), 'damp' (*umido*), 'rich' (*ricco*). Another family near Larino had a relative in a soil-testing laboratory at Pescara and used more technical vocabulary. I have found the less technical approach to be more common throughout the country; both, however, used the soil-texture field test described in n. 11. A division between the 'field and the laboratory' is implied by Columella. Some theorists attempted to classify the *plurimae varietates* of the soil, but that should be no concern of the farmer (2. 1. 2). It was a writer like Theophrastus, as Varro observed, who was the least practical help (see Introduction, p. xi). His works divided agriculture into *partes innumerabiles* and were of more use to those interested in theoretical study than to those 'qui agrum colere volunt' (1. 5. 1–2).

Thus cereals are to be cultivated in the rich soils of the farm most suited to them. In the case of the small farmer living at, or only a little above, subsistence level this is easily understandable. The cereal crops on which he depended for his livelihood would be allocated the best soils at his disposal. However, that such advice occurs in the agricultural texts, which were written by and for landowners with capital and an interest in intensive agriculture, is surely something quite unexpected. It amounts to no less than a reversal of the emphasis of modern studies that intensive, market-oriented agriculture in Roman Italy in the period under consideration concentrated on the 'cash-crops', vines and olives, and that

[10] Fogs are common throughout the winter in the Po Valley and in the upland valleys and basins of the Alps and Apennines: D. S. Walker, *The Mediterranean Lands* (1960), 174.

[11] The test of soil texture by working moistened soil in the hand and comparing its feel with one's experience is still a recognized and valid field test. From Columella's indications a clayey loam is being sought. (For further remarks on soil testing see P. 17. 27–41.) The colour of soil is, as Columella asserts, only of limited value as a test of its fertility. While organic matter will darken a soil, some black soils, as he notes,

can be infertile (Col. 2. 2. 16). Cf. K. D. White, 'Virgil's Knowledge of Arable Farming', *Proceedings of the Virgil Society* 7 (1967–8), 19.

[12] J. Percival, *The Wheat Plant. A Monograph* (1921), 420: 'Although wheat will grow on almost all types of soil from the heaviest clays to the sands and gravels, the highest yields are only obtained on rich, deep, well-drained loamy clays, the physical character of which is fairly uniform down to a depth of two to three feet.' The soil depth recommended by Percival (and Columella) is not related to ploughing depth but to the depth reached by the plant's roots.

6

CHAPTER I

cereals were grown only in order to meet the subsistence requirements of the workforce employed in profitable arboriculture (see Introduction, ix).

Part of the answer to this paradox is that some varieties of vines and olives can flourish on hilly ground in thin, gravelly soils, which would produce only a poor crop of cereals. In this way the richer soil of the plain and valley could be drained and set aside for cereals. But that is not a wholly satisfactory explanation, since other varieties of vines and olives thrive on flatter terrain, in those medium loam or clay soils (provided they are well-drained) which are most suitable for cereals.[13] This ability to share common conditions is reflected by the information that in 1936, while viticulture was practised on 15 per cent of the productive surface of Italy, specialized vineyards occupied no more than 3.4 per cent of the productive surface: the large majority of vines was intercultivated with cereals and forage crops.[14]

There is plenty of evidence for the Roman period, largely literary but also some archaeological, for intercultivation (*arbustum*) of both vines (trained up trees) and olives with grain.[15] The specialized vineyard (*vinea*) was probably no more common then than in 1936, despite some modern studies which lead one to suppose that the greater part of Italy was covered with vines. As today, there can be no doubt that grain was the most extensively cultivated crop, and it is important to realize that therefore it would usually have been grown alone in separate fields.[16]

One explanation for the prevalence of the *arbustum* over the *vinea*—that it was an expedient solution to share inferior vine land with cereals in order to supplement the sales of low wine yields—is a typical deduction from the modern scholarly emphasis on the supposed preference for vines or olives over grain, referred to above. Yet such an explanation pays little attention to the available ancient evidence or to the agricultural reality.[17]

Varro's comment that progress had been made with the more rational layout of *arbusta* so that a greater quantity of both wine and grain was produced, shows that intercultivation was rather a question of the intensive use of a limited amount of good land (V. 1. 7. 2). In fact, if the appropriate types of olives or vines were

[13] Various soils for vines and olives: Cato 6; 43–4; 61–2; V. 1. 23. 1; 24. 1; 26 (agrees with Cato); Col. 3. 1–2; 5. 8. 6; P. 17. 25 ff.

[14] Naval Intelligence Division, *Italy*, Geographical Handbook Series (1944–5), I, 36.

[15] For a collection of references to intercultivation of grain and olives: Duncan-Jones, *Economy of the Roman Empire*, 36 n. 1; of grain and vines: T. Frank, *An Economic Survey of Ancient Rome* (1940, repr. 1975), v, 141 n. 5; cf. K. D. White, 'Wheat Farming in Roman Times', *Antiquity* 37 (1963), 207–12. As for archaeological evidence of trenches or planting holes, it is necessary to realize that a vine *arbustum* was not usually 'vines planted irregularly between trees' (Duncan-Jones, 57) but two or more vines planted around the base of each tree and trained up it (Col. 5. 6. 19; P. 17. 202). Thus, 'vine trenches' identified in the Ager Veientanus (A. Kahane, L. M. Threipland, J. B. Ward-Perkins, 'The Ager Veientanus North and East of Rome', *PBSR* 36 (1968), 168) signify a *vinea*, since traces of an *arbustum* would involve spaced rows of holes for the tree trunks,

surrounded by smaller holes for vine stems. Aerial photographs of the Tavoliere plain of Puglia show closely parallel vine trenches and rows of olives of the Roman period, where the soil's calcium carbonate crust or *crosta* has been punctured: J. Bradford, 'Buried Landscapes in Southern Italy', *Antiquity* 23 (1949), 58–72. Vineyards inside Pompeii were *vineae*, and a carbonized bean found in one suggests that intensive use of urban space might lead to market-garden intercultivation in the specialized vineyard (W. F. Jashemski, *The Gardens of Pompeii, Herculaneum and the Villas destroyed by Vesuvius* (1979), 242). Grain and olives were perhaps intercultivated at Francolise in Campania: C. Pavolini, 'Review of M. A. Cotton, *The Late Republican Villa at Posto, Francolise*', *Gnomon* 53 (1981), 371–5.

[16] Brunt, *Italian Manpower*, 126 ff. White, 'Wheat Farming', misleads with his supposition that the most usual form of grain growing was intercultivation with vines or olives.

[17] Duncan-Jones, *Economy of the Roman Empire*, 59.

planted in rich soil, it was assumed that the area was already under cereal cultivation. Hence the repeated formulation, *pingue et frumentarium solum*, 'rich and
grain land'. If such land were to be planted also with vines or olives, the trees
should be placed far enough apart so as not to damage the cereal production.[18]

On the other hand, vines might still be trained on trees (thus technically
constituting an *arbustum*), in soil which was too poor to make the growing of
cereals worthwhile (Col. 5. 6. 11; 5. 7. 3). In this case the vines would be planted
closer together, since there were no cereals to damage. Why then bother to train
the vines on trees in the first place? There might be several reasons. Some vines
produced better quality wine when trained on trees (Col. 3. 2. 24); the trees
provided leaves which served as welcome animal fodder (Col. 5. 6. 5); the trees of
an *arbustum* near a town could provide marketable firewood and timber
(Cato 7. 1).

We can only conclude, in rebuttal of previous theories, that scrutiny of the
evidence shows that high priority was allocated to cereal cultivation on the type of
estate envisaged by the agricultural writers. This will become increasingly clear
throughout this study. They sought high yields and a surplus, no doubt for a
mixture of reasons: as security against the risk of a year of poor harvest; to feed
not only the rural workforce but also their urban slaves, as well as, perhaps, the
*familiae* of less productive (e.g. maritime) villas; and for sale as a cash crop, when
the price was right, in the nearby town.[19]

Where possible, then, according to the agricultural writers, cereals should be
sown in rich soils. However, only a few areas of the productive surface of Italy
have soils which are ideally adapted to cereal cultivation, and the agronomists
show themselves well aware of this. Their two preferred soils—rich and easily
worked, rich and worked with greater difficulty—which can be identified as light
to medium, well-drained loams and clays, and heavier alluvial soils which require
drainage (as emphasized by the agricultural writers, see below p. 38 f.), are to be
found in the following general areas: the finer alluvial soils of the middle and
lower reaches of the Po valley; clayey alluvium of the Marengo plain (Ales-
sandria); the alluvial coastal plains from the Apuan Alps to the southern limits of
the Latian plain; the terraces and floors of the Arno river between Pisa and
Florence and the plains of Lucca and Pistoia; the Valdichiana south of Arezzo
and the broader stretches of the Tiber valley; the lowland regions of Campania
where the volcanic soils, as in parts of Latium and Tuscany, are very fertile; the
upland basins of the central Apennines—Foligno, Terni, Sulmona, Fucino and
Aquila; the sandy clays of the low hills and the alluvial soils of the narrow coastal
plains and the broader river valleys of Le Marche; certain alluvial soils on the
Tavoliere plain of Puglia and the sandy clays of the Pre-Murge depression
stretching to the south-east of the Tavoliere; parts of the Ionian coastal plain
around the 'instep' of the peninsula.[20]

---

[18] Col. 2. 2. 17; 5. 9. 7.

[19] For the idea that maritime villas were fed by
agriculturally productive estates in Campania: Cic.,
*Leg. Agr.* 2. 78 and M. W. Frederiksen, 'Republican
Capua: a Social and Economic Study', *PBSR* 27
(1959), 121.

[20] Useful works: Naval Intelligence Division, *Italy*,
III, 28–32; P. Principi, *I terreni italiani. Carat-
teristiche geopedologiche delle regioni* (1961); the
series of maps showing soil and agricultural use (*Carte
della utilizzazione del suolo*) together with their
explanatory and detailed guides (*Memorie illustrative*

The above is merely the result of a rapid glance at the soil map of Italy. Within the outlined areas there are naturally many different types of soil, but the overall suitability of the soil therein for cereals makes the regional summary a valid one. There are, of course, climatic factors to be taken into account in the sense that the best soils will not produce good cereal yields if the climate is unfavourable. Thus the cereal potential of soils on the east coast and south of Italy is limited by scanty rainfall, as explained in more detail below.

The chief favoured areas of cereal cultivation in Roman Italy included the Po plain, areas of Etruria, Campania and Apulia.[21] It is most likely that it was especially in these regions that cereals were grown for profit. Although precise details of the location of the renowned areas (especially in Etruria and Apulia) are mostly lacking in the ancient sources, it can be safely assumed that they coincided with the zones of suitable soils as outlined above. If this identification based on a combination of ancient literary evidence and modern soil classification is accepted, then comparative evidence for cereal cultivation in those regions can be applied with useful effect.

However, wholesale acceptance must be tempered by an awareness of the various changes to the countryside since Roman times. Such changes comprise deforestation, alluviation and the reclamation of arable land by drainage. It is generally agreed, for example, that a major period of alluviation occurred in the early medieval period, which means that a lesser extent of alluvial soils was available for agricultural exploitation in the Roman period.[22] The question of deforestation, however, has never been satisfactorily tackled, and it is hoped that this will have high priority in future regional studies and field surveys in Italy.

---

*delle carte della utilizzazione del suolo*) by various authors, produced by the Consiglio Nazionale delle Ricerche, Rome; Tassinari, *Manuale* (1980), 122 ff.; R. Almagià, *L'Italia* II (1959), 732-4. Cf. the geological map in T. Cornell and J. Matthews, *Atlas of the Roman World* (1982), 16.

[21] What follows is a representative list. (1) Etruria: P. 18. 86, 109; V. 1. 9. 6; 1. 44. 2. (2) Campania: Strabo 5. 4. 3; P. 17. 2. 8; 18. 86, 110, 111, 191; V. 1. 2. 6; Cic., *Leg. Agr.* 1. 21. (3) Apulia: V. 1. 2. 6; 1. 57. 3; 2. 6. 5; Col. 3. 8. 4; Strabo 6. 3. 9. (4) Picenum: P. 18. 106; Martial 13. 47. (5) Northern plain: Polybius 2. 15. 1-2; P. 18. 66, 69 (Alps), 101, 109, 141, 182; Strabo 5. 1. 12. (6) Upland basins: Ovid, *Amores* 2. 16. 7 (Sulmona).

[22] C. Vita Finzi, *The Mediterranean Valleys: Geological Changes in Historical Times* (1969). Cf. J. B. Ward-Perkins, *Landscape and History in Central Italy* (1964) and C. Delano Smith, *Western Mediterranean Europe* (1979), 268. It is uncertain how uniform such alluviation was or why traces of Roman buildings are sometimes visible in river valleys, e.g. site 134 on the Tiber floor, M.-P. Muzzioli, *Cures Sabini*, Forma Italiae, Regio IV, II (1980), and the river port at Orte (ancient Horta), G. Nardi, *Le antichità di Orte. Esame del territorio e dei materiali archeologici* (1980). Perhaps the Tiber at least has now cut back to something like its original level. From the

agricultural point of view it is better to see alluviation as a continual process. Certainly the Romans were well aware of it, as appears from the writings of the land surveyors (e.g. Agennius Urbicus, *de controv. agr.*, p. 42 (C. Thulin, Teubner text, 1971 edn.) (Lachmann 82. 5 f.), cf. p. 64 (La. 16. 23 f.), Hyginus, *de gen. controv.*, p. 87 (La. 124)) and of the lawyers (cf. *Dig.* 41. 1. 7; 43. 12). River floods must have been common enough throughout the Roman period despite the construction of river banks and drainage (Brunt, *Italian Manpower*, 173 ff.); for some remarks on drainage to aid arable cultivation see pp. 38 f., 57 f. below. There are ancient references to deforestation (cf. Brunt, 176 f.), which no doubt caused some erosion (known to the agricultural writers: Col. 3. 11. 8; 3. 12. 6), but despite C. A. Yeo, 'The Overgrazing of Ranch-lands in Ancient Italy', *TAPhA* 79 (1948), 275-307, deforestation and its negative results probably did not become a problem until the demographic increase of the later Middle Ages (cf. G. Cherubini, 'Le campagne italiane dall'XI al XV secolo', in *Storia d'Italia* IV, ed. G. Galasso (1981), 309 ff.), and in less-populated southern regions until the construction of railways (E. Magaldi, *Lucania romana* (1947), 47 f.; E. Sereni, *Storia del paesaggio agrario italiano* (1961), 370, 409). The best solution is for regional archaeological surveys to attempt an estimate of the amount of landscape change in their local areas.

There is also the argument (discussed pp. 27–40) that even much of the alluvial soil available was too heavy to be worked by the Roman ox-drawn plough.

If soil conditions on a given estate were not ideal for cereals, the practice of soil-mixing could be adopted. Columella's uncle in southern Spain occasionally mixed clay with gravel to produce luxuriant crops of grain (Col. 2. 15. 4). The mixing of sand or gravel with clay enables the clay to become more permeable and friable and thus to yield its natural richness; equally clay can be added to a thin sandy soil to aid the latter's water retention. Yet on anything more than a small localized scale such an operation would pose considerable labour and transport problems. However, if nearby deposits of the complementary type of soil existed and the market possibilities were favourable, a certain amount of soil-mixing of a considerable acreage could have been economically rational. Whether it was practised much or at all in Roman Italy is perhaps doubtful. Columella's reference is to Baetica; it might be implied for Italy, but we cannot be sure. Its practice today is known but seldom seen.[23]

Another form of soil-mixing, marling, is used to counteract acidity which is harmful to cereals. But this is not necessary in Italy with its mainly alkaline or neutral soils.[24] Scrofa referred to the practice near the Rhine (V. 1. 7. 8), and Pliny appears to limit it to Gaul or Britain (17. 42–8).

Apart from soil-mixing, another clear indication that the agricultural writers were well aware that ideal conditions for cereals could not always be found is the attention paid to the separate pedological needs of the diverse types of cereals. While all cereals will do best in the rich soils already discussed, there are some cereals which will do better than others in poorer soils. Bread wheats, *triticum* and *siligo*, because they need more nutrition than other cereals, require rich soil for best returns (V. 1. 23. 2); *far* (emmer wheat) can grow in wetter ground than *triticum*; barley can be cultivated in drier soils (V. 1. 9. 4; Col. 2. 6. 4); and millet and panic can grow almost anywhere. (See below for an explanation of the agricultural requirements of these various cereals.) Columella, noting that each farm's land can consist of several types of soil, actually advises the selection and sowing not only of different species of cereals but also of different breeds of the main species (2. 6. 1–4).

What Varro and Columella are recommending is the maximum utilization of the available soil conditions for cereal culture. It is interesting that this concentration on suiting soil to the different species and breeds of grain was one of the 'ten practical rules' to increase yields and the extent of cereals in the Fascist drive to render Italy self-sufficient. The similarity of the agricultural advice is a clue to what may have been an expanding, specialized form of cereal cultivation tied to growing urban markets throughout Italy in the late Republic and early Empire. Grain was increasingly produced on specialized cereal farms to feed an increasing urban population, which no longer grew its own staple foods. It would be impossible to demonstrate this conclusively, but certain other passages in the agricultural texts on clearing woodland to sow cereals support the argument.[25]

---

[23] A. Quattrochi, *Agraria*[3] (1979) I, 97–8. Between 750 and 1,000 cubic metres of sand are necessary to ameliorate in this way one hectare of very clayey soil.

[24] Cf. Naval Intelligence Division, *Italy* III, 9.

[25] The Fascist drive, that is the so-called *Battaglia del Grano*. L. Paoletti, 'Norme pratiche per la semina', *Il Contadino Pisano* (October 1925).

Furthermore, the urban market, composed of various economic and social levels, would require a variety of cereals. Thus the specialized grain farmer could exploit to the full the different soils of which his land might be composed, in the knowledge that all the cereal varieties would find a market.

On the specialized cereal farm, then, polyculture of cereals would be practised if the soil was not uniform. At the other end of the scale, the small landowner would also practise polyculture of cereals, but the motive would be to provide against the possibility of a bad year. If his cereal crop consisted of different grains such as emmer, barley and millet, there would be less chance of losing the whole crop than if he practised monoculture. (For the common wisdom, see Pliny, *Ep.* 1. 20. 16.) Yet to envisage the cultivation of cereals as being undertaken only on specialized grain farms or by peasant cultivators would be to falsify what must rather have been a complex situation consisting of a wider range of cereal culture. There would also have existed, for example, (1) large, self-sufficient estates practising mixed farming; (2) mixed farms which produced several crops, including grain, for the market; (3) estates which tended to specialize in other crops and which grew grain only for the subsistence of the workforce; (4) on estates which reared livestock for the market, various cereals could be grown for feed. An example of this last category could be the villa near Potenza in Basilicata. The plant remains recovered include barley, emmer wheat, hard and soft wheats and oats. From the bone evidence, it seems that animal husbandry played a major part in the economy of this estate, with pigs in the majority followed by sheep, goats, cattle and equines.[26] To take evidence from one agricultural writer only: pigs ate 'barley and other grains' (V. 2. 4. 6; cf. 2. 15, 20, 21: barley; 2. 3. 21: wheat). Calves ate wheat bran and barley flour (V. 2. 5. 17), horses barley (V. 2. 7. 7, 12), asses barley (V. 2. 6. 4; 3. 17. 6) and emmer (V. 2. 6. 4). Thus for several reasons polyculture of cereals was much more prevalent in Roman than in modern Italy.

## CEREAL VARIETIES

It is thus necessary to emphasize from the start that a wide variety of cereals was cultivated throughout Roman Italy. The varieties selected depended to a certain extent on broad climatic regions, on regional custom, on the variable agricultural conditions of the individual farm and on market forces, as will be made clear below. The widely held view that, by the first century A.D., husked or hulled grains, such as emmer wheat, had been largely ousted by naked grains should be discounted.[27] The following survey of some of the literary and archaeo-

[26] Clearing of woodland: Col. 2. 2. 8–14; P. 17. 39; cf. Virgil, *Georgics* 2. 207–11. A. M. Small, 'The Environment of San Giovanni', in *Archaeology and Italian Society. Prehistoric, Roman and Medieval Studies*, ed. G. W. Barker and R. Hodges, Papers in Italian Archaeology 2, B.A.R. Int. Series 102 (1981), 203–12. Now see: L. Costantini, 'Piante coltivate e piante spontanee a San Giovanni di Ruoti (Potenza)', in *Lo scavo di San Giovanni di Ruoti ed il periodo tardoantico in Basilicata*, ed. M. Gualtieri et al. (1983), 85–90.

[27] 'In Pliny's and even Varro's day the *far* of early Rome had largely disappeared from the human diet . . . in favour of those wheats which can be freed from their husks on the threshing floor and from which

good bread can be made', L. A. Moritz, *Grain Mills and Flour in Classical Antiquity* (1958), xxii–xxiii. See also N. Jasny, *The Wheats of Classical Antiquity* (1944), 141 ff.; and pp. 93–8 below. Moritz and others see the supposed disappearance of husked wheats as the result of a growing taste preference for naked wheats. Jasny rightly limits this preference to a small minority of the Roman population. He still believes that husked wheats had almost disappeared by the end of the classical period but ascribes this to their bulkiness, which made transport and trade in them uneconomic. This view is argued especially in his article 'Competition among Grains in Classical Antiquity', *American Historical Review* 47 (1941/2), 747–64.

logical evidence will serve to show that polyculture of cereals existed everywhere throughout the period.

Well-known texts such as Ovid's characterization of the agriculture of early Rome as comprising cultivation only of *far* and beans (*Fast.* 2. 519–20; 6. 180); as Pliny's statement that the Roman nation ate only *far* for three hundred years (18. 62); or the use of *far* in ancient religious rites (P. 18. 10; 18. 84); or that it is the only grain mentioned in the Twelve Tables (III. 4); while they certainly attest the antiquity of emmer's cultivation in Italy, cannot be taken to prove its disappearance by the first century A.D.

Emmer (*Triticum dicoccum*) is mentioned often by the agronomists. It usually appears in their texts as a robust wheat grown in soils and under climatic conditions which it can tolerate rather than do best in (wet, heavy and chalky soils: Col. 2. 9. 3; dry soil and when the autumn rains are late: Col. 2. 8. 5; cold, hot, dry and poorly cultivated soils: P. 18. 83). It was the hardiest of known grains and could be grown from Gaul to Egypt (P. 18. 81–2, 109).

This hardiness and tolerance are attested also by modern experts in similar terms.[28] Furthermore, as a husked wheat it was less prone to attack from insects and rust in the ear and, since it was stored in the husk, it was more secure than naked wheats in the granary. Since it was not threshed like naked grain, the risk of rain damage between reaping and storing was also minimized. This would be especially so if the ears only were gathered, which was one of the three main Roman reaping methods. Moreover, recent experiments with the cultivation of emmer have produced surprisingly high yields. It is also more nutritious than naked wheat.[29] All these points will be discussed in more detail later.

Emmer's robustness, its tolerance of poorly prepared soil and its other agricultural advantages over naked wheats must surely have been appreciated by the subsistence cultivator. On the villa estate it would usually have accounted for a considerable proportion of the slave diet as a flat bread or, more commonly, porridge, and it was probably also transported to the city to feed the urban *familia*. It was also on sale in the city, where it was no doubt purchased by large numbers of the urban poor and by the slave owner whose workforce did not eat the produce of his rural estate. That, surely, is the point of Martial's quip, 'You feed your vinedresser (sc. on your suburban farm) on urban emmer' (3. 58. 48). Thus the large cereal producer in the town's *territorium* would have his eye on this bulk market, clearly worthwhile, even though emmer was somewhat cheaper than naked wheats.[30]

---

28 Percival, *The Wheat Plant*, 188; R. F. Peterson, *Wheat: Botany, Cultivation and Utilization* (1965), 12; Jasny, *Wheats*, 118.

29 P. J. Reynolds, *Iron Age Farm. The Butser Experiment* (1979), 60–4 reports on the high yield and food value of emmer. After seven years of annual cropping, yields are still close to those of *modern* bread wheats: id., 'Deadstock and Livestock', in *Farming Practice in British Prehistory*, ed. R. Mercer (1981), 97–122. These figures cannot of course be applied directly to Italy but they do give some indication of the advantages of emmer. For doubt about

how long such high yields will last, see G. W. Barker, *Prehistoric Farming in Europe* (1985), 51.

30 The necessary parching process (see below) destroys much of the flour's gluten content and so bread from emmer was flat: L. A. Moritz, 'Husked and Naked Grains', *CQ* n.s. 5 (1955), 129–34. It was probably more common to eat it as porridge (P. 18. 83). Emmer for slaves: V. 1. 63 (on the farm); Juv. 9. 123 (urban slaves?); Horace, *Sat.* 1. 5. 69; Jasny, *Wheats*, 115. Yet it would appear that Columella's workforce ate a mixture of bread-wheat and barley (2. 9. 16), and Cato's slave rations are in

Before consumption emmer wheat had to be separated from its husk by being grilled or parched. Thus the husks became brittle and could be removed and flour produced by pounding with mortar and pestle or by grinding with a quern. The inconvenience of this prolonged preparation was, however, far outweighed by the manifold advantages outlined above, especially as concerns the small cultivator. So emmer remained in cultivation throughout classical antiquity, during the Middle Ages and into the present century among the peasants of the south, where its drought-resistant quality was much appreciated, and in the mountains of the Abruzzo, where it tolerated cold, wet and poor soils.[31]

Then again, its importance as fodder cannot be underestimated. Firstly, it was fed green in a mixture with barley, vetch and other legumes as *farrago* (P. 18. 142; V. 1. 31. 5). In the grain it provided fodder for the ass (V. 2. 6. 4), which was an animal to be found on all farms, large and small alike. For this purpose it did not require any preparation, since animals digest it better in its husked state. It also served the more specialized and growing market of *pastio villatica*, which was the breeding of certain types of animals and birds in confined spaces for pleasure or profit. Thus *far* could be fed to the wild animals in the private game park, or be used to fatten thrushes and snails for the urban market. Exponents of *pastio villatica* for profit might often purchase such grain rather than grow it themselves, and thus provided another market for the cereal producer.[32]

And finally, it is clear that certain types of emmer wheat were highly prized as food and were thus grown on good soils (rather than relegated to those they could tolerate). Such was *arinca*, which made a very sweet bread (P. 18. 92). *Alica*, or *far halicastrum*, which was a spring-sown wheat, was so highly sought after that certain growers used their best naked wheat to imitate it, and some African dealers also tried to invade the lucrative market with a spurious mixture. Within Italy itself the geographical location of the most renowned regions for the production of *alica*, around Verona, Pisa, and in Campania, again demonstrates the wide adaptability of emmer wheat (P. 18. 109–16).

This adaptability is shown also by a glance at the available archaeological evidence. Emmer has been recovered in contexts throughout Europe and the Middle East, which amply justifies Pliny's statement that it was cultivated from Gaul to Egypt (18. 81–2, 109). It was the most commonly grown cereal in the prehistoric period, and within Italy traces of it have been found from the *palafitte* of the north, where its tolerance of wet conditions was paramount, to the Tavoliere plain of Puglia in the south-east, which is one of the driest regions of the

*triticum*, perhaps naked wheat, but see below p. 106 n. 11. Other literary evidence for the consumption is in J. André, *L'Alimentation et la cuisine à Rome* (2nd edn. 1981), 50–72. Some proof that *far* was sold in towns comes from Pompeian graffiti: *CIL* 4. 2567; 4. 5380 (*alica* and porridge). Mortars have been found in bakeries in Pompeii, which indicate the pounding of husked grains: Moritz, *Grain Mills*, 26.

[31] Grilling and pounding: V. 1. 63; P. 18. 97.

Emmer in the medieval period: P. J. Jones, 'Medieval Agrarian Society in its Prime: Italy', in *Cambridge Economic History of Europe* I, ed. M. M. Postan (1966), 372; in the present century: P. Scheuermeier, *Il lavoro dei contadini. Cultura materiale e artigianato rurale in Italia e nella Svizzera italiana e retoromanza* (1980) II, 177 f. and pls. 283, 284, 286.

[32] Emmer for such animals: thrushes and snails, V. 3. 5. 4; 3. 14. 5; for asses, V. 2. 6. 4. Market for cereal producers: pp. 143 f. below.

country.[33] This evidence, which derives from pre-classical sites, might seem at first to confirm the view held by Moritz and others, that emmer disappeared during the Roman period. Instead it reflects the fact that many fewer Roman sites have been excavated with such botanical priorities in mind. Nevertheless, the few recoveries of emmer from Roman contexts indicate clearly enough its Italian-wide cultivation, from the earliest period to the fourth century A.D. This is a picture that can confidently be expected to emerge in greater detail as more excavation of the right sort is undertaken.[34]

*Far* used commonly to be misidentified as 'spelt' (and is still occasionally so translated). Some archaeological evidence suggests that spelt (*Triticum spelta*) was known in the Bronze and Iron Ages in the north of Italy and perhaps also at Rome. Einkorn (*Triticum monococcum*) was quite widely cultivated in the pre-classical era, but it seems clear from the silence of the evidence, both literary and archaeological, that during the Roman period it had become much less significant. There can be little doubt that emmer was the most widespread husked wheat in Roman Italy.[35]

As regards other, 'inferior' grains, rye (*Secale cereale*) is confined by Pliny to a limited area in the north-west of Italy, and a recent archaeological find seems neatly to bear out the literary evidence. Even there, according to Pliny, it was mixed with emmer to make it more palatable, a clear indication of the ubiquity of both emmer and the practice of polyculture (18. 141), and in fact the rye sample found contained some grains of emmer wheat, among other cereals. Rye has also been found at San Giovanni in the 30 B.C.–A.D. 200 level, which suggests that Pliny's delimitation was inaccurate. This is a clear case of the inestimable importance of archaeological discovery. We must await more evidence. Until now it has always been thought that the much greater extent of rye cultivation in Italy

[33] Evidence of finds of emmer and other cereals in prehistoric contexts: D. Evett, J. Renfrew, 'L'agricoltura neolitica italiana: una nota sui cereali', *Rivista di Scienze Preistoriche* 26 (1971), 403–9; G. Forni, 'Origini delle strutture agrarie nell'Italia preromana', in *L'azienda agraria nell'Italia centro-settentrionale dall'antichità ad oggi, Atti del convegno di Verona* (1979), 13–66; H. Helbaek, 'Agricoltura preistorica a Luni sul Mignone in Etruria', *Acta Instituti Romani Regni Sueciae* 25 (1967), 274–82; A. Oliva, 'I frumenti, le leguminose da granella e gli altri semi repertati a Belverde', *Studi Etruschi* 13 (1939), 343–9; H. N. Jarman, 'The Plant Remains', in *A Faliscan Town in Southern Etruria. Excavations at Narce 1966–71*, ed. T. W. Potter (1976), 308–10. Prehistoric and Roman botanical evidence: L. Castelletti, 'Contributo alle ricerche paletnobotaniche in Italia', *Rendiconti dell'Istituto Lombardo di Scienze e Lettere* 106 (1972), 331–74; id., 'Rapporto preliminare sui resti vegetali macroscopici delle serie neolitico-bronzo di Pienza (Siena)', *Rivista Archeologica dell'Antica Provincia e Diocesi di Como* 156-7 (1974-5), 243–51. Iron age: H. Hjelmquist, 'Economic Plants from Monte Irsi', in B.A.R. Supp. Series 20 (1977), 274–82. A. Donvito, *Monte Sannace* (1982), 161: grain and barley. Fourth–third centuries B.C.: J. C. Carter, L. Costantini et al., 'Population and Agriculture: Magna Graecia in the Fourth Century B.C.', in *The Human Landscape*, ed. C. Malone, S. Stoddart, Papers in Italian Archaeology 4.1, B.A.R. Int. Series 243 (1985), 281–312.

[34] Early Rome: H. Helbaek, 'Vegetables in the Funeral Meals of Pre-Urban Rome', *Acta Instituti Romani Regni Sueciae* 17 (1956), 287–94; N. H. Nickerson, 'An Analysis of Vegetal Remains' in *Satrianum*, ed. R. R. Holloway (1970), 124–5. Early Empire near Potenza in Basilicata: Small, 'The Environment of San Giovanni'. Third–fourth centuries A.D. at Matrice in Molise: J. L. Lloyd, *The Roman Villa at Matrice: Interim Report* (1980) and personal communication. Emmer occurs in the third–sixth-century A.D. levels at the villa of Settefinestre in the Ager Cosanus; barley and bread(?)-wheat from the first century B.C. For the complete list of finds see M. K. Jones, 'I resti vegetali' in *Settefinestre. Una villa schiavistica nell'Etruria romana*, ed. A. Carandini (1985) II, 306–9.

[35] Jasny, *Wheats*, 120 ff. argues conclusively that *far* meant emmer rather than spelt. His denial that spelt was cultivated in Italy until after the Roman period seems disproved by Helbaek, 'Agricoltura preistorica a Luni'. Find of einkorn: in Puglia, Evett and Renfrew, 'L'agricoltura neolitica'; Etruria, Helbaek, ibid.; near Bergamo, Castelletti, 'Contributo', 346 f.; Roman forum, Helbaek, 'Funeral Meals'.

in the Middle Ages was not a Roman development. Millet and panic, however, were grown throughout Roman Italy, although their importance has been hitherto almost ignored (see pp. 90–6 below). Oats (*Avena sativa*) were ground into flour and eaten as porridge by Germans (P. 18. 149), and this observation, together with uniform silence elsewhere in the sources, indicates that oats were not part of the Roman diet. Archaeological evidence, from San Giovanni near Potenza and Aquileia, thus presumably reflects the use of oats as animal forage. Oats can succeed in the poorest soils but require more water than other cereals. Aquileia receives over 1,000 mm of annual rainfall, and San Giovanni stands at 640 m above sea level in the mountains of Basilicata. Both places, therefore, suit the crop's water requirement. It was cut green for forage, and only a sufficient amount of grain for the next year's sowing was allowed to mature (Col. 2. 10. 32). This factor no doubt accounts for the rarity of seeds in archaeological finds. Use of the oat *grain* as fodder had to wait for a later period and was associated with the greater utilization of horsepower in agriculture.[36]

The cultivation of barley has been underestimated in Roman Italy. Although less tolerant than emmer of wet soils, it has the great advantage of a shorter vegetational cycle than wheat. Thus, as a general point, it is exposed for less time to risk of disease (P. 18. 79). Its early ripening also means that barley can succeed in both hotter and colder regions than wheat.[37] Thus in Italy it can be cultivated higher in the mountains and is in less danger in such southern regions as the Tavoliere, where parching summer winds can seriously damage the slower ripening wheat (see below).

This wide climatic adaptability is well borne out by the abundance and diversity of finds of barley from archaeological contexts of the Neolithic onwards.[38] It is nowadays a preponderantly husked grain, and the classical literary and archaeological evidence concurs, although one find from the Roman period at Aquileia indicates that naked varieties were known. Further from the literary evidence, it is clear that two main species were cultivated: *Hordeum hexastichum* (six-row) and *Hordeum distichum* (two-row), the latter mainly spring-sown (Col. 2. 9. 14, 16; P. 18. 78).

That it was not prized as human food seems clear, since, at least from the third century onwards, it was distributed as punishment rations in the army.[39] Yet commonly it was sown along with wheats as a reliable safeguard against shortage, as is clearly explained by Pliny the Younger (*Ep.* 1. 20. 16; Col. 2. 9. 14). Or, if autumn-sown cereals failed, barley could be sown in the spring, in January in a

[36] Some 650 whole grains of rye were recovered from a context of the second–third centuries A.D. near Pavia. The size and quality of the sample suggest strongly that the rye was cultivated rather than a weed. Also recovered, although 'incidental to the main find', were the following, which attest polyculture: emmer, bread wheat, millet and six-row barley; see L. Castelletti, 'Segale (Secale cereale L.) subfossile a Lomello', *Atti Centro Studi Italia Romana* 6 (1974), 55–71. San Giovanni: Costantini, 'Piante coltivate e piante spontanee'. For the diffusion of rye after the Roman period: C. Parain, 'The Evolution of Agricultural Technique', in *Cambridge*

*Economic History of Europe* I, ed. M. M. Postan (1966), 163. Oats at Aquileia: L. Castelletti, 'Resti macroscopici di vegetali da Aquileia', *Aquileia Nostra* 53 (1972), 147–68; at San Giovanni: Small, 'The Environment of San Giovanni'. Oats were best known as a weed to the Roman agronomists (p. 61 below).

[37] Peterson, *Wheat*, 122.

[38] From the instep of Italy to Aquileia in the north. For convenient surveys of the evidence: Castelletti, 'Contributo', 340; Hjelmquist, 'Economic Plants'.

[39] André, *L'Alimentation*, 50.

region of mild winters, or otherwise in March. Columella thought favourably of spring barley and fed it, along with wheat, to his slaves (Col. 2. 9. 16). It could be eaten as either flat bread or porridge. For the latter, it was best to harvest before full maturity, which shortened the vegetational cycle even further and avoided the risk of shedding, since barley in particular becomes fragile and brittle as it approaches full ripeness (P. 18. 80 and pp. 66–7). Barley's use in a medical potion called *tisana* is thought to have been widespread.[40]

Moreover, barley was grown everywhere in Italy in the Roman period as the principal animal fodder (Col. 2. 9. 14; 6. 3. 3). Barley tillers (puts out more shoots) more than wheat, and is thus most suitable for grazing and cutting green. In the grain, it was nutritious fodder, suitable for all animals. Sale to breeders engaged in *pastio villatica* could also prove profitable.[41]

Naked wheats, soft (*Triticum aestivum* or *vulgare*: bread wheat) and hard (*Triticum durum*: macaroni wheat), dominate in Italy today. Both naked wheats can be threshed freely and are ready for milling after threshing. Both were used for bread in the Roman period. While it can be assumed that both types were cultivated in Italy from the Neolithic (although see below), there are difficulties with the terms used by the Roman agricultural writers, and with archaeological identification. Jasny, building on the work of earlier scholars, took *triticum*, as used by the agronomists, to mean hard wheat with reference to Egypt and North Africa, but poulard wheat (*Triticum turgidum*) when it applied to Italy. He explained *siligo* as soft wheat, either bread wheat or club wheat (*Triticum compactum*). He further suggested that autumn-sown *siligo* was usually bread wheat, and the spring-sown variety club wheat. Before commenting further, it is important to consider some of the agricultural factors involved.[42]

Soft wheat is much less drought-resistant than hard wheat, while hard wheat is much less tolerant of cold conditions than soft. In broad terms, therefore, soft wheat is confined to the north of Italy, hard wheat to the south, and there is an overlapping zone in the centre. But the climatic frontier cannot be so precisely drawn, since in the mountains of Basilicata, for example, soft rather than hard naked wheat will succeed, because of the harsh winter. Or again, in the dry Tuscan Maremma hard wheat preponderates.[43] Nevertheless, on climatic grounds, hard wheat will not be expected in north Italy, and in fact, all our literary and the considerable archaeological evidence for naked wheats indicates the presence of soft wheat only in that region. Archaeological finds of soft wheat are usually identified under the category *aestivum–compactum* (bread–club), since it proves impossible in practice to separate the two with certainty. Thus Jasny's differentiation of autumn- and spring-sown soft wheats, as bread and club varieties respectively, remains unsubstantiated.[44]

[40] André, ibid., 62.

[41] Barley for peacocks, V. 3. 6. 3; geese, 3. 10. 6; chickens, 3. 9. 13; Col. 8. 5. 18. It was perhaps this, together with its consumption by the urban poor, that made barley too costly to use as normal livestock fodder in the region of cities (Col. 7. 3. 22).

[42] Jasny, *Wheats*, 95 ff. The term *triticum* was sometimes used inexactly to include naked and husked wheats: ibid., 54 ff.

[43] Tassinari, *Manuale*, 45 ff. For detailed provincial analyses of modern cereal culture in Italy, the series, *Memorie illustrative delle carte della utilizzazione del suolo*, is invaluable.

[44] Archaeological finds of soft wheat are surveyed by Castelletti, 'Contributo'.

Unfortunately there has been only one identified find of hard wheat: from the south, as could be expected, but from the elevated site of San Giovanni near Potenza, which makes it less easy to explain, since the area can commonly experience winter temperatures of -15°C. Clearly hard wheat could not have been the major cereal grown on the estate, since it could succeed there only with difficulty. In fact, the cereal finds also include emmer, barley and soft wheat, all much more suited to the prevailing conditions.[45] One possibility is that the hard wheat found at San Giovanni was a three-month variety, sown in the spring. Although, whereas the agronomists refer specifically to spring-sown soft wheat, they do not make explicit mention of spring-sown hard wheat.

One leading palaeobotanist has recently called into question the possibility of distinguishing securely between grains of soft and hard wheats, especially in a carbonized state.[46] Yet in Italy, at least, all finds of soft wheat have fitted well with the requisite climatic conditions and have probably thus been safely identified. The sample of hard wheat at San Giovanni, however, might be placed under suspicion. Better archaeological evidence for *durum* must remain a hope for the future. Yet the present lack of evidence should not lead to agreement with the supposition that hard wheat was 'brought by the Arab invaders into Northern Africa, Sicily and Spain . . . the Romans grew only soft wheat'.[47]

As for Jasny's interpretation of *triticum* in Italy as poulard wheat, there have indeed been several identified finds of *Triticum turgidum*, although neither from the Roman period, nor from the area around Rome to which Columella (who gives a description of one type of *triticum* called *robus*: 2. 6. 1) particularly referred, according to Jasny.[48] Yet another eminent palaeobotanist has seriously doubted the various identifications of *Triticum turgidum* that have been made and would prefer to subsume most under the category *aestivum–compactum*.[49] Agriculturally, poulard wheat yields highly, which clearly commends it. However, since it is a semi-hard, semi-soft wheat, it suffers from the disadvantages of both hard and soft wheats, in that it has a low tolerance of cold and drought. It is unlikely, therefore, to have been as diffuse as the hitherto identified finds have suggested.[50] It might, as today, have been grown in small quantities in Latium, for example, as Jasny suggested, and it thus contributed to polyculture of cereals in the transitional climatic zone between north and south, to which it is reasonably suited. But Jasny was wrong to reach this conclusion on the supposition that Columella (or any other agronomist) limited his purview just to the 'area around Rome'. It is clear from the agronomists that *triticum* in the specific sense was a

[45] Small, 'The Environment of San Giovanni'. Olive stones were also found at San Giovanni, although the site is above the altitude of successful olive culitvation. Perhaps olives were purchased elsewhere and transported to the villa. It is just possible that the hard wheat was also brought in from elsewhere to satisfy human or animal preferences. Cereals found in the uplands of Molise include bread wheat, spelt, emmer, barley, oats and millet but no hard wheat, which well fits the agricultural expectations: Lloyd, *The Roman Villa at Matrice* and personal communication.

[46] W. van Zeist, 'Aperçu sur la diffusion des végétaux cultivés dans la région méditerranéenne', in *Colloque de la Fondation L. Emberger sur la mise en place, l'évolution et la caractérisation de la flore et la végétation circumméditerranéenne*. Naturalia Monspeliensia, N. Hors Série (1980), 129–45.

[47] Parain, 'Evolution of Agricultural Technique', 160.

[48] Jasny, *Wheats*, 95, 102.

[49] Castelletti, 'Contributo', 356.

[50] Agricultural details: Tassinari, *Manuale*, 458. So-called *Triticum turgidum* has been identified at Cetona in Tuscany and throughout the Po Valley: Oliva, 'I frumenti a Belverde'. 'Semi-hard, semi-soft' is meant in a loose sense; genetically it is a hard wheat.

major wheat, ranked along with emmer and soft wheats, and as such enjoyed considerable diffusion. It is then best to conclude that, whether in North Africa or Italy, *triticum* signifies *Triticum durum*.

## TOPOGRAPHY

The topographical formation of the land is also important. Grain was considered best adapted to the plains, vines to the hills and forests to the mountains (V. 1. 6. 5). This undoubtedly was what the well-run estates, which would typically consist of plain, hill and mountain—or at least two of those configurations (V. 1. 6. 2)—looked like in Varro's period. Such was the Tuscan estate of Pliny the Younger. It was a landscape which reflected established human occupation: the original or 'climax' woodland of the lowlands and hillslopes had been cleared and the land cultivated. Climax vegetation may still have existed in the higher areas but it too was utilized: for pasture (V. 1. 6. 5; 2. 3. 6; 2. 5. 11; 2. 10. 3), for timber (Pliny, *Ep.* 5. 6. 8) and vine props (Col. 1. 2. 4).

Yet in some areas the 'perfect' landscape was altered through choice or necessity.

> Some of the hills should be bare of trees to serve for grain crops only; still, these crops thrive better in moderately dry and fertile plains than in steep places (*praecipitibus locis*), and for that reason even the higher grainfields should have some level sections and should slope as gently as possible just like the land of the plain. (Col. 1. 2. 4)

This is a model farm and rare, as Columella admits (1. 2. 5). The advice against 'steep places' is surely a recognition of the fact that cereals *were* grown in some areas under such conditions. However, the point to be emphasized is that on this model farm (Col. 1. 2. 4), where the flat land was devoted mainly to cereals (along with some hay-meadows and willow thickets), the recommendation that further land on the hill slopes should be set aside for cereals (not intercultivated with either vines or olives—*vacui arboribus*) surely suggests surplus cereal cultivation for profit.

Thus, either through choice or necessity, hills and mountains were utilized for grain cultivation. This is hardly surprising given that plains occupy only about one-fifth of the country, while the remaining area is divided more or less equally between hills and mountains.[51] In a discussion of labour times for various agricultural tasks, Varro comments that there is a great difference between the plains of Gaul and the mountains of Liguria (1. 18. 6). The inhabitants of Liguria ploughed and dug, but the arable land was extremely poor. Posidonius had referred to their agricultural activity as 'quarrying' rather than ploughing (Strabo 5. 2. 1). Pliny notes in passing that grain is grown in 'rocky places' ('locis saxosis', 18. 299), and this may refer to a similar situation. From these passages the unfavourable conditions under which at least some cereals were grown are evident.

---

[51] Naval Intelligence Division, *Italy* III, 26. One definition of 'mountains' is an altitude above which vines are unable to grow with ease (between 900 and 1300 m). Cf. F. Braudel, *The Mediterranean and the Mediterranean World in the Age of Philip II*, trans. S. Reynolds (1972) I, 30.

Other references serve to reinforce the picture. Varro notes the difference in sowing and reaping times between the mountain and the plain (1. 6. 3). Pliny records that mountain wheats are inferior in quality to those grown on the plains (18. 63). 'Mountain people dispense with oxen and do their ploughing with hoes' (18. 178). In steep and rough terrain it would have been difficult and hardly economical to use oxen and ploughs (V. 1. 18. 4). Reaping and the breaking up of ground are still these days carried out by hand in mountainous regions or on small plots of land everywhere.[52] Primitive methods are not always due to the unavailability or non-development of more advanced techniques; they are often dictated by the lie of the land, and the size of the area owned.

Therefore, while the agronomists certainly recommended the cultivation of cereals in ideal conditions if possible, they were well aware that often the reality was otherwise. Another indication of this realistic attitide are the varied sowing amounts for thin or thick soil (V. 1. 44. 1), or Cato's three grades of contract: 'on good land the share tenant should receive one-eighth of the unthreshed grain, on fairly good land one-seventh, on land of third quality one-sixth' (136).

The above indications of the topographical ubiquity of cereal cultivation could imply that pressure existed on some sections of the rural population to move to unfavourable areas as a result of either the occupation of the best cereal land by the richer landowners or an increase in the rural population as a whole.

## CLIMATIC FACTORS

'It has been recognized that climate decides what can be cultivated, whereas soils indicate mainly to what extent climatic opportunities can be realized.'[53]

Italy, in comparison with other countries, was considered to have a temperate climate favourable to agriculture (V. 1. 2. 4--6). Yet this is the generalized type of comment expected from the modern, northern tourists who visit the favourite resorts at the best time of the year.[54] In reality the weather (the day-to-day manifestation of climate) is extremely variable (Col. 1. *pr.* 23), and even a well-run farm is at risk (Col. 1. 7. 1). Although the climate of Italy cannot be simplified —certainly the label 'Mediterranean' will not do[55]—several regions are nevertheless, for convenience, usually recognized.[56]

Only the main climatic differences need be outlined for the purposes of this study. In Peninsular Italy (i.e. excluding the Po plain) the south is drier than the north, the east drier than the west, the hills wetter and colder than the plains. In

[52] Autopsy: reaping by hand is visible everywhere in hilly country (I was taught to reap near Potenza in July 1981); breaking the ground with hoes is likewise common, especially in the south. See Pl. III, 1.

[53] Peterson, *Wheat*, 118.

[54] Almagià, *L'Italia*, 426.

[55] Braudel, *The Mediterranean and the Mediterranean World* I, 231, observes rightly that the label 'Mediterranean climate' can be strictly applied only to the 'narrow coastal ribbons' of the countries bordering the sea. A large part of Italy is thus excluded. One way of conceiving of the Mediterranean climate is to consider the area in which the olive can grow. See the map in Cornell, Matthews, *Atlas of the Roman World*, 111. However, any detailed study of the agriculture of Italy must emphasize climatic complexity, rather than any supposed unity. One cannot, therefore, with White, *Roman Farming*, 173, generalize about the climate of Italy as 'Mediterranean'. Equally uncritical are the remarks of G. Rickman, *The Corn Supply of Ancient Rome* (1980), 97–9. Walker, *The Mediterranean Lands*, 16 ff., is instructive.

[56] The Alpine region, the Northern Plain, the Ligurian Coast, the West Coast, the East Coast, the Apennines. Cf. Almagià, *L'Italia*, 420 ff.; Naval Intelligence Division, *Italy* I, 432 ff.

the far south the rainfall tends to concentrate in the winter. Proceeding north it separates into autumn and spring maxima, although winters are still rainy. The driest and hottest summers occur on the Ionian coast, the Tarentine hinterland and the Tavoliere, where very little rain falls between May and August; there only, if anywhere in Italy, can the typical Mediterranean climate be identified. North of the Gargano promontory on the east coast and along the west coast the driest and hottest months are limited to July and August. Winters are mild in the lowlands of the south. Nowhere (or only very occasionally) do temperatures fall to zero on the west coast. The east coast, however, has a higher temperature range than the west between summer and winter.

The Po plain experiences a high annual range of temperature, from freezing in winter (snow, frost and frequent fogs) to summers almost as hot as in the extreme south of the peninsula. The rainfall maxima occur on either side of the summer months (May–June, late September–October), and in the Alps the maximum actually occurs in summer.[57]

Although it is useful for any study of Italian agriculture to recognize these climatic regions, it must again be emphasized that weather conditions throughout the country are unstable. The agriculturalist should be aware of the prevailing conditions but must be prepared for annual variations. 'Summer and winter do not come every year with the same countenance; the spring is not always rainy or the autumn moist' (Col. 1. *pr.* 23).

Since it has already been argued that cereal cultivation in Roman Italy was ubiquitous, and since the climatic diversity of Italy has been stressed, it will be as well to point out immediately that even soft wheat—among the least robust of the various cereals grown—is, climatically speaking, a very adaptable plant. 'It can be grown from beyond the arctic circles to the equator.'[58] High yields, however, can be obtained only when both climatic and soil conditions are favourable. As will become clear during the following remarks, such optimum conditions rarely occur in Italy, and, despite much discussion, there is no convincing evidence to suggest that the climate in Roman times was significantly different.[59]

[57] Other less general features: (1) upland basins in the Apennines can receive much less rain than the surrounding hills (cf. n. 60 below), and can suffer from persistent fogs due to temperature inversion; (2) the Ligurian coast, despite its northerly latitude, enjoys a favourable climate not found elsewhere on the west coast above Naples because of its sheltered position and southern aspect; (3) the northern lakes have a milder local climate than elsewhere in the Po plains (which might account for the feeling of Catullus 31).

[58] Percival, *The Wheat Plant*, 4.

[59] Vita Finzi, *Mediterranean Valleys*, 113. Yet H. H. Lamb, *Climate Past, Present and Future* II. *Climatic History of the Future* (1978), 424–9, argues that the late Republic and early Empire was a moist period with wet, thundery summers unlike those of today. Varro and Columella warn against rain at harvest time (V. 1. 13. 5; Col. 1. 6. 24; see p. 75 n. 31). But summer thunderstorms are not infrequent in Italy today (Naval Intelligence Division, *Italy* I, 534 f., Table 7 and 541, Table 14) especially in the north but also in the centre and south. If summers were wetter, maturation of the crop would have been slower, but

no secure conclusion can be drawn from comparison between modern and ancient harvesting times (see p. 66 n. 1; despite H. Nissen, *Italische Landeskunde* (repr. edn. 1979) I, 400, who collects most ancient evidence on the subject of the Roman climate). Other remarks of Columella reveal a lack of consensus also in the Roman period: some argued that the climate was becoming more temperate and thus allowing diffusion of cultivation of the vine and olive (Col. 1. 1. 5); others claimed that the climate was deteriorating (Col. 1. *pr.* 1). The remarks of R. L Raikes, 'Climate of the Mediterranean and Middle East semi-arid zones from the Monolithic to the Chalcolithic' in *Papers in Italian Archaeology* I, 1, ed. H. McK. Blake et al., B.A.R. Suppl. Series 41 (i) (1978), 1–23, emphasize the dubious nature of the evidence for climatic change and note instead frequent annual fluctuations of weather which are most important for the 'micro-climate'. Again, local surveys should consider the possibility of zonal changes in climate due to deforestation, drainage and other aspects of human intervention rather than give automatic credence to climatic changes on a continental scale. For recent work on the question of climatic change see

CHAPTER I

Adequate water, of course, is necessary for successful agriculture (V. 1. 1. 6), but irrigation was not necessary for wheat in Roman Italy.[60] 500–700 mm of annual rainfall are easily sufficient for soft (bread) wheat, while hard (macaroni) wheat which is more drought resistant can succeed with as little as 300 mm. The annual precipitation in no part of Italy falls below the latter level. In the drier regions, especially the lowlands of the south, hard wheat is the main cereal crop. Thus the *triticum* of Apulia acclaimed by Varro was certainly of this type (1. 2. 6). While this rainfall constraint will limit the cultivation of soft wheat and cold temperatures that of hard wheat, other cereals such as emmer, barley and the millets can be grown throughout Italy, as explained above. However, equally or more important than the total annual rainfall is the seasonal distribution.

At sowing time there should be sufficient water to encourage germination, but excess water, especially if it is allowed to collect in the fields in puddles, can asphyxiate the new seed or young plant, while heavy rain can wash it away. This is a danger in most parts of Italy where autumn and winter rainfall maxima occur, since most wheat is sown in that period. In the south of Italy where the lack of spring rain is certainly a formidable obstacle to good yields, excessive rain in the winter months is the greater fear: 'I granicoltori dell'Italia meridionale non devono preoccuparsi tanto della siccità quanto dell'umidità eccessiva'.[61] Careful attention to drainage at this point is therefore essential. It often means that much of the precious annual rainfall has to be channelled off and therefore lost to the crop. Cato gives a dramatic account of the activities involved (155), and in the agricultural land around Metapontum in the south, drainage channels have been discovered, which were no doubt cut to cope with this danger from torrential winter rain.[62]

Rain is required in the spring during the heading and flowering stages and for filling the ear. Spring rainfall can often be very scarce in the south and on the east coast, and so poor yields result even when soil conditions are good. It has been calculated that for the best yields in southern Italy the following rainfall distribution is necessary.[63]

| | Autumn | Winter | Spring | Summer |
|---|---|---|---|---|
| Maximum | 200 mm | 160 mm | — | 120 mm |
| Minimum | 100 mm | 60 mm | 80 mm | — |

Yet the amount of spring rain in the lowlands of south Italy is aleatory, and if it falls at a time when temperatures begin to rise rapidly it will disappear through evaporation without benefit to the crop.[64]

now: J. L. Bintliffe, W. van Zeist (eds.), *Palaeoclimates, Palaeoenvironments and Human Communities in the Eastern Mediterranean Region in Later Prehistory*, B.A.R. Int. Series 133 (1982).

[60] The only exception to this was what appears from Pliny (17. 250) to have been irrigation of wheat in the Ager Sulmonensis. Because of the very low rainfall in the upland basin of Sulmona, crops are irrigated there today; sources of water, other than rain, are comparatively plentiful. Naval Intelligence Division, *Italy* III, 104.

[61] Tassinari, *Manuale*, 468.

[62] Drainage at Metapontum: G. Uggeri, 'Κλῆροι arcaici e bonifica classica nella Χῶρα di Metaponto', *Parola del Passato* 124 (1969), 51–71. At Foggia (in the centre of the Tavoliere) approximately one-third of the annual precipitation occurs in a total of twenty-four days between October and December: Naval Intelligence Division, *Italy* I, 533, Table 2.

[63] Ibid., III, 28.

[64] C. Colamonico, *Memoria illustrativa della carta della utilizzazione del suolo della Puglia* (1960), 53. Any fall in rain less than 10 mm from spring through to autumn is lost in evaporation.

Where the spring-rain maximum merges into summer, as in parts of the northern plain, there is danger of wind and rain flattening the ripening crop. Spring rain, combined with melting snow in the Alps, often caused severe flooding in the northern plain before the Po and its tributaries were brought under control this century. This would have been a significant disadvantage for cereal cultivation in the Roman period. It was undoubtedly one reason for the extensive cultivation of millet in the area, since, as a three-month crop, it could be sown if autumn cereals had been destroyed (see pp. 90–6). Summer rainstorms, which are more common in the Po valley than elsewhere in Italy, can cause problems during the reaping, drying and threshing periods. Spring hail, another climatic feature of the northern plain as well as of the Roman Campagna, can badly damage the newly-formed ears of grain.[65]

Thus the question of the water requirement of the wheat in Italy is much more complex than a calculation based on the mean annual rainfall of any one given area. Temperature is the other main controlling factor. It has been calculated that winter-sown wheat in Italy needs a total of 2,053 daylight degrees centigrade.[66] This means that maturation takes longer in colder places and is the reason why sowing and reaping times vary with altitude, from north to south and from west to east. At about 1,000–1,200 m in Italy wheat reaches its altitude limit, since at that height it can take up to twelve months to complete its vegetation cycle. One problem of a long growth period is that it exposes the plant to greater danger of disease and adverse weather. Mountain dwellers at higher altitudes might depend rather on barley, since it completes its growth cycle in less time (see p. 14 above).

For successful germination of the seed a minimum of 3–4°C is required. Germination should occur in time to allow the plant to develop enough below and above the ground to resist winter cold. However, too much growth will increase the danger of winter injury. Thus sowing times have to be regulated by anticipation of the onset of winter temperatures; in colder areas (the highlands and the northern plain) sowing occurs earlier than in the south and the coastal plains. One difficulty experienced in regions with mild winters is the rapid growth of vegetation matter at the expense of the grain; for best yields a period of winter cold is required.[67] Snow in the winter months can be beneficial in that it allows such a cold period without freezing the plant, while it protects the young crop from ice or harsh winds. If, however, snow cover lasts more than two months it can seriously retard the growth cycle. In mountainous regions where snow lasts for two months or more or where autumn rains are too heavy to allow a successful sowing, spring wheat is preferred.[68]

The temperature should rise gradually in spring when the stem lengthens and flowering takes place at a minimum of 16°C. A hazard in this growth period are

[65] For the number of days with hail: Naval Intelligence Division, *Italy* I, 542, Table 15.

[66] C. Manetti, 'Pane e frumento', *Minerva dei campi* 16–17 (1931), 308; cf. Peterson, *Wheat*, 50.

[67] Many Italian farmers ascribe this to the idea that the cold makes the wheat healthier by killing parasites. Whatever the explanation, it is an observed fact that

'winter wheat requires a cold period in order to flower and produce grain': M. R. Jarman, D. Webley, 'Settlement and Land Use in Capitanata, Italy' in *Palaeoeconomy*, vol. II of *Papers in Economic Prehistory*, ed. E. S. Higgs (1975), 179.

[68] See further pp. 43 f.

sudden changes of temperature. On the Tavoliere, for example, rapid growth encouraged by mild winters and quickly climbing temperatures towards early spring can be endangered by harsh frosts, which are not uncommon, especially in February but also as late as April and May.[69] Another serious danger in the south in the spring and early summer is the searing wind from North Africa, known locally as the *favonio*, which hastens the crop to an abortive maturation.[70]

Light is essential for plant growth (V. 1. 2. 4–5), for the process of photo-synthesis. The clear skies of the south help to accelerate the vegetative cycle of wheat, while the persistent fogs of the northern plain and mountain valleys and basins retard it, and cause a greater risk of rust and related diseases.

Apart from the need to understand the prevailing climatic characteristics of the various regions and their effect on crops during the year—a knowledge which the Roman agronomists had, as the following chapters will demonstrate—the agriculturalist must also be aware of the so-called 'micro-climate'. Land which remains in the shade for much of the day will be considerably less useful for ripening crops than a south-facing hillside; both conditions may obtain on the same farm. When planting and sowing, therefore, the aspect of the place should be taken into consideration (V. 1. 39. 1). The 'micro-climate' will dictate what type of cereal should be sown; rich soil is best for all cereals, but in an area prone to fogs (perhaps a low-lying part of the estate) millet should be planted instead of wheat (Cato 6. 1). Ploughing and sowing times are governed not only by the prevailing regional climatic conditions but also by the lie of the land and the 'temperature' of the soil.[71] The differences in temperature with respect to altitude are, as noted, all important for vegetation. Pliny the Younger grew cereals on his Tuscan estate both in the Tiber valley and on the gently sloping hills; those on the higher ground ripened later and were harvested later in the season (*Ep.* 5. 6. 8–9).

Once the soils had been chosen and the climatic factors taken into account, the land had to be worked skilfully if it was to yield abundantly (Col. 2. 2. 21). The Romans recognized two *formae* of the countryside: one natural and one created by cultivation (V. 1. 6. 1). It was the well-ordered, man-made, rural scene which not only produced more profit but also appealed to their aesthetic sense. Or rather, because it was profitable, it was also beautiful (V. 1. 4. 1–2). The greater the regard had for appearances, the more bountiful the agricultural produce (ibid.). According to Varro, there had been an increase in practical recognition of the relation between investment in time and money and profitable agriculture: 'our ancestors used the same land as we, but laid it out poorly, and therefore produced less wine and grain and of a poorer quality' (1. 7. 2).

---

[69] Colamonico, *Memoria illustrativa della Puglia*, 52, 'while most frosts occur in autumn and winter, they can occur also in April and as late as May. Coming in these later months they are always damaging, and sometimes disastrous, for the agriculture of the region'. For the number and distribution of days with frost: Naval Intelligence Division, *Italy* I, 531, Table 4.

[70] Colamonico, *Memoria illustrativa della Puglia*, 43. Cf. the brief reference in Pliny 17. 11.

[71] 'Temperature' of the soil as regards ploughing will normally depend on the amount of water retained in the soil. The drier the soil the more quickly it will heat up for ploughing. But temperature of local soils is affected by other factors such as amount of sunlight received, altitude, colour, cf. Col. 2. 8. 3.

# CHAPTER II: PLOUGHING

What is good cultivation? Good ploughing. What is the next best? Ploughing.

Quid est agrum bene colere? bene arare. quid secundum? arare. (Cato 61. 1)

*Bene arare* as a defintion of *bene colere* emphasizes the overwhelming importance of careful ploughing in the type of agriculture described by the Roman agronomists. The paradoxical second answer, *arare*, serves to stress the first. At the same time it implies that some ploughed better than others.

The explanation of why, when, and how to plough, the discussions on how soil is affected by wind, sun and rain, and remarks on the problems of evaporation and water conservation, all reveal strict attention, based on practical experience, to technique and reason; a level of attention reached again in Italy only in much more recent times, if the agricultural writers of the Fascist regime are to be believed.[1] It would be uncritical to imagine that all or most Roman farmers who possessed ploughs adopted the methods of the agronomists. However, it is reasonable to suppose that those who were intent on obtaining high yields, inasmuch as they were bound by the soils available and the local climatic conditions, developed similar or the same methods of soil preparation. Again, any ideas that the Roman agronomists only wrote theoretically about techniques applicable to ideal soils must be dispelled. Their instructions acknowledge the varied reality: rich, water retentive soils in flat land (Col. 2. 4. 1 f.); rich soil on hillsides (2. 4. 9); thin soil on sloping ground (2. 4. 11); thick soil in flat or hilly land (2. 5. 1); medium soil, as opposed to either *pinguis* or *gracilis* soil (P. 18. 242).

## DRY FARMING

Generalizations about the climate of Italy have led to a misunderstanding of the systems of fallowing and rotation adopted in the Roman period.[2] In particular, the long-standing contention that the ancient Italian farmer had to use a fallowing system because 'he required the carefully husbanded rainfall of two years to produce the crop of one' calls for refutation.[3]

'Dry farming is farming under conditions of water shortage when irrigation cannot be used, and it includes the systems of agriculture in use throughout the

---

[1] See for example, A. Oliva, *La politica granaria di Roma antica dal 265 a.C. al 410 d.C.* (1930), 183 and *passim*; G. F. Guerrazzi, *Nuova agricoltura vecchia. I lavori profondi al grano* (1926), 2 ff.: praise of the 'Cato Club' led by the great agriculturalist Giulio Del Pelo Pardi. On ploughing and the other topics mentioned, Columella presents the most systematic treatment. Cato, Varro and Pliny are briefer. Their remarks, often incidental, imply that knowledge of most of that set out at greater length by Columella was assumed. See for example, Col. 2. 4; 3. 12. 1–4; Cato 50. 2; 131; V. 1. 27. 2–3; 1. 32; 1. 37. 5; P. 18. 1. 174 f.; 18. 181; 18. 242.

[2] For further discussion of fallowing and rotation, see pp. 117–22.

[3] C. E. Stevens, 'Agriculture and Rural Life in the Later Roman Empire' in *Cambridge Economic History of Europe* i (1966), 97. Cf. D. B. Grigg, *The Agricultural Systems of the World, an Evolutionary Approach* (1974), 135, writing of the Mediterranean basin in the Roman period, 'dry farming was well understood and almost universally practised'; White, *Roman Farming*, 113 appears to recognize the misunderstanding: 'above all, *in areas of low rainfall* (my italics), the cultivated fallow allows for two years' precipitation to be available instead of one'. Elsewhere (173) a distinction is made but not explained between Italy and Greece: 'the Mediterranean farmer learnt from very early times to practise "dry farming" methods. Thus in Greece (as a normal routine), and to a lesser extent in Italy, the land was allowed to remain fallow in alternate years.'

semi-arid regions of the world.'[4] Although there is bound to be controversy over what constitutes a semi-arid region, nevertheless a dominant characteristic is a maximum annual rainfall of some 250–375 mm mainly confined to one season, usually winter. As is clear from rainfall maps and from the preceding observations on p. 20, there are very few areas of Italy which can be classified as semi-arid according to this definition. The Tavoliere and the Tarentine hinterland are possible candidates but these areas are, it must be emphasized, exceptions. The annual rainfall and its seasonal distribution in most parts of Italy simply do not necessitate the adoption of dry farming techniques.[5]

There is in fact considerable archaeological evidence, with a bearing on Roman agriculture, from the Tavoliere, although its full worth cannot be assessed before publication of the long-awaited study by G. D. B. Jones.[6] One solution to suit the semi-arid conditions, namely the medieval and modern large, extensively-managed cereal and pastoral estate, does not seem to have been dominant during the Roman period here under discussion.[7] Air photographs (p. 6 n. 15) reveal that more than half of the Tavoliere was centuriated and settled, and that 60 per cent of the centuriated zone was under vines and olives. This arboriculture, as noted above, appears to have been intensive. Regarding cereals and forage crops, they were probably grown mostly in separate fields located in those portions of each farm's land, visible from the photographs, which were clearly not planted with vines or olives. This is most noticeable in the area of settlement near Luceria.

Varro remarks on the export of wine, oil and grain from Apulia (2. 6. 5), and it should thus perhaps be presumed that all three were produced on the sort of intensive basis recommended by the agricultural writers. Farms on the Luceria centuriation grid seem to have been between 80 and 100 *iugera*, easily large enough to produce a surplus for the market. There is some discernible evidence that a few original properties were amalgamated towards the end of the first century A.D., but into estates which continued to practise intensive agriculture, not pastoral *latifondi*. Kolendo's recent attempt to characterize Roman cereal farming in Apulia as large scale and extensive is probably therefore to be rejected. He appears to misinterpret a dense passage of Varro on *occatio* (see p. 49 n. 30) and, typically, ignores archaeological evidence.[8]

Excavation of a small farm building, dating from the end of the second century B.C. until (probably) the early second century A.D., at the very eastern edge of the Luceria centuriation zone (and thus perhaps it can be assumed that

[4] E. J. Russel, *Soil Conditions and Plant Control*, 8th edn. revised by E. W. Russel (1950), 390–6. For some other details which appear here on dry farming see A. D. Hall, *The Soil, an Introduction to the Scientific Study of the Growth of Crops*, 3rd edn. (1920), 102.

[5] Rainfall maps: Almagià, *L'Italia*, 420; Cornell, Matthews, *Atlas of the Roman World*, 13.

[6] Prior notice of this publication stretches back to Toynbee, *Hannibal's Legacy* II, 563 ff. and Brunt, *Italian Manpower*, 366. See now G. D. B. Jones, 'Il Tavoliere romano', *Archeologia Classica* 32 (1980), 85–107.

[7] See now J. Frayn, *Sheep Rearing and the Wool Trade in Italy during the Roman Period* (1984), 22 ff.,

who makes only the most general attempt to locate the cereal/livestock estates of the Roman period owned in Apulia by such as Varro. Evidence of a large villa near Troia, but outside the centuriated area, is one possibility: Jones, 'Il Tavoliere', 88.

[8] J. Kolendo, 'L'Agriculture en Apulie d'après Varron (R.r. 1. 29. 2)', *Dialogues d'Histoire Ancienne* 5 (1979), 267–71. Varro has personal knowledge of agriculture in Apulia (see Introduction, xi). Columella praised Apulian cereals in a general way (3. 8. 4). An inscription to him at Tarentum suggests some first-hand acquaintance with the driest areas of the south (*CIL* 9. 235): L. Keppie, 'Colonisation and Veteran Settlement in Italy in the First Century A.D.', *PBSR* 52 (1984), 84.

PLATE I

1.　Eared plough, Alba Fucens, Abruzzo, 20 March 1982. The 'ears' cover the seed in ridges.
The upright rod in the sharebeam is used to alter the ploughing depth (see p. 33 and Fig. 1).

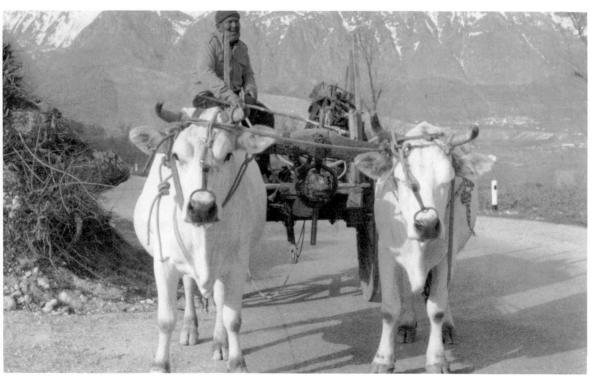

2.　Ploughing oxen used for transport, Alba Fucens, Abruzzo, 20 March 1982
(see p. 34 n. 29).

PLATE II

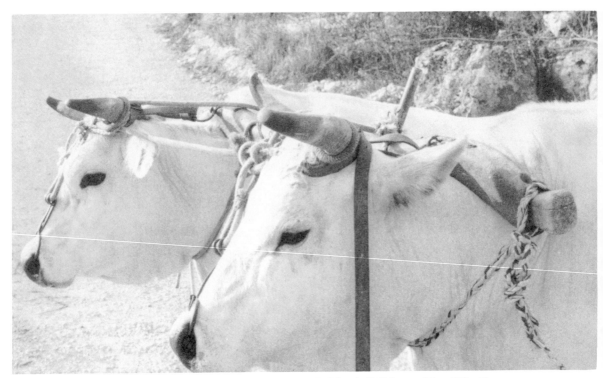

1.   Neck yoke, Alba Fucens, Abruzzo, 20 March 1982 (see p. 36 and Fig. 2).

2.   Toothed harrow, nr. Francolise, Campania, 21 April 1981. The large teeth break up the clods of earth left after ploughing. On the underside are smaller teeth for harrowing in the seed (see p. 52 and Fig. 3).

PLATE III

1. Reaping by hand, nr. Ruoti, Basilicata, 28 July 1981. One person reaps, about halfway up the culm, and leaves bundles to be tied by the other into sheaves, which in this case were taken direct to the threshing floor (see pp. 66–73, 138 n. 19).

2. Threshing and winnowing tools, nr. Ruoti, Basilicata, 2 August 1981. All these tools, for turning the wheat on the threshing floor, for winnowing and for cleaning the threshing floor, are easily made on the farm. Made entirely of wood, they do not survive in the archaeological record (see pp. 74 f.).

PLATE IV

1. Leaves as forage, nr. Poppi, Tuscany, 22 December 1982. These leaves come mainly from the supporting trees of the farm's *arbustum*, as does the firewood (see pp. 7, 36, 120 n. 10).

2. Sledge, nr. Poppi, Tuscany, 22 December 1982. Used for transport over open fields or on unmade roads (see p. 145). The conical haystack in the background indicates the presence of working animals (see p. 123).

settled intensive agriculture occupied still more of the Tavoliere than the cen-turiated areas), shows evidence for olive and vine cultivation of the sort now expected. No cereal seeds have been recovered, but a quern, and bone evidence of mature oxen strongly indicate arable activity. The dry conditions of *siticulosa Apulia* (Horace, *Epod.* 3. 16) are eloquently confirmed by a well, several troughs placed to catch rainwater from the roof, and a pumping device. Such things no doubt went some way to providing human and animal requirements. Yet there is no evidence at present to suggest that special dry farming techniques were necessary to achieve the renowned agricultural success of the area.

The error of assuming that the reason for the fallowing system in Roman Italy was to store the rain of the year for use by the crop in the next would appear to be a result of a conflation of two misunderstandings: (1) the characterization, as already noted, of Italy's climate as 'Mediterranean' with rainy winters and droughty summers; (2) the false syllogism—annual fallowing is a technique of dry farming, the Romans practised fallowing, therefore they practised dry farming. The following considerations will further expose the error of this reasoning.

The fallow field under the dry farming system should be made to store as much water as possible. The land should therefore be ploughed after the grain harvest in order to allow maximum penetration of the winter rains and to minimize run-off. The breaking up of the soil will also remove the grasses and weeds which had been growing among the cereal crop or which have sprung up after the harvest. This is necessary, since grasses and weeds use up the water which should be stored for the following year's grain crop. Repeated ploughing during the year is advisable both to eradicate further growth of grass and weeds and to impede evaporation of the water which has already penetrated.[9]

Not one of the Roman agronomists states that the land should be ploughed after the harvest in order to absorb the autumn and winter rains. Instead the first ploughing is carried out at some stage in the following year. The only exception regards the preparation for the sowing of lucerne, a crop treated in a highly individual way (Col. 2. 10. 26; P. 18. 145). The time for working the soil is dictated by its 'warmth', which means in effect its water content. In dry and warm areas, where the water content of the soil was low and the soil therefore manage-able, the first ploughing could take place in February. Usually, however, it was carried out in spring when the rains had eased and the heavier and wetter ground became more workable.[10] The rains were thus considered sufficiently abundant to percolate the soil of their own accord, without recourse to the dry-farming technique of a preliminary autumn ploughing. In fact the rain was seen as more of an enemy than a friend; careful drainage was required to cope with its excess and to prevent waterlogging or erosion. (See further below and on pp. 57 f.)

Moreover, before the fallow land was broken for the first time in the spring it could be put to good use as pasture. Sheep could be pastured on the stubble left

[9] Repeated working of the soil produces more pockets of air among the soil particles than when the soil is left compact. The air pockets act as a form of insulation; the topsoil becomes dry under the sun but the water from lower down will be less easily transferred to the surface. In dry, compact soil on the other hand, this transferring or capillary action from one soil particle to another occurs much more easily.

[10] Ploughing in February: Col. 2. 4. 9; water-retentive flat lands ploughed after the Ides of April, id. 2. 4. 3. See also the sensible remarks by C. L. Smith, 'Virgil's Instructions for Ploughing, Fallow-ing, and the Rotation of Crops', *AJPh* 2. 8 (1881), 425–45.

after the harvest (V. 1. 53; 2. 2. 12). In fact sheep eat very little of the actual stubble, since it rapidly dries out after the harvest, if it has not already lost all of its succulence even before reaping. They do eat the fallen ears of wheat if gleaning has not been carried out. Their main sustenance, however, comes from the grasses and edible weeds, which were therefore purposely allowed to grow over the winter period contrary to the requirements of dry farming. (See Col. 6. *pr.* 1; 7. 2. 3; 7. 3. 9; 7. 3. 19; and p. 125 below.)

The danger from weeds and grass on the fallow arises not so much from their consumption of water as from their competition with the new crop to be planted in the following autumn. If not checked, they compete with the newly-sown crops for the soil's nutrients and moisture, grow faster and obscure light, mature earlier and drop seeds, and thereby compound the problem in ensuing years. It was necessary, therefore, after utilizing such grass growth as pasturage over the winter period, to remove it with the first ploughing in spring before it ripened and cast its seeds (V. 1. 27. 2; Col. 2. 4. 1).

The Roman plough, since it was a sole-ard and did not turn over the sod (p. 28 n. 15), would tend to eradicate only the shallow grass and weed growth. Weeds would not then be a problem in light shallow soils. Deeper root systems in heavier soils might be sliced off (cf. P. 18. 172) but not properly removed. New growth would therefore usually appear after the first breaking of the soil in spring. Yet this too was utilized as very welcome pasture (Col. 7. 3. 20). Such land, to combat weeds, would require a greater number of ploughings than light soil.

Thus the number of ploughings between spring and the autumn/winter sowing depended on the texture of the soil. Four ploughings, including the covering of the seed, are advised as a general rule by Columella (2. 4. 8). Pliny recommends four before sowing and, in parts of Etruria where the soil was particularly heavy, nine (18. 81). Varro describes three ploughings including the covering of the seed (1. 29. 2). Again, diversity indicates the agricultural reality rather than the agronomists' inaccuracy. Repeated working of the soil was not to store water but was necessary to provide a well-aerated seed bed free of weeds, so that the greatest number of the new plants of the next sowing would be able to spread their roots quickly and as far as possible, to explore the soil's fertility and to build up resistance before the onset of the cold weather. Of course a friable soil would also absorb water more easily if any rain fell during the summer (V. 1. 27. 2); and it would prevent undue evaporation, although the Roman agronomists thought otherwise. They instead counselled against the ploughing of light soil until after the summer, according to the mistaken reasoning that a previous working of such soil would expose what moisture it contained to evaporation by the sun (P. 18. 242; Col. 2. 4. 11).

Regarding management of heavier soils, however, the summer heat could be beneficial, since it helped to break down large clods into a friable tilth (V. 1. 27. 2). Pre-summer or post-summer ploughing, heavy or light soil, in either case the essential point was the preparation of a good seed bed for the autumn sowing. There was never any doubt that the rains which fell during the sowing season were sufficient for the new seed. Again, the danger of harm through excess was paramount (Col. 2. 8. 5).

It must therefore be concluded that the biennial fallow in Roman Italy was not of the dry-fallow type. Its prime purpose was to give the land a rest after bearing a cereal crop. On the more intensive farm this method of restoring fertility combined providing winter pasture for animals, which would in turn provide manure for the soil, with the careful preparation of the ground for sowing, and with the removal of weeds, which would otherwise impede the following year's crop during the crucial first stage of growth.

If, however, the soil was particularly fertile, or plenty of manure was available, or fertility was restored by a legume rotation, then fallowing was not necessary and could be suppressed. This would have been the case on some of the estates which specialized in cereal and legume production for the market. At the other end of the scale the pressures of subsistence on a small farm could give rise to continual cropping. In such a case, where it is likely that manure was scarce and soil poor (if it is accepted that small farmers would tend to be pushed on to the poorer soils), yields would rapidly decline unless a legume rotation was practised (cf. P. 18. 187).

Biennial fallowing was the sign of a settled, as opposed to a nomadic, agricultural community, and in most areas of Roman Italy it can be assumed that enough food was produced for the existing population even though approximately half of the productive arable land at any one time might be under fallow. In some favoured situations where market possibilities permitted, or in other cases where the pressures of subsistence demanded, fallow could be suppressed. The controlling factor was not the amount of rainfall.[11]

## PLOUGH TYPES

The central argument of this section opposes the contention that the available agricultural equipment and technology of the Roman period were not sufficiently developed to exploit heavy soils which had rich arable potential.[12] The course of the argument will permit exposition of various features of ploughs and of the ploughing operation.

It is important to note at the outset that the argument that light, easily-worked soils were selected in preference to heavy, although fertile, soils was one which was developed from surveys of prehistoric sites.[13] The assumption then made seems to be that farming techniques had not changed or had not improved sufficiently by the Roman period to enable exploitation of heavy soils. The thesis may then be backed up by the view that the Roman world saw little or no techno-logical advancement.[14]

This argument, since it is based on what appears to be agricultural logic and is endorsed by some of the leading British archaeologists working in Italy today, is

[11] See further pp. 117–22.

[12] Clear expositions of this contention occur in G. W. Barker, J. Lloyd, and D. Webley, 'A Classical Landscape in Molise', *PBSR* 46 (1978), 35–51; G. W. Barker, 'The Archaeology of Samnite Settlement in Molise', *Antiquity* 51 (1977), 20–4; cf. Jarman and Webley, 'Settlement and Land Use in Capitanata, Italy', 180.

[13] See n. 12 and G. W. Barker, 'Prehistoric Terri-tories and Economics in Central Italy' in *Palaeo-economy, Papers in Economic Prehistory* ii, ed. E. S. Higgs (1975), 111–75; id., *Landscape and Society* (1981), 25; R. W. Dennel and D. Webley, 'Prehistoric Settlement and Land Use in Southern Bulgaria' in *Palaeoeconomy* ii, 97–109.

[14] M. I. Finley, 'Technical Innovation and Eco-nomic Progress in the Ancient World', *Economic History Review* 18 (1965), 29–45.

likely to be adopted by researchers unaware of alternative possibilities. Although the evidence is confined to only one area of Italy (which nevertheless, since it lies along the Biferno river valley, traverses several climatic, topographical and pedological zones), the theory elaborated from it is considered to be applicable throughout the Mediterranean. The following remarks, which seek to combat such arguments from environmental determinism, deal in detail with some fundamental issues such as types of plough, ploughing techniques, draught animals and drainage.

I assume with White that the Roman plough was of the sole-ard or body-ard variety.[15] However, while it might be agreed that the sole-ard was the dominant kind, it is most important to recognize that there were several types of it in use. The relevant literary evidence is set out in Table 1 and then discussed.

TABLE 1

| Author | Type | Use |
| --- | --- | --- |
| Cato | (1) 'Roman' (135. 2) | Heavy soil (*terra valida*) |
|  | (2) 'Campanian' (135. 2) | Blackish soil (*terra pulla*) |
|  | (3) 'Detachable ploughshares (*vomeris indutilis*) are best' (135. 2) | For both Roman and Campanian ploughs |
|  | (4) 6 ploughs and ploughshares (10. 2) | Oliveyard of 240 *iugera* with 3 yoke of oxen |
|  | 2 ploughs and ploughshares (11. 2, 4) | Vineyard of 100 *iugera* with 1 yoke of oxen |
| Varro | (1) Light plough (*aratrum leve*) (1. 20. 2) | Training oxen in sandy or light soil ('per harenam aut molliorem terram') |
|  | (2) Light plough (1. 20. 4) | Drawn by an ass, cow, or mule in light soil, as in Campania |
|  | (3) Small boards (*tabellae*) attached to the *vomer*[16] (1. 29. 2–3) | Covering the seed in ridges and making a drainage furrow (*sulcus*) between two ridges (*porcae*) |

[15] White, *Agricultural Implements*, 213–16 for the argument (and the technical vocabulary for the component parts of the plough). In support of White and against the argument that Virgil's plough (*Georgics* 1. 169–74) was a beam-ard, some comparative evidence (G. Caselli, 'Per uno studio tipologico dell'aratro', *Archeologia Medievale* 4 (1977), 281–96) together with limited archaeological evidence of socketed ploughshares can be noted (assembled by M. S. Spurr in *Enciclopedia Virgiliana* (1986–), s.v. *Aratro*. Add to this the Bronze Age sole-ard from the northern edge of Lake Garda: L. Barfield, *Northern Italy Before Rome* (1971), 72, and the plough and yoke from Lavagnone: R. Perini, 'Der frühbronzezeitliche Pflug von Lavagnone', *Archäologisches Korrespondenzblatt* 13 (1983), 187–95.

[16] Some idea of what this might have looked like can be derived from ploughing models of the Roman period which display what are assumed to be these boards, 'which run back from the tip of the share to the base of the stilt, where they are supported by arms': W. H. Manning, 'The Piercebridge Plough Group' in *Prehistoric and Roman Studies*, ed. G. de G. Sieveking, *British Museum Quarterly* 35 (1971), 132–3. It must be emphasized that the *tabellae* are not to be identified as 'mould-boards', as in *Marcus Porcius Cato on Agriculture, Marcus Terentius Varro on Agriculture*, trans. W. A. Hooper, revised by H. B. Ash (Loeb Library, 1967) ad loc., 251.

| Author | Type | Use |
|---|---|---|
| Columella | (1) Very light ploughshare (*leve admodum vomer*) and 'smallish' ploughs (*minora aratra*) (2. 2. 23) | With horn yokes rather than neck yokes in very light soils. Cannot efficiently break up fallow ground |
| | (2) Small shares and sharebeams (*exigua vomera et dentalia*) (2. 2. 24) | Light ploughing with small oxen if the farmer wants to save money |
| | (3) Heavy shares and large oxen (implied) (2. 2. 24) | To slice off surface olive and vine roots which can damage cereal yields in intercultivation |
| | (4) The lightest ploughpoint? ploughshare? (*levissimus dens*) (2. 2. 25)[17] | Fertile light soils of Numidia and Egypt |
| | (5) The smallest ploughs (*minima aratra*) (2. 10. 33) | Preparing ground to depth of 4 fingers (3 in.) for planting fenugreek |
| | (6) Light ploughs (7. 1. 2) | Drawn by asses in easily worked soils as in Libya and Baetica |
| Pliny the Elder | (1) Coulter (*culter*) fixed in front of sharebeam (18. 171) | Cutting soil before it is broken up by *vomer* |
| | (2) Common type of ploughshare shaped like the prow of a ship (18. 171)[18] | (Supposedly) normal ploughing. Fig. 1a |
| | (3) Ploughshare which is merely an iron tip on the point of the sharebeam ('non toto porrectum dentali sed exigua cuspide in rostro') (18. 171) | Easy soil (*solum facile*). Possibly Fig. 1c |
| | (4) Larger type of ploughshare sharpened into a point with sharp lateral edges (18. 172). Overall shape is like a spade blade (18. 172/3) | Breaking soil and slicing off weeds. Fig. 1b |
| | (5) The same type of plough as (4) but fitted with small wheels (18. 172–3) | Turns (*versat*, not overturns) the (grassy) clods of soil (*caespites*) in cultivated or nearly fallow land. Invented recently in *Raetia Galliae*. |
| | (6) A board (*tabula*)[19] attached to the plough (18. 180) | For covering the seed in ridges (*lirare*) where 'local custom allows' ('ubi consuetudo patitur') |
| Pliny the Younger | The strongest ploughs (*fortissima aratra*) (5. 6. 10) | Drawn by huge oxen (*ingentes boves*) in very stiff soil (*tenacissimum solum*) in the Tiber valley at Tifernum |

[17] *Dens* could mean only the tip of the sharebeam (White, *Agricultural Implements*, 130), but Columella's usage elsewhere seems to indicate that the term signifies the tip of the sharebeam together with the ploughshare (2. 4. 6).

[18] There is a textual difficulty here. *Rostrati vectis* has been taken to refer to a 'tanged' rather than a 'socketed' ploughshare: White, *Agricultural Implements*, 135. In my view it refers to a socketed ploughshare shaped as in Fig. 1a. *Rostrati vectis*, which causes confusion, is probably a 'poeticizing' of what would have otherwise been a very ordinary description, since the ploughshare in question was of the common type. The ship metaphor inherent in *rostrati* could have been borrowed from Virgil, *Georgics* 1. 50, 96–7. See p. 34.

[19] *Tabula* is singular. Despite White, *Agricultural Implements*, 140, a single board would have been able to *lirare*, which is defined by Varro (1. 29. 2) as ridging, covering the seed *and* cutting a furrow. It depends on how the field was divided up for ploughing and on the ploughing directions. For various possibilities: Scheuermeier, *Il lavoro* I, 103–4.

| Author | Type | Use |
|--------|------|-----|
| Palladius | (1) Simple ploughs (*aratra simplicia*) (1. 42. 1) | Contrasted with (2) and thus supposedly used in dry land or hilly areas where water was least likely to collect |
| | (2) Eared ploughs (*aratra aurita*) (1. 42. 1) | In flat, water-retentive areas |
| Virgil | Plough with two 'ears' (*aures*) fitted to the sharebeam (*Georgics* 1. 172) | To make a wider furrow (Servius ad loc.) |

As would be expected, there are several factors which, singly or in combination, regulate the use of a variety of ploughs and ploughshares. These factors include the texture of the soil, the depth of ploughing necessary for different crops, regional custom, the type of draught animals available, the wealth of the owner and his approach to farming.

It would appear from the Catonian evidence that while ploughs were made in each particular area to suit prevailing local soil conditions, the intensive agriculturalist might purchase two ploughs, one heavy and one light, for the different ploughing operations on his estate.

The ard plough is usually classified as a light plough.[20] On this view, heavy ploughs are mould-board ploughs. But what must be emphasized here is that there were also light and heavy *ard* ploughs. What is meant above by 'different ploughing operations' is that the first breaking up of the soil in spring would require a heavier plough than later ploughing of the same soil. Large arable farms of the Campagna Romana at the turn of this century possessed heavy ploughs for breaking up the fallow, and lighter ones both for later ploughings and for working stretches of light soils.[21]

This then is likely to have been the reason governing Cato's instructions. Since he recommends the purchase of two ploughs and two ploughshares for each yoke of oxen, his ploughs were not designed to be fitted with a variety of shares. That possibility is, however, clearly implied by Pliny (see below p. 34), and signifies a considerable improvement in ploughing method. The small farm could be characterized as one which has only one yoke and, perhaps, a single plough (Cic., 2 *Verr.* 3. 27). This was no doubt due to economic necessity. Yet different ploughing depths could be achieved with the same plough by altering the angle between the share and ploughbeam, as explained below. The richer farmer could resort to the better expedient of buying more than one type of plough.

According to White,[22] Cato's Campanian plough had a wooden rather than a metal share, and the reference to 'detachable ploughshares' indicates that fixed ones were still in use. However, there is nothing in the passage to suggest that the

---

[20] H. C. Bowen, *Ancient Fields* (1961), 7 f.
[21] A. Cervesato, *Latina Tellus, la campagna romana*    (1910), 95–6.
[22] *Agricultural Implements*, 132.

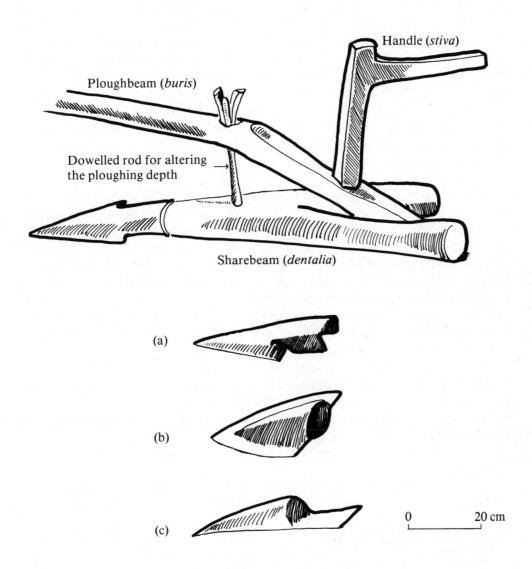

Fig. 1. Sole-ard and various socketed ploughshares.

The sole-ard was the most common general variety of plough in use in Roman Italy. It differs from the beam-ard in that the ploughshare is inserted into the sharebeam. Ploughshares: (*a*) the most usual type (P. 18. 171). It no doubt varied in length depending on the depth of ploughing required; (*b*) good for breaking heavy soil and slicing through weeds, perhaps also through shallow vine and olive roots in intercultivation. Pliny describes it as spade-like (18. 172–3); (*c*) used for the lightest soils worked with small ploughs (Col. 2. 2. 23; P. 18. 171).

Campanian plough had a wooden share, and the recommendation of 'detachable ploughshares' seems rather to apply to both the Roman and the Campanian ploughs. A further doubt arises when one tries to imagine what a 'fixed share' was. Surely any type of metal share could be removed or replaced; it would be inconceivable, for example, to discard the whole plough when the ploughshare wore down. *Indutilis*, rather than meaning simply 'detachable', probably refers to a variety of socketed share which was 'drawn on and over' (*induo*) the tip of the sharebeam, shaped, at a guess, like the representation of Pliny's second example (Fig. 1a). It is thus implied that other types of shares existed, or just possibly, that the alternative was a wooden share, in which case the recommended use of metal shares could indicate a concern with difficult soils and more difficult ploughing.

When Varro recommends the training of oxen with a light plough there is no doubt that he expects the farm equipment to include also heavier ploughs. In light soils such as those of Campania (and this is a personal observation by Varro), it is noted that asses, mules and cows can be used as draught animals with light ploughs. It is unclear whether double or single yoking is meant, although from the Columella passage (7. 1. 2) single yoking seems to be implied. This is perfectly possible and can still be seen in Italy today.[23] Yet we have no firm details from the agricultural writers. The choice between an ass or mule and a cow should take into consideration that an ass or mule requires less fodder but a cow is more productive (*fructuosior*, V. 1. 20. 4/5). This must mean that the cow would be used to produce milk (and therefore cheese) and calves, and thus would not be the same as the sterile cows which, in Columella's words, 'can endure toil and work quite as well as oxen' and should be broken in to the plough (6. 22. 1).[24] Thus, to summarize, it is most important to realize that several types of animal were used for ploughing, whether on the same or on different farms: in light soils with light ploughs, asses, mules and cows either singly or perhaps in pairs; in heavy soils, oxen and sterile cows.

The small boards attached to the plough for ridging in order to cover the seed could represent an advance in ploughing method since Cato's time. None of the

[23] I have seen single yoking of a cow in fertile but friable soil in the upper Liris valley near Ceprano (7 April 1982), and of an ass in light brown earth at the site of San Giovanni di Ruoti (25 October 1980). In the latter case an all-metal plough was being used, but the same practice had been adopted in earlier years with a wooden ard fitted with a ploughshare.

[24] While an ox (a castrated bull) is not of course *fructuosior*, it can be resold for slaughter after a working life of between five and nine years. One calculation of the costs of maintaining oxen on a farm in tropical Africa demonstrates that the resale price of a pair of oxen is 62.5% of the purchase price. It is to be further noted that if the oxen are trained on the estate (as the Roman agronomists advise), which was not the case in that particular calculation, then the purchase price is far less. For details: United Nations, Food and Agricultural Organization, *Manual on the Employment of Draught Animals in Agriculture*

(1972), 239–45. Towards the end of last century in Sardinia it was observed that the meat of old slaughtered oxen differed little from younger beef in taste: R. Tennant, *Sardinia and its Resources* (1885), 82. Profitable resale for slaughter is probably the explanation of Cato's 'sell the oxen which are getting old' (*boves vetulos*, 2. 7). Given these observations, beef might not have been as despised an item of Roman diet as is usually thought: White, *Roman Farming*, 277. It is relevant that bone samples from Bronze Age, Iron Age, Roman and medieval sites indicate that cattle were bred principally for work, and then died or were killed at a mature age and were eaten: G. W. Barker, 'Animal Husbandry and Economic Change at Monte Irsi' in *Monte Irsi, Southern Italy. The Canadian Excavations in the Iron Age and Roman Sites, 1971–1972*, ed. A. Small, B.A.R. Suppl. Series 20 (1977), 265–73.

agronomists' treatises pretends to be a complete guide to contemporary agriculture, and so it would be difficult to press this argument *e silentio*. It appears that the *tabellae* described by Varro could be attached or removed at will, and so the plough used for ridging may well have been the same as that used for earlier working of the soil.[25] Pliny's reference to *tabula* suggests the same conclusion. The statement of Palladius, however, clearly demonstrates that the 'eared' plough which was used for ridging was different from a normal or 'simple' plough. It might be assumed that both Palladius' and Virgil's eared ploughs are to be identified with the ridging plough of Varro.[26] What follows briefly here is a new interpretation based on modern comparative evidence.

The plough from Alba Fucens (Pl. I, 1) has a short length of wood attached halfway along the sharebeam on either side, which projects outwards, backwards and slightly upwards at an angle of about 45° to the sharebeam, and is fastened at its other end to the upright handle by a smaller piece of wood. These wing-like projecting lengths of wood are in fact called locally 'ears' (*orecchia*), and the plough is used for ridging.[27] The ploughshare and the sharebeam make the furrow, and the 'ears' raise the earth into ridges on either side. The 'ears' are not detachable, and the plough is a light one used only for ridging and covering the seed in soil that has already been broken up and worked into a suitable tilth by a heavier plough. In my view this is the type of plough described by Virgil and is the *aratrum auritum* of Palladius. While the *tabellae* attachments of the Varronian plough would have served the same purpose as the 'eared' plough, it is important for an understanding of the agricultural diversity of Roman Italy to recognize that there were at least two methods of carrying out the same ridging operation.

That the ridging system had become widespread by the late Republic is indicated by the existence of a vernacular term among *rustici* (V. 1. 29. 2; cf. Col. 2. 4. 8), and by certain late Republican *responsa* in the *Digest* (39. 3). Noteworthy is the situation put before Alfenus (39. 3. 24. 1), where one farmer channelled off water from his land by drainage furrows and ridges ('per sulcos itemque porcas') to the detriment of his neighbour at a lower level.

The remarks of Columella imply the existence not simply of ploughs that were either light or heavy but of a gradation of plough weights to suit various soils, crops, and economic possibilities. When sowing fenugreek, the soil should not be worked to a depth of more than three inches, and this observation provides an indication of the penetration of the 'smallest ploughs'. In an *arbustum*, however, the soil should be worked deeply and powerfully in order to break off spreading tree roots which could prejudice the success of the cereal crops (Col. 2. 2. 24). A ploughshare similar to the Pliny example (4) was no doubt used.

Part of Columella's discussion of suitable ploughing methods provides an interesting insight into an agricultural rationale different from his own. Celsus had advised the purchase of small oxen and small ploughs in order to save money. This is opposed by Columella, who argues that the initially greater investment in stronger animals and heavier ploughs will be more than repaid by higher yields

[25] The Piercebridge plough model appears to represent such a plough with the boards removed: Manning, 'The Piercebridge Plough Group', 132 f.

[26] For the state of the argument: White, *Agricultural Implements*, 140.

[27] For some possible parallels, cf. Caselli, 'Per uno studio tipologico dell'aratro', 281–96.

D

from land that has been worked deeper and more efficiently (2. 2. 23–4).
Columella's attitude is that which will be adopted on the intensive estate, yet
doubt remains that the view of Celsus indicates the existence of 'extensive
farming' as defined above (p. 1). This is because it is clear from the remarks of
Columella that inferior equipment was not a labour-saving device: breaking the
ground with light ploughs and small oxen would require no less time than
ploughing the same soil deeply with large oxen and heavy ploughs. Instead, the
advice of Celsus, if it is to be taken seriously, is representative of those estate
owners who, for whatever reason, did not seek to derive profit from their *cereal*
land, but were content to work it with as little expense as possible.

While Columella refers to a range of plough sizes, Pliny provides information
on various types of ploughshares. It is to be observed that the simple wooden
share, which perhaps still existed in Cato's period, is not mentioned; even the
lightest soil required some form of iron share (Pliny the Elder, example (3) ). The
list suggests that any given plough could be fitted with a variety of shares,
although it is surely more likely that example (4) was suited especially to a heavy
plough and heavy soils. Such a plough could be carried only with difficulty, and
this would be a reason for the addition of wheels. Its heaviness and its use in heavy
soils are further suggested by the need for two or three pairs of oxen to draw it
('protelis binis ternisque arant', 18. 173).[28] One of the advantages of a light sole-
ard is that it can be easily carried by the ploughman from its place of storage to the
field. Yet it should not be deduced from this that even the heaviest ploughs
mentioned by the Roman agronomists were light enough to be carried by one
man, just because no transport difficulties are discussed. In modern practice, if a
heavy animal-drawn implement is to be employed at some distance from the farm
buildings, it is simply carried there in a cart pulled by the same oxen which are
going to use it.[29]

As to the diffusion of the wheeled plough in Roman Italy, Pliny provides
precise information. Raetia Galliae (Table 1, Pliny the Elder (5)) should be
understood as the valleys and slopes of the Alps behind and between Como and
Verona. Despite this and Pliny's statement that it was a recent introduction,
Kolendo wishes to argue that the use of the wheeled plough was widespread.[30]
Another discussion of the question accepts Servius' explanation of *Georgics* 1. 174
and links it to Pliny's wheeled plough.[31] Yet Virgil, by the use of the term *currus*
may simply have been extending the plough-as-ship metaphor from 1. 50, since
*currus* can refer to the keel of a ship (as Catullus 64. 9). Against widespread
diffusion is the fact that Pliny's near contemporary, Columella, does not mention
the wheeled plough. By the late medieval period it was in use in the lower Po plain
and some northern valleys of the Marche.[32] It is best to assume that it was more
confined in the Roman period, although its introduction should be seen as
another stage in the ability and need to work heavy soils.

---

[28] Cf. n. 39 below.

[29] Pl. I, 2 shows a cart drawn by two oxen. In the
cart was a harrow which the oxen had used in the field
(Alba Fucens, 20 March 1982).

[30] Kolendo, *L'agricoltura*, 70–127.

[31] G. Forni, 'Il "Plaumaratum" (aratro a carello)

di Plinio nel quadro della storia dell'aratrocoltura in
Italia' in *Tecnologia, economia e società nel mondo
romano. Atti del Convegno di Como 27–29 settembre
1979* (1980), 99–120.

[32] Cherubini, 'Le campagne italiane', 299.

One other useful indication of the functioning of ploughs is provided by Pliny. When using a ridging plough to cover the seed 'it is usual to make inter-mediate drainage funnels by driving a deeper furrow' (18. 179). I interpret this to mean that at regular intervals the depth of penetration of the ridging plough was altered. There are two ways of doing this: (1) shortening the length of the plough-beam between the share and the yoke by pushing it further through the yoke attachment; this increases the angle between the ploughbeam and sharebeam and results in deeper penetration of the ploughshare; (2) a short dowelled rod of wood is fitted in an upright position on the sharebeam and inserted into the ploughbeam. The ploughbeam, since it is slightly flexible, can be wedged at various heights on the dowelled rod and thereby the angle between the sharebeam and ploughbeam can be widened or reduced.[33] Since none of the descriptions of the working parts of the Roman plough mentions the existence of the latter device, it is perhaps better to assume that the former, more simple, method of altering the depth of ploughing was usual.

From Pliny's description of the function of the *culter* there can be no doubt that it was similar to a modern coulter, namely a blade which is attached to the ploughbeam and cuts vertically into the soil just in front of the ploughshare along the (future) furrow wall. It is particularly useful for the first ploughing of heavy soils. In light soils or in later ploughing of heavy soils it would not be required and could be removed.[34] That such a coulter is mentioned by neither Cato nor Varro could signify that it had been an invention of the early Empire; yet that Columella, a near contemporary of Pliny, makes no reference to it indicates that its diffusion was not wide. There can, however, be no doubt that it existed somewhere in Italy, since Pliny is scrupulous in noting foreign provenance (for example in the case of the wheeled plough). The existence of the coulter serves to emphasize again a concern with working heavier soils as well as contributing further to the picture of agricultural diversity.[35]

## OXEN AND YOKES

It is clear that different sizes and breeds of oxen were known, and it was recognized that they had different working capacities (Col. 6. 1. 1–2; V. 2. 5. 9–10). For difficult land oxen had to be very powerful and could 'often leave the plough stuck in the ground with a broken beam' (V. 1. 19. 2). Strong oxen could plough deeper than smaller ones (Col. 2. 2. 24). Some oxen were bred and trained for ploughing level country, others for steeper terrain (V. 1. 20. 2). This meant that locally bred oxen were usually best for any given farm, and if oxen were purchased and brought from another region, they would perform best when the lie of the new land was similar to that of their place of origin (Col. 6. 2. 12–13). The

[33] See Pl. I, 1 and Fig. 1.

[34] Again in the Piercebridge model there is evidence that a coulter could be fitted if necessary: Manning, 'The Piercebridge Plough Group', 133.

[35] To my knowledge there have, however, been no finds of coulters in Italy from the Roman period. For examples of coulters found in England see S. Rees, *Agricultural Implements in Prehistoric and Roman Britain*, B.A.R. British Series 69 (1979), 60. White, *Agricultural Implements*, 70, 133, does not believe that the coulter (as it is understood in modern times) existed in Roman Italy but that Pliny's reference (18. 171) was to a 'ground opener'. This would, however, still indicate cultivation of heavy, stiff soils.

sturdiest animals should be chosen, and methods of selection, based on appearance, differ little from modern advice.[36] As already observed, it would be on the intensively managed estate that the strongest animals most suited to the prevailing soils and topography would be bought.

Two types of yoke were known and their advantages and disadvantages recognized. The first was the 'head' or 'horn' yoke, the second was the 'neck or shoulder' or 'withers' yoke (see Fig. 2). Columella, who was interested in greater traction power and deep ploughing, was correct in advocating the use of the latter type, especially since long-necked cattle had been recommended.[37] One disadvantage of the shoulder yoke is the frequency of sores, a problem of which Columella was well aware (cf. 6. 16. 1).

Yoking systems and ploughs could only be as good as the draught animals which used them, and for efficient work the oxen had to be kept well nourished. The agronomists recognized that conditions varied:

> If the fertility of the district supplies green fodder, there is no doubt that this food is to be preferred to all others; but this is only to be found in irrigated or dewy areas . . . On drier farms the oxen must be fed at their stalls, the fodder provided varying according to the nature of the district. . . .. The best foods are vetches, chickpea and meadow hay. We are not looking after our cattle so well if we feed them on chaff, which is a universal, and in some districts the only, resource. (Col. 6. 3. 2–3)

It would be in the last mentioned areas that the oxen, after a winter of inactivity and little fodder, would be in a poor condition for the strenuous first ploughing in spring. Yet on the more favoured arable estate more nutritious and plentiful fodder was available; it is recommended that the amount of hay should be increased in March and April for the initial breaking of the soil, and that during the sowing period in November and December oxen should be given all the food they want (Col. 6. 3. 6).[38]

*Heavy Soils*

In the above discussion what has been revealed is the diversity and complexity of the ploughing operation in Italy from the early second century B.C. to the late first century A.D. The evidence as it appears suggests a considerable improvement over time, and although this must remain a tentative observation, it would accord with other indications that the late Republic and early Empire witnessed an increasing

---

[36] 'The ox . . . must be powerful, compact, sturdy, with well developed muscles, particularly those of the back and hindquarters. Its legs must be strong and as short . . . Its chest must be ample and deep. It must have strong hooves', United Nations, F.A.O., *The Employment of Draught Animals*, 12. Columella 5. 1. 3 (following Mago), 'The oxen which should be purchased are those which are young, squarely built, with large limbs . . . the neck long and muscular . . . the chest broad, the shoulder huge . . . the flanks should be extended, the loins wide, the back straight, the buttocks round, the legs compact and straight but short . . . the hooves large' (cf. V. 2. 5. 7–8).

[37] Discussion of yokes: Col. 2. 2. 22–3. Short-necked cattle can be used with head yokes, although the jolts and checks received during ploughing when obstacles are encountered by the plough can cause serious injury to the animals' heads. The animals are unable to move their heads freely with this type of yoke, and this increases their discomfort. Longer-necked cattle harnessed to the head yoke (against which practice Columella argues) are unable to produce their potential traction power: H. J. Hopfen, *Farm Implements for Arid and Tropical Regions* (1969), 19–20.

[38] See further pp. 119 f.

(a)

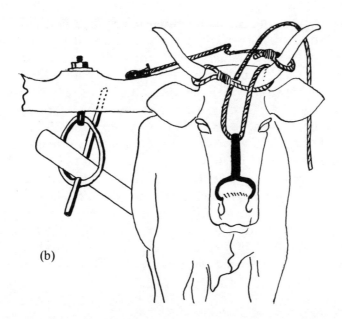

(b)

Fig. 2. Head and neck yokes.

The head yoke (*a*) suits only short-necked oxen and light soils. Columella rejects this
(2. 2. 22–3) and advises the use of long-necked oxen, which can only perform to their full
capacity with the neck yoke (*b*). Cf. Pl. II, 1.

concern with the practice of intensive arable farming, at least in the vicinity of urban centres.

The agricultural writers wrote about an Italy they knew, and described ploughing which ranged from the use of asses in thin soil to the heaviest equipment drawn by robust and well-fed oxen. Whereas it is this latter mode of arable agriculture that they promote (most clearly Varro and Columella), considerable information is also provided about other existing methods.

In the preceding chapter it was observed how the richest soils were recommended for cereals. The best soil was fertile and easily worked. The next choice fell on that soil which was rich but heavy and clayey; the considerable expense and labour required to work it was repaid by high yields. The worst soil was dry, stiff and heavy, and infertile; even that could be ploughed but the extremely poor yields would not compensate for the effort. Even if it was decided not to work such land but rather to leave it for grazing, it yielded poorly (Col. 2. 2. 5–7). It is essential to note that the choice presented itself: to plough or not to plough was decided on the basis of yields set against expense and labour. Wet meadow land was highly praised because it produced fodder spontaneously, without any human effort (V. 1. 7. 10). If it was left as such, instead of being drained and cultivated, that was because it was a prized asset, not because it was considered impossible to plough.

There is no suggestion in any of the literary evidence that even the heaviest soils could not physically be worked. Because Pliny the Younger had a ready market for his produce (Rome), it was worth possessing the largest oxen and the strongest ploughs to cultivate the heavy alluvial soils of the upper Tiber valley at Tifernum. There was no question about the difficulty of ploughing such soil; to pulverize it properly even with the best equipment required nine ploughings (*Ep.* 5. 6. 10). Particularly hard was the first ploughing, and it was best to wait for some rain to dampen the soil to render it more tractable (Col. 2. 4. 8). Then when ploughing began, oxen had to be rested on reaching the end of each furrow and the yoke pushed forward to ease their shoulders (Col. 2. 2. 28). The ploughbeam might break (V. 1. 19. 2), and, particularly hazardous for both oxen and ploughman, the share could stick or jump out of the ground leaving patches of hard unworked soil (Col. 2. 4. 3, 6). Yet the soil was finally broken up, even if, as in some heavy land, two, three or four teams of oxen had to be yoked to the one plough, a practice known at least since Cato's period.[39] If the capital was available and the decision taken, the most tenacious soils could be ploughed.

Drainage, of course, was an essential part of the process, and all agronomists put considerable emphasis on this. In a discussion of bringing damp and wooded (and thus presumably low-lying) areas under arable cultivation, Columella provided detailed instructions on the construction of ditches (*fossae*). It would be

---

[39] Cato, *Orig.* 5, fr. 103, 'sed protelo trini boves unum aratrum ducent'; P. 18. 70, 'protelis binis ternisque sic arant'. The word *protelum* indicates that the oxen were yoked in pairs one pair behind the other: Kolendo, *L'agricoltura*, 67. The relative efficiency of each animal actually decreases as more animals are used, although the overall traction potential is greater. When using a pair of oxen of the same strength the potential ploughing effort of a single ox is multiplied by 1.9. If two pairs are used the power of one pair is multiplied by 1.7, and three pairs would only double the potential of one pair: United Nations, F.A.O., *The Employment of Draught Animals*, 24–5.

especially this type of ground which, once worked and sown, would require ridging and the cutting of drainage furrows to carry water off into the earlier constructed main ditches, as Pliny the Elder advised (18. 179). His nephew was careful to point out that the soils of the Tifernum estate were well drained (*Ep.* 5. 6. 11), and it is important to realize how necessary this was for successful cultivation.[40]

One region where rich alluvial soils required careful drainage was in the northern plain. That the soils of the area were worked is clear from the extensive visible traces of centuriation and field divisions.[41] There is good evidence that the alluvial sandy-clay soils of the Ravenna region in the Romagna plain had been drained and were under intensive cereal cultivation of the type recommended by the agronomists, since several *villae rusticae* with capacious granaries dating from the early first century B.C. have been excavated in the area; and it is argued with all probability that the cereals were transported by land or by water to be sold at the market centre of Ravenna.[42]

It is not for a moment suggested that heavy soils were automatically ploughed. The equation of capital and labour costs to yield and profit possibility had to be carefully considered. The richest soils, according to Pliny the Elder, are always hard to work, to the extent that their very merit of fertility can be said to 'afflict' the farmer (17. 28). Pliny the Younger vividly describes the effort involved:

> In meadows and wheatfields the land can be broken up only by the heaviest oxen and the strongest ploughs. The soil is so heavy that it is thrown up in great clods at the first ploughing and is not thoroughly broken until it has been gone over nine times. (*Ep.* 5. 6. 10)

We should, therefore, resist any hypothesis which excludes the possibility that Roman agriculturalists, unlike prehistoric farmers, were capable of ploughing the heaviest soils. How widespread such heavy ploughing was should become increasingly quantifiable as detailed archaeological surveys, interested in the agricultural resources of Roman settlement in Italy, increase. A survey in Spain demonstrates quite a remarkable coincidence between villa sites and the most fertile soils.[43] While such a study might be questioned on the ground that it concerns such an extensive area, detailed research on Roman and pre-Roman ploughing in Britain will inspire more confidence. It has recently been stated, in

---

[40] Ditches were important for drainage: Sic. Flacc., pp. 111–13 Thulin; La. 147, 21–149; cf. *Dig.* 39. 3. 1 for draining land where rainwater collects (pp. 20, 57 f. below). Concern about river floods and alluviation has relevance in this context; presumably the soil prone to flooding was often worked (p. 8 n. 22). One expedient was construction of river banks combined with ditches, as along the Tiber just north of Rome (V. 1. 14. 3; cf. *Dig.* 43. 13. 7). But such drainage work probably required capital (cf. Col. 2. 2. 12/13). Thus poor veterans allotted *paludes et silvas* (Brunt, *Italian Manpower*, 310 f.) would be unlikely to succeed.

[41] F. Castagnoli, *Le ricerche sui resti della cen-*

*turiazione*, Note e Discussioni Erudite 7 (1958), 28, where traces of Roman fields are observed 120 feet (1 Roman *actus*) wide. It is considered that the heavy soil of these fields was ploughed transversely, since Columella states that oxen should not plough a furrow longer than one *actus* without stopping (2. 2. 27).

[42] For these villas and the interpretation stated here, see D. Scagliarini, *Ravenna e le ville romane in Romagna* (1968), G. Mansuelli, *La villa romana di Russi* (1962), *passim*.

[43] J. G. Gorges, *Les villas hispano-romaines. Inventaire et problématique archéologiques* (1979), 67 ff.

accordance with the view argued above, that the Roman farmer was neither restricted to the easiest land nor excluded from soils worked extensively in later ages.[44]

An example of a promising, detailed archaeological survey in Italy is that currently under way in the Albegna valley in Tuscany, just north of the Ager Cosanus. It appears that the villas sited along the valley terraces utilized the rich alluvial soils for grain cultivation. Convenient local markets could be found at Saturnia and Heba, while a good road or the river itself (when not in flood) ensured easy access to the coast and markets beyond.[45]

*Digging*

Mountain dwellers 'ploughed' with hoes rather than oxen (P. 18. 178). I take this to mean that ploughs were common enough elsewhere, even among peasant-cultivators, although not necessarily drawn by oxen. As the preceding discussion has shown, single asses or cows could be used, and Pliny elsewhere observed that one of the main functions of asses was ploughing (P. 8. 167). Economical to feed (Col. 7. 1. 2) and coupled to a light and simple plough, the ass would have been inexpensive and its forage not difficult to find even on the peasant farm.

Only in steep and rugged terrain, or in small garden plots, would the plough have been uneconomical. There hoes or mattocks were (and are) used instead (cf. p. 17 and Horace, *Odes* 3. 6. 38-9). Yet there are indications in Varro that land under cereal crops on the intensive arable estate was also *dug* rather than ploughed (1. 18. 2; 1. 37. 5). This is another insight into diversity of practice. Arthur Young (during a visit to Italy in the late eighteenth century) noted that the spade was sometimes used in place of, or in combination with, the plough in grain land; a method which he damned as primitive, although from his own testimony the crop yields achieved were high. At the start of this century, Azimonte referred to a rotation of maize followed by wheat, which began with a thorough digging of the soil with spades (*vanghe*). It is possible then that the same occasional, deep working of arable land occurred on intensively-run estates during the late Republic and early Empire, the purpose being to increase yields.[46]

[44] P. Salway, *Roman Britain* (1981), 623.

[45] I. Attolini et al., 'Ricognizione archeologica nell'Ager Cosanus e nella valle dell'Albegna. Rapporto preliminare 1981', *Archeologia Medievale* 9 (1982), 365–86; id., *Archeologia Medievale* 10 (1983), 439–65.

[46] Arthur Young, see Table 2, pp. 86 f. E. Azimonte, *Il frumento, come si coltiva o come si dovrebbe coltivare in Italia* (1914), 221. Spades have altered little in Italy since the Roman period: White, *Agricultural Implements*, 17 ff. A deep working of the soil leads to greater yields: Azimonte, 105, reports the results of experiments with deep ploughing. The same piece of land worked at a depth of 10 cm yielded 5.8 quintals per ha, at 30 cm 7.06 qu. per ha, at 50 cm 7.36 qu. per ha, while at greater depths yields dropped dramatically.

# CHAPTER III: SOWING AND CULTIVATION

## SEED SLECTION

Careful seed selection is of crucial importance for improved cereal yields and was emphasized as a feature of rational agriculture by the agricultural writers. If it is carried out year after year, the purity of the species is maintained, weeds are restricted, and it can thus lead to higher yields. On a large arable farm in Puglia (managed by a farmer-owner who sought to cultivate cereals as intensively as the profits and labour market allowed), during the last quarter of the nineteenth century, the method of selection was to take note of the best looking parts of the crop as it grew and then to thresh and store them separately.[1] This is probably how Varro's statement on the subject should be interpreted: 'The crops which were the largest and best in the field [*seges* = crops in the field] should have their ears threshed separately so that the best seed can be obtained' ('quae seges grandissima atque optima fuerit, seorsum in aream secerni oportet spicas, ut semen optimum habeat') (1. 52. 1). Seed selection should conform with this method according to Columella (who here quotes Celsus) when the harvest is average (2. 9. 11). When the yield is good, all the grain should be sieved and the best seeds chosen in this way. The second procedure, especially when employed on a large cereal growing farm, would have been extremely labour intensive, and underlines the strict attention paid to seed selection (ibid.).[2]

Since a variety of cereal crops might be cultivated on the same farm, the same process would have to be carried out separately for each. It would have been important to keep the threshing floor swept clean, to avoid contamination not only by different cereals but also by the various legumes, such as beans, which had been threshed there earlier. Careful maintenance of seed purity would, it could be supposed, have been easier on the smaller farms, but my experience of contemporary peasant practice would, however, indicate the opposite. I observed in various locations in the highlands of Basilicata that several types of cereal including barley, oats, and hard and soft wheats were grown and threshed together. The reason was not the one commonly suggested as an explanation of crop diversification: the fear of putting all one's eggs into the same basket. Rather, it was due to careless seed selection and cleaning of the threshing floor.[3] The problem compounds itself from year to year. It means also that some of the cereals ripen before others and are practically useless for producing flour by the time that the 'majority crop' is reaped.[4]

Although the general advice was, and still is, to keep to the tried and tested

---

[1] V. Testini, *Il frumento: coltura e trebbiatura nella Puglia Barese* (1885), 18 f.

[2] Further recognition of the importance of seed selection is demonstrated by the criteria used: size, weight, colour, texture (Col. 2. 9. 11-13; P. 18. 195). Columella offers a fatalistic comment on the recognized limitations of the empirical method: weak crops *can* grow from strong seed but strong crops will never grow from weak seed (2. 9. 12). Against those who argue that Celsus represented a system of extensive farming it is to be noted that his recommended method of seed selection was highly *intensive* (even if done with sieves). Five *modii* of wheat were usually sown to the *iugerum* (V. 1. 44. 1); each *modius* would have contained approximately 175,000 selected seeds. Such a method of seed selection is incompatible with any form of extensive agriculture.

[3] See p. 97 n. 39.

[4] This was emphasized by a local miller at Ruoti near Potenza in Basilicata. Observations about mixed cereal crops: from interviews with small cereal farmers between Melfi and Potenza (20-30 July 1981).

types, some farmers experimented (in the tradition of the progressive agri-culturalists of the age, V. 1. 18. 8) with the importation of seed. Pliny confirms that this happened but condemns the practice as *falsa diligentia* (18. 197). Yet Columella, without explanation, asserts that a type of emmer from Clusium was, among others, in common use (2. 6. 3).[5] Such experimentation would have been the luxury of the larger landowner, too risky for the peasant. A possible danger of refining and developing seeds to increase yields can be a decrease in resistance of the growing crop to rust, mildew, and attack by insects and birds. It is no doubt true that more bread wheats were being cultivated in Varro's and Columella's time than in an earlier age, and while they may have yielded better than the more primitive emmer and were certainly milled more easily, the husked cereals were yet more resistant to attack from birds and fungi.[6] Thus husked cereals would have appealed more than did naked wheats to *rustici*. On the larger estates where naked wheats were grown for sale, much more attention had to be given to the protective measures of drainage, hoeing and weeding to ensure a profitable yield. Such measures might also include attempts to disinfect the seed (P. 18. 156; Col. 2. 9. 10).

## SOWING TIMES

There were two sowing times for grain: autumn and spring. Within these two seasons the precise time to sow depends on the climate, especially the micro-climate. Where it is colder because of latitude, dampness, shade or greater altitude, the vegetational cycle of wheat is longer, and therefore it is necessary to sow earlier than in warmer areas. Coastal farms of south Campania carry out the autumn sowing early in November; in the colder and higher areas of Molise near Campobasso I have seen sowing begin as early as mid-September. Yet sowing times can also vary on the same farm when soils and aspects differ. Columella is succinct: 'In areas that are wet and poor in fertility, or cold, or even shaded, it is usually best to sow before 1 October' (2. 8. 3). Otherwise he recommends from the last week of October until the winter solstice (*c.*25 December) (2. 8. 2). Pliny advises commencement on 10 November or better, when nature gives her infallible sign and the leaves begin to fall. Yet he notes that most people begin sowing eleven days from the autumn equinox (which fell nine days before 1 October) (18. 224–5). Varro, always the most explicitly aware of variations in conditions and practice, states that sowing can continue from the autumn equinox until the winter solstice (1. 34. 1). There was, then, as it might first appear, a certain confusion. But this would be to misunderstand the reality. It is impossible to fix dates for sowing, and the variants offered by the agricultural writers reflect this. As a modern Italian handbook observes: 'Soltanto l'osservazione attenta e ripetuta può essere di guida' ('Observation of local established practice is the only sure guide').[7] Another axiom is to sow early rather than late, if in doubt: 'sementa anticipata, rare volte fu sbagliata'.[8]

---

[5] Pliny observes that seed was imported from cold, late-ripening areas to warm, early-ripening areas and vice versa. During the Fascist encouragement of wheat growing in Italy, seed experimentation was not a practice found to be favoured by the small farmer, as the consequences of crop failure were too serious. A. Oliva, *Il frumento nella montagna* (1936), 16.

[6] Cf. p. 11.

[7] Tassinari, *Manuale*, 470.

[8] Paoletti, 'Norme pratiche', 9. Cf. Col. 11. 2. 80: 'While every operation of agriculture should be performed with alacrity, this is especially true of sowing. It is an old proverb among farmers that an early sowing can often deceive us, late sowing never

Sowing at the correct time is crucial for the successful germination of the seed. This will depend on the type of grain and on the climate and soil conditions. Emmer could be, and was, sown earlier than other cereals. It could also withstand poorly prepared land. The early sowing time for unfavourable conditions mentioned by Columella may therefore refer to emmer. So, perhaps, does Pliny's observation that *most* people sow eleven days after the autumn equinox, since quantitatively the small farmer was prevalent in Italy throughout the Roman period, and Pliny asserted that he wrote for *rustici*.[9] The late October or early November dates were applicable to warmer, more favourable soils and climatic conditions suitable for the more delicate bread wheats. Sowing right up until the winter solstice could occur only in the lowlands of the south of the peninsula, where winters are milder and an earlier sowing might have the undesirable consequences of a too rapid growth and thus an increased chance of frost damage in early spring. In such regions the autumn sowing can also be late when the first winter rains are delayed.[10] The variable climatic factors account for the difficulty in prescribing dates.[11]

In areas of Italy where autumn merges rapidly into winter, a spring sowing of wheat is more practical. Pliny records a recent spring sowing after the failure of a winter-sown crop in the Trier region: 'The crop was nipped by an extremely cold winter, so that they sowed the fields again in March, and had an excellent harvest' (18. 183). According to Columella, spring sowing was most commonly practised in cold and snowy regions where autumn planting was difficult due to the early bad weather (2. 9. 7). This remark is a further indication of the widespread cultivation of grain in Italy. Pliny specifically mentions a spring-sown wheat used throughout the Alps where heavy snow prevented successful sowing in autumn (18. 69). Yet in more temperate regions, autumn sowing was considered better for all cereals because with a longer growing period they yielded more (Col. 2. 9. 8).[12]

Yet there is no doubt that spring sowing was not confined only to cold and mountainous areas. It was carried out also on the plains (V. 1. 6. 3) and in warm regions (Col. 11. 2. 20). This needs explanation. White comments that 'the Roman evidence suggests that spring-wheat only did well in cold climates'.[13] Knowledge of present Italian agriculture can again be of use. Firstly, however, it must be pointed out that while spring sowing appears often in Columella's treatise, it mostly refers to legumes or forage crops.[14] Millet and panic could also be sown in the spring and, as is argued on pp. 94–102, those crops would have been much commoner in the Roman period than now. Other cereals which could succeed (because they grew quickly) as spring-sown crops, according to Columella, were a species of three-month emmer, Galatian barley and *siligo* (2. 9. 8; 2. 6. 3). While it is probable that at least the first two of these last, along with

—it is always a failure'.

[9] 18. 323; cf. 18. 24; 1 *pr.* 6 and Frederiksen, 'Plinio il vecchio', 82–3. The early sowing might also refer to barley; cf. P. 18. 71 and p. 14 n. 37. Emmer: p. 11.

[10] A. Grimaldi, *Coltivazione erbacee* (1979), 29–30; and see pp. 20 f. on the requirements for successful germination.

[11] Germination period: V. 1. 34. 1; growth of roots during autumn and winter: V. 1. 45. 3; Col. 2. 8. 3.

[12] Cf. Percival, *The Wheat Plant*, 422.

[13] White, *Roman Farming*, 188.

[14] Legumes suitable for spring sowing: Col. 2. 10. 9, 16, 17, 20, 21, 26, 33. For a discussion of legumes see pp. 103–16.

millet, were commonly grown as a standby in case of a poor harvest from the autumn cereals, some perspective of the ratio between autumn- and spring-sown wheat may be derived from the observation that in 1945 spring-wheat accounted for only 2 per cent of the total wheat crop.[15] While there is little doubt that the ratio also in the Roman period must have been heavily weighted in favour of autumn-sown cereals, there is reason to believe that spring-sown cereals counted for more than 2 per cent.

Why were cereals planted in the plains and warm regions in the spring? In the south of Italy, if the rains (which have the tendency of contracting their range to the winter months) are delayed and arrive too late to render the soil workable and to provide the moisture requirements for successful germination, the sowing (of a quickly developing variety) is put off until early in the new year. By January the rain should have arrived. It is then important to sow as early as possible (usually the second half of January) to allow the crop to grow and ripen before the summer drought. This would be one explanation of Columella's advice to sow three-month wheat ('trimestrium satio', 11. 2. 20) in warmer regions in January (for other possibilities, see n. 15). As for Varro's reference to spring sowing in the plains (1. 6. 3), it is possible that, having just alluded to the Tavoliere of Puglia as an example of a hot lowland area, he had continued to keep this in mind when speaking of the sowing of spring crops.

Yet quite apart from the possibility of difficulty with an autumn-sown crop because of bad weather in cold mountainous areas, or because of lack of, or too much, autumn rain in the dryer lowlands of the south, spring wheat was also grown in northern Italy. This is deduced from the appearance of a normal spring-sowing date of February or early March (Col. 11. 2. 20; 2. 4. 9) as a definite date on the agricultural calendar, and from the fact that this is the usual spring-sowing period in modern times 'nel Settentrione'.[16] The reasons for this will have been various: (1) the failure of (Col. 2. 6. 2), or a preventative measure against, a poor harvest from the autumn crop; (2) less commonly perhaps, due to a rotation pattern; (3) to capture a special part of the market.[17] Certainly the question of spring sowing was much more complex than is usually assumed.[18]

## SOWING TECHNIQUES

The method was to scatter the seed by hand. The Latin terms *iacere* and *spargere* and Pliny's description (18. 197) are unequivocal. Scattering spreads the seeds unevenly, causing some plants to choke others as they grow, leaves gaps in

[15] Naval Intelligence Division, *Italy* III, 29. For the following remarks on an early spring sowing in the south, Grimaldi, *Coltivazione erbacee*, 30. (Testini, *Il frumento*, 26 observed that spring-sown grain was not common in Puglia, although in Sicily it could be used if heavy late-autumn rains had inhibited sowing or if the land was put under a short-fallow over the winter.)

[16] Tassinari, *Manuale*, 460. In Italian, February sowing or January sowing in the south and parts of central Italy are known as 'winter sowing' (*semina invernale*) instead of 'spring sowing'. I have kept to the usual English differentiation between autumn- and

spring-sown wheat. It would be better, however, to think in more flexible terms, given the various climatic regions of Italy. Where winters are mild, 'autumn sowing' is postponed into December and 'spring sowing' is brought forward to the second half of January.

[17] Specialities for the markets: cf. the three-month wheat which made the best starch (P. 18. 76); three-month emmer was 'excellent both in weight and goodness' (Col. 2. 6. 3). Rotation patterns, see below pp. 117–22.

[18] See White, *Roman Farming*, 157.

other places, and makes hoeing and weeding, if practised, difficult. There is also the tendency to sow more in order to make up for the defects of the method. Thus have spoken Italian experts since at least the last century. Yet still in Italy today sowing *a spaglio* continues, especially in the more inaccessible areas or on small plots where tractors are not used. An experienced sower can minimize the defect of uneven distribution, and Pliny (ibid.) emphasizes that the task requires skill.[19] Yet if inefficient, it is at least considerably quicker than dropping the seeds at regular intervals along the furrow by hand or with an elementary seed drill. Given the importance of sowing at exactly the right time according to climatic conditions, the broadcast method would thus have suited large and small farmers alike. Recognition of the speed of the operation permits modification of the often-heard statement comparing seed time and harvest time as the peak periods of the year in that they both require an intensification of labour.[20] *No* extra labour was required for sowing with the broadcast method, which could be performed much more rapidly than reaping. The truth behind the idea that both were labour-intensive methods is simply that generally, in all countries, they were the only times of the year when the cereal crop was tended.

## COVERING THE SEED

The seed when cast was not abandoned to its fate; instead it was covered over in a variety of ways: (1) with an 'eared' plough, (2) *sub sulco*, (3) *occatio*.

(1) The 'eared' plough created ridges separated by furrows to drain off any excess water, as discussed on p. 33. It was probably a practice derived originally from the cultivation of the *hortus*. In the vegetable garden consisting of damp soil, the asparagus seed must be placed on the ridges so that it is not harmed by excessive moisture (Col. 11. 3. 44). Transposed to the grain field, the system provided run-off furrows for the sometimes violent autumn and winter downpours. The reference to asparagus cultivation implies that the main reason for the ridges was to drain soil that was naturally heavy and water-retentive, and not just to avoid excessive rainfall. This would also have been applicable to grain cultivation in heavier soils. There is another important advantage of the ridging method of covering the seed in heavier soils: since such soils cannot be ploughed deeply by the ox-drawn ploughs of whatever size, the heaping up of the soil into ridges provided a permeable seed bed of a satisfactory depth for the covered seed. The regular ridges and furrows would, moreover, have aided the operations of

---

[19] Defects of broadcast sowing: G. Paolino-Pistone, *Sul modo di seminare il frumento* (1884), 1 ff. Interestingly the sowing tends to be carried out in Italy by the older women of the family who are endowed with the traditional skill (autopsy throughout the south of Italy; I was taught to sow at Montorio nei Frentani by the grandmother of the family with whom I stayed). It also indicates that sowing is not particularly heavy work. However, in the Roman agricultural treatises the only work performed by women is spinning wool (Col. 12. 3. 6) and keeping hens (Col. 8. 2. 7). Children's work included vine trimming (Col.

11. 2. 44), cutting down ferns (Col. 2. 2. 13), hen-keeping (Col. 8. 2. 7), watching the flock on the estate (V. 2. 10. 1).

[20] This has become an unwarranted truism. Cf. M. K. Jones, 'The Development of Crop Husbandry' in *The Environment of Man: the Iron Age to the Anglo-Saxon Period*, ed. M. K. Jones and G. Dimbleby, B.A.R. British Series 87 (1981), 105: 'The main advantage of mixed autumn and spring sowing is that it spreads the labour load at sowing and harvest time, the peak seasons of the year'.

hoeing and weeding, thus counteracting one of the disadvantages of broadcast sowing.[21]

Ridging is therefore only necessary in heavy soils or where water is likely to collect. However, from comparative evidence of earlier this century, it is clear that this method was adopted even in well-drained, light and porous soils.[22] Given the commonness of *porcae* and *sulci*, if the evidence of the *Digest* is interpreted correctly (*Dig.* 39. 3. 1, 5 and n. 60 below), it cannot be ruled out that the use of the ridging plough had spread to such soils also in the Roman period, at least by the late Republic. Ridging of lighter soils, besides being unnecessary, would have been detrimental to the cereal crop. It had the effect of completely drying out soil which was already low in moisture. It would also have exposed light, dry, friable soil to an increased danger of erosion by the wind whipping, as it were, across the crests of waves. Moreover, the furrows which occupy a good portion of the field's total area are inevitably without seed under the ridging method, a disadvantage outweighed in heavy and rich soils by their increased productivity, but with serious consequences in poorer soils. Given this, it is not then surprising that another method of covering the seed was advised for thin soil on sloping, and therefore self-draining, land. 'Such land is not to be sown in ridges but in the furrow' (*sub sulco*, Col. 2. 4. 11).

(2) White observes rightly that the phrase of Columella, *sub sulco*, because of its very laconicism, implies a common, familiar method. Yet his explanation of the passage, equally brief, must be at least partially erroneous:

> in dry soil the seed would appear to have been sown along the furrows *after ridging* [my italics], and not by broadcasting, and then covered by means of rakes or harrows.[23]

This is erroneous because Columella is explicit that thin soil is *not* ridged.

It was only in the kitchen garden (when the soil was not water-retentive) that sowing in furrows took place. It would not have been worthwhile to employ such an intensive method of sowing in grain land consisting of poor soil. In the garden context, the sowing process is described in detail, leaving no doubt as to the placing of the seed 'in the bottom of the furrows as though in little troughs' (Col. 11. 3. 44). *Sub sulco*, however, was a much more general term, and there can be no doubt that grain seed was sown broadcast on poor soil as elsewhere.

Kolendo discusses this term at much greater length than White, although he arrives at basically the same conclusion. He interprets *sub sulco* to mean that in poor soil seed was sown in furrows, which had been ploughed beforehand, and then was covered over with earth by means of hoes. This, Kolendo admits, required more work than sowing in ridges. It is asserted that more draught

---

[21] These and following details and criticisms of ridging (these ridges are still called *porche* in the vernacular, although the practice is rapidly disappearing now that heavy soils are increasingly worked with mechanical means) are taken from Azimonti, *Il frumento*. Note also the observations of Goethe, *Italian Journey 1786–88*, trans. W. H. Auden and E.

Mayer (1968), 104: 'At sowing time they heap up small narrow ridges with deep furrows between them in which the rain water can run off. The wheat grows on the top of the ridges, so that they can walk up and down the furrows when they weed' (near Arezzo).

[22] Ibid., 214 ff.; Paoletti, 'Norme pratiche', 10 f.

[23] White, *Roman Farming*, 179, 485 n. 31.

animals were necessary with the *sub sulco* method, although it is then strangely surmised that this method was adopted by peasant farmers.[24]

The views of Kolendo and White cannot be credited. They clearly reveal the difficulty of interpreting that type of 'partial evidence' presented by the Roman agricultural writers, obscure to us but obvious to their contemporary audiences. It is precisely for the resolution of this type of problem that comparative evidence and first-hand knowledge of Italian agriculture are so useful.

It is impossible to believe that poor soils required a more labour-intensive method of sowing than rich soils. *Pace* Kolendo, the sole-ard, unless it has *aures*, does not create the type of furrows into which seed can be dropped and then be covered over with hoes. As was noted against White, and as Kolendo himself is careful to explain, *sub sulco* clearly does not refer to the ridge-and-furrow technique of the 'eared' plough.

*Sub sulco* instead must correspond to what used to be a non-intensive sowing method widespread in central and southern Italy earlier this century termed *a solchi*.[25] Seed was scattered on ground that had been previously worked poorly or not at all and was then crudely ploughed in by breaking the soil with an ard. This was usually then followed by a smashing of the larger clods of earth left after the ploughing (*rompere le zolle*) with hoes or mattocks (*zappe*).

Columella, since he sought to achieve the best yields from all soils, advised two ploughings and a manuring of thin, sloping land before sowing *sub sulco*. It can safely be assumed that on less intensively worked farms, and where manure was scarce, such soils would have been broken at the most only once before the seed was sown. More often, perhaps, the remarks of Columella on the sowing of lupins would have been applied to grain: 'they can succeed on poor soil, are scattered on unbroken land, can be covered in any way, and tolerate every carelessness of the farmer' (2. 10. 2; 2. 15. 5). Pliny's note that labour can be saved when sowing beans and vetch by scattering seed on unbroken ground might be similarly indicative (18. 181).

One noted danger of the *sub sulco/a solchi* method compared with sowing in ridges arose from the absence of drainage furrows. Unless ditches, however rudimentary, were dug around the borders of the field to direct as much as possible of the torrential rainfall away from the sown crops, a good proportion of the new seed could be washed away.[26]

If it is true that the 'eared' ridging plough represented a development in ploughing techniques since the time of Cato, then it may be assumed that the simpler and less labour-intensive method of sowing *sub sulco* had until then been most common. It no doubt continued to be widespread, even though ridging had probably become increasingly diffuse by the late Republic. There is, however, too little evidence either way on which to base any quantitative judgements on diffusion patterns.

Diffusion should of course be dictated by soil needs, as it would have been on the well-run cereal estate. There, both ridging and *sub sulco* would have existed side by side, at least if variety of soil and topography demanded. But practice is

---

[24] Kolendo, *L'agricoltura*, 89, 91, 107–12.

[25] Azimonti, *Il frumento*, 221.

[26] Azimonti, ibid.

not always controlled by rationality. Thus Pliny, in his discussion of ploughing techniques, refers both to 'where circumstances require' and to 'where custom permits' (18. 180; see below n. 35).

One final doubt can be dispelled. Despite reference to *sulci*, Virgil (*Georgics* 1. 111–13) speaks of luxuriant crops which run the risk of 'lodging'. (This means flattening by wind or rain and is a sign of weak culms.) How would this be possible in thin soil? The answer is that not all thin, light soil was infertile. Virgil here is probably describing a Campanian scene, certainly not the Po valley with its generally heavy soils. Campanian fields could be ploughed by one donkey or a cow, it will be remembered, since this fertile soil was easily worked. Thus the rich crops are compatible with the *sub sulco* technique.

It yet might still be objected that Virgil refers to the young crop as 'growing level with the *sulci*' (ibid.). Thus actual furrows seem imagined. This again can be explained by close attention to the agricultural reality. If a light soil has been worked once and then ploughed again to cover the seed, even if no 'ears' are used but just the simple plough, *slight* furrows and ridges will occur which could then be called *porchettine strettissime* ('very narrow little *porche*').[27]

(3) *Occatio* is usually rendered 'harrowing' in English translations of the agricultural texts. 'To harrow' in English usage is to draw a harrow over the soil to crush and pulverize it. A 'harrow' is defined as a heavy timber or iron frame with teeth, which breaks clods, stirs and pulverizes the soil, roots up weeds or covers over the seed.[28]

There are two initial observations to be made which will direct the ensuing discussion. Firstly, as regards Roman agriculture of the period, it is clear that *occatio* was not commonly carried out by a 'harrow', but by rakes, hoes and primarily by the plough. Secondly, as the term *occatio* appears to have at least two, and perhaps three, meanings, it will be necessary for the better understanding of Roman agriculture to determine which meaning is required in any given passage.

The subject of 'harrowing' has often received a confused treatment in earlier works. White has done much to clarify the situation, and Kolendo has shown how complex it is.[29] Both these writers surmise that the harrow was introduced into, or invented in, Italy in the latter half of the first century A.D. as a symptom of a supposed decline in the slave supply and resulting agricultural labour shortage. For Kolendo, the appearance of the harrow was also associated with the spread of an extensive system of farming. These views are considered in more detail on pp. 140–3. The discussion which follows here is divided under five separate headings: (*a*) pulverization of the soil; (*b*) *occatio* before sowing; (*c*) *occatio* as covering the seed; (*d*) 'combing' of the cereal crops; (*e*) *occa* and *irpex*.

(*a*) Pulverization of the soil. Most references to *occatio* which occur in the

---

[27] Azimonti, ibid. Ploughing had been well done, according to Pliny, when it proved impossible to tell, by looking at the field, in which direction the plough had gone. This is clear evidence that the land was not furrowed in appearance (P. 18. 97).

[28] *Oxford English Dictionary* definitions.

[29] White, *Agricultural Implements*, 143 ff.

Kolendo, *L'agricoltura*, 88 ff. The discussions of the question of harrowing in both these works are not countered here in detail, although I believe that both are at least partially misleading and that Kolendo in particular shows little knowledge of the agricultural reality.

agricultural texts require the sense of pulverizing the clods of earth left after ploughing. In this sense it was not confined only to land under sown crops, as Varro demonstrates: 'Digging and ploughing the new vineyards is followed by the operation of *occare*, namely the breaking up of clods' ('id est comminuere, ne sit glaeba', V. 1. 31. 1). Any doubt as to definition is dispelled by Columella who explains that *occatio* was rustic vernacular for *pulveratio* (11. 2. 60—again in the context of viticulture).

As regards cereal and legume cultivation, this type of *occatio* seems to have been carried out most commonly after ploughing and sowing but before hoeing and weeding. Its aim was to complete the work of the plough in providing a friable seed bed for successful germination. Breaking of the remaining clods allowed an easier and more even growth of the new plants above ground. It also prepared a more permeable surface for the absorption of rainfall, and facilitated later hoeing and weeding.

Ideally, however, the main implement for such pulverization of the soil was the plough itself. The first working of the ground turns up large clods which the second and later ploughings break up (V. 1. 29. 2). Since the aim of ploughing was to prepare a fine tilth, the heaviness and texture of the soil were the regulating factors as regards the number of ploughings. Both Pliny and Columella cite the ancestral axiom that a field had only been ploughed properly when it required little or no *occatio* (P. 18. 97; Col. 2. 4. 2). Thus, if *occatio* in this sense was necessary, it would mean that either only rudimentary or careless ploughing had been carried out, or that the soil was of such a (clayey) composition that it resisted even repeated and attentive ploughings and required 'finishing off' with other implements. It would also depend on the type of crop under cultivation, since it is clear from the agricultural texts that land destined for cereals was worked with much more care than that set aside for some legumes (cf. Col. 2. 15. 1; P. 18. 181), at least on the intensive arable farm.

The various implements used for *occatio* include *sarcula*, hoes (Col. 2. 17. 4), *rastra*, rakes or drag hoes (Virgil, *Georgics* 1. 94–5), *ligones*, mattocks (Isidore, *Etym.* 17. 2. 4). All these tools required the same manual chopping or downward swinging action, although the choice of tool and the height of swing would depend on the size and texture of the clods to be broken.

It is clear that *occatio* could follow both the ridging and the *sub sulco* methods of ploughing and sowing. It is not unreasonable to suppose that in order to be ridged, the soil would usually already have been well pulverized, and thus any remaining clods would have been small and infrequent. This might aid the comprehension of a compressed passage of Varro where he seems to say that on small farms *occatio* could be performed after ridging during the later hoeing operation.[30] As regards sowing *sub sulco*, Virgil describes the breaking of clods with rakes (*rastra*; the term *occatio* is not actually used) and then the drawing over the soil of a drag made from osiers (*cratis viminea*, *Georgics* 1. 94–5). Servius'

[30] V. 1. 29. 2, 'Non nulli postea, qui segetes non tam latas habent, ut in Apulia et id genus praediis, per sartores occare solent, siquae in porcis relictae grandiores sunt glaebae.' Here *per sartores* can be translated as 'during the hoeing operation'. This seems to mean that some Apulian cereal farms were small and intensively worked, and thus bears out the discussion on pp. 24 f. Yet the exact significance of the passage remains enigmatic.

explanation, and comparison with a passage of Columella, demonstrate that the purpose of the osier drag was to level the field after sowing.[31] Levelling is clearly not applicable in a ridged field and will, should it be necessary to classify ploughing methods as either one or the other, refer to the *sub sulco* technique discussed above.

This *cratis viminea* cannot be strictly termed a harrow. It fulfilled only the special function of levelling soil in a field which had already been sown. It is clear too that it was separate from clod smashing; as White rightly argues against earlier explanations, it would have been incapable of this.[32] Nor can it be assumed that such a drag was an essential accompaniment of *sub sulco* ploughing. It was instead an indication of an intensive approach to cereal cultivation as compared with what was, as surmised above, a more common and rudimentary form of the *sub sulco* method, which comprised just one ploughing and then a breaking up of only the larger clods of earth.

No safe assertion can be made concerning the diffusion of the osier drag. Virgil and Columella mention it, but clearly for Columella its use was very specialized. Varro refers to the making of *crates* out of osiers (1. 23. 5), although he nowhere describes their use. Nor is it certain that osier drags are meant rather than sheep hurdles (cf. V. 2. 2. 9).[33] Yet since the fabrication of such a drag was simple, it might already have been of considerable antiquity. However, it by no means ought to be identified as a 'bush-harrow', *pace* White, which was rather a type of 'proto-plough' characteristic of nomadic cereal cultivation, and not simply a light drag for levelling off a field.[34]

(*b*) *Occatio* before sowing. Both Pliny and Columella state that during the careful preparation of ground for the cultivation of lucerne *occatio* should take place *before sowing* (P. 18. 145; Col. 2. 10. 26). This is obviously a special case. It was, for example, the only crop sown in spring which required a preliminary working of the soil in the preceding autumn (ibid.). Further, lucerne might have been a new crop to Italy, since it was not mentioned by Cato and was considered almost miraculous by Pliny and Columella. As still today, the practice was to provide a thoroughly pulverized seed bed. Thus *occatio* in this case was advised even before sowing, although what this operation comprised, and by what tools it was carried out, are not explained.

Presumably of more general significance is a clear reference in Pliny to an *occatio* after ploughing but before sowing 'where circumstances demand it', performed with either a *cratis* or a *rastrum* (18. 180). 'Harrowing' (with a harrow) before sowing is common enough in Italy today; the purpose is to contribute to the preparation of the seed bed by breaking up clods and by removing any remaining weeds. Both these operations, in my view, were performed by the Plinian, pre-sowing *occatio*, although this is not explicitly stated. A *rastrum* was

---

[31] Servius ad loc., 'The *crates* which country people call *irpex*, to be understood as used for levelling the fields', cf. Col. 2. 17. 4.

[32] White, *Agricultural Implements*, 147; see Fig. 3a.

[33] White translates 'bush-harrows', ibid., 146. But *crates stercorariae* (see p. 55 below) or sheep hurdles (cf. Col. 12. 15. 1) are alternative possibilities. See

White, *Farm Equipment*, 78, where V. 1. 23. 5 is translated 'hurdles'.

[34] G. Forni, 'Tipologia e nomenclatura dell'aratro tradizionale', *Acta Museorum Italicorum Agriculturae* 6/7 (extract from *Rivista di Storia dell'Agricoltura* 2 (1981)), 220–3 and Table 2.

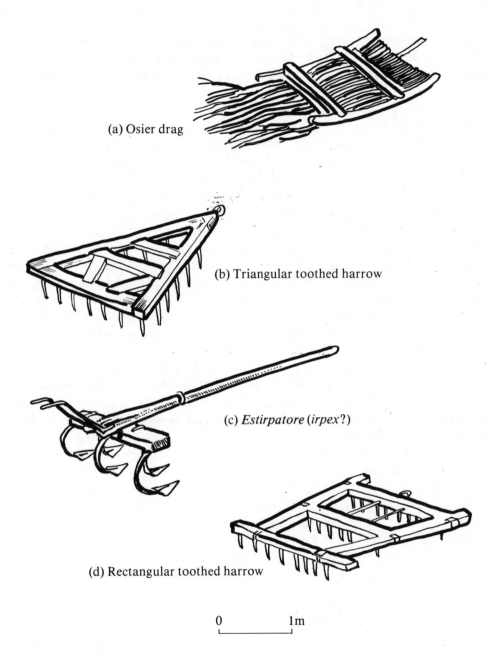

(a) Osier drag

(b) Triangular toothed harrow

(c) *Estirpatore* (*irpex*?)

(d) Rectangular toothed harrow

0        1m

Fig. 3. Harrows.

(*a*) was used for levelling ploughed fields where the clods of earth turned up after ploughing had already been pulverized; (*b*) and (*d*) break up the clods and then, turned over, harrow in the seed and level the field; (*c*) the modern *estirpatore* for scarifying the soil and light weeding possibly resembles the Roman *irpex*. Cf. Pl. II, 2.

usually a heavy implement used with a swinging action for breaking earth, but it could also weed, and turn soil.[35] Since the *rastrum* could be replaced by a *cratis*, according to Pliny, it can be assumed that both implements performed the same or very similar tasks. The *cratis* in question was therefore not an osier drag, but rather a 'toothed' harrow (*cratis dentata*). There is not a secure description of this type of *cratis*, but from comparative evidence it can reasonably be suggested that it was similar to what are still called 'toothed harrows'. These consist usually of a horizontal wooden frame with crossbeams to which are attached wooden or iron 'teeth' on the underside. For the breaking of clods and weeding, the harrow is drawn over the land with the teeth facing downwards. The only situation in which the smashing action of a *rastrum* could be more suitable is when the soil is heavy and the clods have dried out before breaking. (See Figs. 3b, d; Pl. II, 2.)

In the same passage Pliny observes that a *cratis* can also be used to cover the seed when the ridging method of ploughing and sowing has not been adopted. This *cratis* will be the same 'toothed harrow', if the traditional emendation of *dentata* is accepted for the manuscript *contenta*. How the same implement was used both for breaking clods before sowing and later for covering the seed is easily explained from modern comparative evidence. For covering the seed the toothed harrow is inverted and the teeth are thus put out of action. One variation is that the toothed harrow has larger teeth on its underside and a set of smaller teeth on top. When the harrow is inverted the small teeth are engaged, which 'harrow in' the seed rather than merely covering it. (See Pl. II, 2.)

While the above explanation is the most satisfying from the point of view of comparison with existing techniques, another emendation can be proposed for *cratis contenta* which has not, apparently, been previously suggested. Instead of *contenta*, *contexta* could be read, and this would clearly signify an osier drag, since *texere* is the natural word to describe the fabrication of this type of *cratis*.[36] A method similar to the Virgilian could then be imagined. Whereas Virgil describes the breaking up of clods with rakes after sowing, followed by levelling-off with an osier drag, Pliny refers to an *occatio* with rakes or a toothed harrow before sowing, followed by levelling-off with an osier drag (*cratis contexta*). While no certainty is possible, the discussion is at least able to continue to indicate the complexity and variety of Roman agricultural techniques.[37]

(*c*) *Occatio* as covering of the seed. 'The earth receives the scattered seed . . . and at first keeps it hidden (*occaecatum*), from which we get our word *occatio*' (Cic., *De Sen.* 51).

Thus *occatio* could also mean 'covering the seed'. In fact this is also clear from a careful reading of the Pliny passage discussed immediately above. The covering of the seed (he states) with a ridging plough or a harrow is called *occatio*,

[35] See the references collected by White, *Agricultural Implements*, 52–3. The dense passage of Pliny under discussion can be quoted here since it is referred to again shortly. 'After the second (crossways) ploughing has been done *occatio* follows, either with a *cratis* or with a rake where circumstances require it and, once the seed has been sown, this (*occatio*) also is repeated, where local custom allows, either with a *cratis* †*contenta*† or with a board attached to the plough (which they call 'ridging') to cover the seed' (18. 180).

[36] For *texere* in the sense of making a *cratis* out of osiers, Virgil, *Aen.* 11. 64–5; cf. Horace, *Epod.* 2. 45.

[37] See further pp. 55f. For yet another tool employed in *occatio*: Palladius 2. 3, *dolabrum* (type of pick-axe) for smashing clods after the first ploughing.

although 'ridging' was more specifically known as *lirare* (18.180). The harrow could be used for this purpose of covering the seed only when *sub sulco* ploughing was carried out, since it would be totally unsuitable in a ridged field.

However, it is equally clear that a harrow was not employed by Columella for this purpose. In the *sub sulco* system as recommended by him, the *plough* covered the seed, and there is besides no hint to the contrary in either Cato or Varro. Only in special cases, such as the sowing of fenugreek or lucerne, was the seed covered by other implements, in these cases hoes and wooden rakes respectively (Col. 2. 10. 33; 2. 10. 27). That these were exceptions is emphasized at the end of the summary of labour times for the various legumes and cereals: 'Lucerne, however, is covered over, as I said, *not with the plough* [my italics] but with small wooden rakes' (2. 12. 6). This is not to say that Columella was ignorant of this other usage of the term *occatio*,[38] but when a distinction is required he uses *occatio* for pulverization of the soil and another term (e.g. *obruo* 'cover over', 2. 12. 4) for covering the seed. In this way the confusion which arises from Pliny (18. 180), where both meanings of *occatio* are juxtaposed, is avoided. It is made clear also in this way by Columella which of the two meanings of the term took priority.[39]

(*d*) 'Combing' of the cereal crop. Pliny mentions the use of a toothed harrow, with iron tines ('cratis et hoc genus dentatae stilis ferreis'), for 'combing' excessive vegetation growth in the early stages of the crop's growth.[40] There can be no doubt that this 'combing' operation with such an implement would also have included the uprooting of weeds and the loosening of the surface soil. Not, however, that such a combination of tasks necessarily saved labour or was utilized as a labour-saving device. As Pliny clearly remarks (ibid.), the crop which had been thus 'combed' was then grazed and, at a later date, required hoeing to loosen the soil after the trampling of the animals.

It is questionable whether this type of harrow enjoyed widespread use, although it enriches our understanding of the diversity of Roman agriculture. There is no indication of such use in any of the other agricultural writers, and this is not, *pace* Kolendo, just because they were exponents of intensive agriculture opposed to the spread of the harrow.[41] It is of some significance that a harrow which combined the operations of combing, weeding and hoeing only appeared in Puglia in the latter part of the last century.[42] Pliny's reference could suggest a location in the Po valley, although that must remain speculative. On the other hand the primary reason for the use of the combing harrow would tend to indicate cereal cultivation in areas with both fertile soil and mild winters which, as discussed on p. 21, can promote too much early growth.

Importantly there is no indication that a combing or harrowing of the growing crop could be included in the term *occatio*. Moreover, separate terms for

---

[38] Col. 11. 2. 60, 80; but cf. 2. 8. 4; 2. 15. 5.

[39] Pliny informs us about one other use of the toothed harrow. It covers the seed and breaks the clods in the wake of the wheeled plough (18. 173). But this use cannot have been widespread; cf. p. 34 above.

[40] 'There are some kinds of ground the fertility of which necessitates combing the crop before the jointing stage' (18. 186). The 'necessity' is explained below pp. 64 ff.

[41] Kolendo, *L'agricoltura*, 147 f.

[42] Testini, *Il frumento*, 35. For the limited southern diffusion of the harrow, see also Scheuermeier, *Il lavoro* I, 94.

hoeing and weeding continued to exist; and Pliny does not suggest that this or any form of harrowing in any way replaced them.[43]

(e) *Occa* and *irpex*. The first of these need not detain discussion, since evidence is almost entirely lacking, besides being late. It is possible that *occa* was a vulgar term for *rastrum*, and that it has crept into the text of Columella (2. 17. 4) as a gloss for *crate*. But this is no more than a conjecture.[44] *Irpex*, however, is of greater interest. It appears in Cato's list of equipment for the oliveyard (10. 3). This implement does not occur in any other agricultural text, but is described by Varro (*LL*. 5. 136) as a wooden bar with several teeth drawn by oxen to eradicate weeds. It is mentioned also in the lexicon of Festus (p. 93 L): '*Irpices* are a type of iron *rastri*, so called because they have numerous teeth for rooting up weeds in the fields'.

White identifies the *irpex* as a lighter model of the *cratis dentata*. This does not fit his other suggestion that the introduction of the harrow was the result of an increasing shortage of labour in the period of Columella and Pliny.[45] Instead Kolendo prefers to argue that the *irpex*, which appears to have originated in Samnium, was a primitive form of harrow which disappeared at some point probably in the first century B.C. and was replaced by the later forms of the *cratis*. To explain the fact that the word *irpex* rather than *cratis* has been transmitted to the modern romance languages (cf. *erpice* in Italian), he cites the comment of Servius on Virgil (*Georgics* 1. 94-5) to the effect that *irpex* remained the country vernacular term for the later substitution ('crates, quem rustici irpicem vocant').[46]

Yet the most recent research into plough typology indicates that the *irpex* of Varro's description was a type of proto-plough, not a primitive harrow. The stages of the plough's development are to be understood as an increasing loss of 'teeth', from the so-called 'brushwood' or 'bush harrow', to a bar with between ten and three teeth on its underside, to the, as it were, 'single-toothed' plough.[47]

It was a common enough practice on small farms some thirty years ago to perform a superficial ploughing, weeding and clod-breaking in one operation with an *estirpatore*, very similar in design to the *irpex* (Fig. 3c).[48] It is possible that in and before Cato's period, when plough types were not as diverse, the *irpex* was used by small farmers as a sort of proto-plough, and that it also continued in use, together with the plough, on intensive farms, for the removal of weeds in fallow cereal land, as well as among olives and vines. This would explain its occurrence among the equipment of a Catonian oliveyard (10. 1).

## Concluding Remarks

As the plough developed, more and more emphasis was placed on it alone for

[43] That 'combing' was not absorbed into the term *occatio*, and that hoeing and weeding maintained their separate identity, further confirms the unlikelihood of widespread use of the harrow for 'combing'. The only instance in which it is stated that harrowing replaced hoeing is in the case of the wheeled plough (P. 18. 173). This must remain enigmatic.

[44] White, *Agricultural Implements*, 59. See further Kolendo, *L'agricoltura*, 91. Note the derivation supplied by J. André, *Lexique des termes de botanique en latin* (1956), s.v. *occa*: 'a thorny bush'.

[45] White, ibid., 148–50.

[46] Kolendo, 133 f. His argument for the disappearance of the *irpex* depends on the fact that later agronomists do not mention it, a dangerous argument at the best of times, especially here, since Varro does describe it in *LL* 5. 136.

[47] Forni, 'Tipologia dell'aratro'. See also Forni, 'Plaumaratum', 110.

[48] H. J. Hopfen and E. Biesalski, *Small Farm Implements* (1953), 27–8.

a deeper working of the soil, the breaking of clods and the eradication of weeds. Various forms of *crates* were adopted (or perhaps invented) to supplement the work of the plough by pulverizing and levelling soil and covering seed. Nevertheless, the *irpex* continued in use, especially on small farms where light soils were not worked deeply or thoroughly. This, coupled with the observation that in rural dialect, if Servius is to be believed, even the *crates* in use on the larger, intensive farms were known as *irpices*, accounts for the most usually accepted modern Italian term *erpice* for 'harrow'.

The modern Italian *erpice* in its various forms accomplishes all the functions of the Roman *crates*: pulverization of clods, covering of seed, levelling of soil, although 'combing' is rarely seen. Two other common uses are collecting manure from pasture land and spreading manure on cultivated land. In this light it is conceivable that the *crates stercorariae* mentioned by Cato were harrows for spreading manure in the field rather than cradles for carrying it (10. 3), which would instead have been performed by the three asses specifically assigned for the purpose (10. 1).[49]

If the argument that Roman 'harrows' owed their introduction to labour shortage is to be abandoned (p. 141), an alternative explanation should be offered. Local custom could be one reason, although that is usually applied to explain the retention of agricultural techniques rather than their introduction. If the 'harrows' *are* to be seen as a new development since Cato's time, then they should be inserted as another element into the picture of improved arable farming in the late Republic and early Empire.

The use of the osier drag, for example, to achieve a smooth finish to a field under cereals or hay, covered and spread seed more evenly than the plough and facilitated the later reaping. This can only be seen as attention to improved methods. As regards the toothed harrow it should again be noted that Varro and Columella, although clearly interested in intensive arable farming, do not mention its use. For them the plough performed all duties in heavy soil, followed, only if required, by manual breaking of remaining clods. The toothed harrow was not seen as necessary.

Yet this does not mean that other farmers did not see the toothed harrow as an improved device, perhaps to aid cultivation of increased areas of fertile heavy soils in response to market demand. But here we move into the realm of speculation, although perhaps less so than those who argue for labour shortage. The basic Roman agricultural profit equation (p. 3) meant that the manning-ratios elaborated by the agronomists were kept to the minimum for the type of agriculture practised and the size of farm. Thus can be understood the calculation recorded by Columella for an arable estate of 200 *iugera*: 2 plough teams and ploughmen, and 6 labourers (2. 12. 7-9). Greater profit would be possible if the

---

[49] The modern use of the harrow for spreading manure: Scheuermeier, *Il lavoro* I, 93. For the suggestion that the *crates stercorariae* are to be thus interpreted: G. E. Fussel, A. Kenny, 'L'Équipment d'une ferme romaine', *Annales ESC* 21 (1966), 309. White, *Farm Equipment*, 77 identifies them as 'hurdles' for carrying manure. One slender reason for preferring the former interpretation is that they are listed along with the ploughs and the *irpex* (10. 3). Whatever the conclusion, it would appear that there was a considerable amount of manure to move around: four *crates*, three manure 'baskets' (*sirpeas*) and three pack asses to carry manure. This is perhaps disturbing for proponents of the view that manure was scarce. See pp. 126–32.

size of the estate could be enlarged without any increase in the workforce, provided that agricultural efficiency could be maintained. One way of achieving the same intensity of agriculture with a reduced ratio of men to land is by intro-ducing a labour-saving device. The toothed harrow could have allowed an increased area of heavy productive soils to be worked with fewer men. Thus greater profit would have resulted.[50]

## SOWING AMOUNTS

Specific sowing amounts are recommended by Varro, Columella and Pliny. Explanations are not provided but accuracy is attested by comparative agricultural knowledge (below). One interesting point is that emmer needs to be sown in approximately double the amount of either bread wheat or barley.[51] This reflects the greater bulkiness of emmer. It was sown with its husk on, of course, and the *modius* is a volume measure. There would therefore be fewer seeds per *modius* than for a naked grain. The Roman sowing rate has been successfully used in the experiments with the cultivation of emmer at the Butser Iron Age Farm.[52] The extra bulk of emmer would lessen its attraction from the point of view of storage and transport; the former a concern for the small farmer, both prob-lematic for the larger producer. Barley too is mostly husked and therefore as voluminous as emmer. However, the smaller sowing quantity is explained by the fact that, since barley tillers more than any other cereal, it needs to be sown in lesser quantity.[53] As for *triticum*, the Roman sowing amounts accord well with those commonly sown broadcast in Italy today, although they are excessive by the standards of the more rational sowing method of drilling.[54]

Besides presenting specific sowing amounts, Varro (like the modern textbooks) suggested local imitation as the best guide (1. 44. 1), and Columella explains that quantities should be flexible depending on soil, topography, micro-climate, and whether they belonged to an early or late sowing (2. 9. 2–6).[55] More seed will be required if the grain is intercultivated with vines, olives or fruit trees. Even though, as Varro pointed out, there had been a considerable improvement in the layout of *arbusta*, which had increased yields (1. 7. 2), the trees would still have drawn soil nutrients and light away from the cereal crop. It therefore needed

[50] That is, (1) less time will be spent in preparing any given area for cultivation by the plough teams, which means that more land can be worked; (2) labourers' time can be directed away from breaking clods to other work necessary on the expanded area. If this is accepted, there is no reason to postulate declining availability of agricultural labour. See further pp. 140–3.

[51] V. 1. 44. 1: *triticum*, 4 *modii* to the *iugerum*; barley 6, emmer 10; Col. 2. 9. 1: 5 of wheat, 10 of emmer on medium land; P. 18. 198: 5–6 of wheat and 10 of emmer.

[52] Reynolds, 'Deadstock and Livestock'.

[53] Peterson, *Wheat*, 239 and p. 15 above.

[54] Amounts recommended for broadcast sowing vary between 150 and 200 litres of grain per hectare: O. Cinelli, 'La mietitura', *Giornale Agrario Italiano* 7 no. 5 (1873), 1, 150 litres in good quality land; Oliva, *Il frumento nella montagna*, 16, 150 kg (*c*.200 litres) in poor land. Taking 5 *modii* as an average Roman sowing rate per *iugerum*, the following data are used: 1 *modius* = 8.75 litres, 1 hectare = 4 *iugera*. Therefore, 5 *modii* = 175 litres per hectare. Columella notes that some people sow 8 *modii* of *triticum* to the *iugerum*; this equals 279 litres per hectare, far in excess of modern amounts.

[55] For similar indications of the factors which affect sowing amounts, see Peterson, *Wheat*, 239.

to be sown more thickly in order to produce as much as an open grain field (Col. 2. 9. 6).

It is interesting that Varro recommended a thicker sowing of richer ground (1. 44. 1), whereas Columella (2. 9. 1) and Pliny (18. 200) increased their amounts for poorer ground. In Puglia towards the end of the last century, the common idea and practice was to sow rich land heavily, because 'like a strong ass it could carry more'. Yet some of the owners of large estates were calling to their aid scientific reports which showed that rich land required less seed than poor and that by sowing less thickly there was less danger of plant suffocation.[56] Economically, a lighter sowing was beneficial, since it meant that more seed could be saved. It is perhaps likely that both notions co-existed in the Roman period. If the Columellan practice was adopted, it would have had its beneficial effect mainly on the large arable estate, where, it can be supposed, there was a reasonable amount of fertile land and thus a *modius* saved per *iugerum* would make a considerable difference to the overall total. The yield would have been greater due to less choking of plants (cf. P. 18. 199). Less difficult too would have been the all-important 'cultivations' of hoeing and weeding during the crop's growth. On the small farm choice of quantity is unlikely to have been common, if it is assumed that the amount of sowing seed set apart was of necessity kept to a minimum. If sown on poor soil a thin crop would result and the problem be compounded.

## CULTIVATIONS

Michon, writing in the middle of the last century, believing (as many still do) that for the Roman agricultural writers wheat growing was of little interest because it yielded little profit, noted with some surprise that Cato advised weeding and hoeing of the crop. He thought this especially remarkable, since in France where cereal cultivation was important, farmers just scattered the seed *à la volée* and did nothing more until harvest time.[57] The cultivations discussed here below are drainage, weeding and hoeing, and grazing of the crop as it grows.

### Drainage

Three main reasons for careful drainage can be identified: (1) when new land which might be heavy and wet was brought under cultivation for the first time; (2) to avoid the collection of stagnant water; (3) to check and divert excessive rainfall. All are in reality interconnected and combine to improve and preserve the cultivable land.[58]

The detailed discussion of Columella on the different types of drains to be constructed when clearing virgin land destined for the plough strengthens the argument that some of the heavy soils of Italy were being cultivated in this period (2. 2. 9–11). Yet once the natural vegetation is cleared for arable cultivation, the effect of the sometimes torrential rain is harsher and soil erosion can occur.[59]

[56] Testini, *Il frumento*, 12 f.
[57] L.-A. J. Michon, *Les céréales en Italie sous les Romains* (1859), 184.
[58] Besides cultivable land, meadow land also had to be drained to avoid affliction from animal parasites.
[59] A. Goudie, *The Human Impact. Man's Role in Environmental Change* (1981), 118, 127.

Cato presents a lively picture of the fight against the first torrential autumn rains when, after the summer, the ploughed earth is most susceptible to erosion:

> The greatest danger from water is in the early autumn when there is dust (since the soil of the fallow land has been worked so thoroughly). When the rains begin the whole household must turn out with spades and hoes, open the ditches, direct the water into the roads, and see that it flows off. (155)

It is after sowing time that all old ditches have to be cleaned and new ones dug (V. 1. 35. 2; Col. 11. 2. 82; 2. 8. 3). Otherwise the rains can wash away the soil together with the seeds and the new plants. Moreover, stagnant water, besides literally drowning the seeds, can, when it freezes in winter, badly damage the roots of young plants (V. 1. 45. 2–3). The ridging system of ploughing, as already mentioned, would greatly have aided the situation. Pliny also advises (as noted previously) the driving of a larger furrow every so often to function as a connecting channel between the ploughed field and the larger drainage ditches (18. 179).

Good drainage not only alleviated the problem of excess surface water but also had the beneficial effect of lowering and stabilizing the water table. This in its turn provided more space for root development and permitted increased aeration and bacterial life in the soil. Further, well-drained soils warm up sooner. This would have allowed an earlier first ploughing in the spring, and more generally have made the working of heavier soils easier. However, an over-enthusiastic drainage policy might cause problems for contiguous properties.

The *Digest* reveals that not only was drainage of farmland common but also that one's neighbour could be a worse enemy than the rain. An action could be brought if it could be shown that damage had been caused by the diversion of *aqua pluvia* from its natural course. It is extremely interesting that the conclusions of the late Republican jurists were that if rain water had been diverted for the purpose of cultivation, a case could not be brought. This exemption particularly applied to the system of ploughing with ridges and *sulci aquarii*, and, for Trebatius at least, was confined to cereal culture. Perhaps we can see here concern to promote cereal cultivation. General ditches, unless specifically dug to dry out land for cultivation, could be the subject of an action. It would have been necessary, therefore, especially in an area of close settlement, to maintain and direct one's drainage channels carefully.[60] Large-scale drainage projects might even cause inter-municipal rivalry, as we learn from a passing reference in Cicero (*ad Att.* 4. 15. 5).

*Weeding and Hoeing*

In order to achieve the highest yields, the weeding and hoeing of the crop as it grows are essential. The many references to both these labour-intensive operations in the agricultural texts demonstrate that this was widely recognized. Various times were recommended for the carrying out of both operations, and it is once

---

[60] *Aquae Pluviae Arcendae, Dig.* 39. 3: 'Quintus Mucius responded that land which had been ploughed was not actionable [sc. under the law governing the damaging redirecting of rainfall], while Trebatius only excluded such land provided that it was under cereal cultivation'.

again clear that diversity of advice reflects cultivation conditions in different areas of Italy and on different types of farms.

Varro explains the general principle of weeding. Weeds should be destroyed when small, otherwise they become too strong and are able to resist eradication by breaking off above ground only (V. 1. 47).[61] This surely refers to a manual weeding action. Roots which are left in the ground stay alive and can produce successive crops of weeds year after year. Careful working of the fallow would reduce this danger, but even so, attentive weeding at a later date was obviously necessary. This would especially have been true of the heavier and more fertile soils. On large farms before the use of chemical weed-killers, weeding was often a task allotted to women and children. As has been noted, the field tasks allocated to women and children by the Roman agronomists were few (p. 45 n. 19); instead weeding was undoubtedly done by the *mediastini* (common labourers on the arable estate).[62]

Certain types of weeds that grew in land under arable cultivation are mentioned by the agricultural writers, alhtough it is not always clear whether the context concerns weeding during the cereal crops' growth period or clearing of the fallow land in preparation for ploughing. Cato refers to pulling up (*vellito*—again a manual action) dwarf elder (*ebulum*: *Sambucus ebulus* L.) and hemlock (*cicuta*: *Conium maculatum* L.)[63] from the *seges*, which should mean 'sown field'.[64]

Columella, again talking about the weeding of *segetes*, advises the removal of brambles (*rubi*) and branches (*rami*), which are then used for fencing (11. 2. 19).[65] Since the reason for removing 'brambles' and 'branches', according to Columella, was to facilitate the 'digging and working of the soil' (ibid.), it seems permissible to take *segetes* as arable land under fallow. On the large arable estates (*domus cultae*) of the later Roman Campagna gangs of workers were hired during the winter and early spring for the *sterpatura* (uprooting) of *sterpi* (thornbushes), *rovi* (brambles) and *ginestre* (brooms) on fallow land in preparation for ploughing.[66] The implements used were hoes and spades, not hands. Quintilian briefly refers to 'cutting out' (*excidere*) brambles from the *arva* (*Inst. Or.* 9. 4. 5), which indicates a tougher task than manual weeding. It would thus appear to make better sense of the Columella passage if it is taken to refer to the preliminary clearing of the fallow land rather than to the weeding of the growing crop.

Were the hemlock and dwarf elder, noted by Cato, weeds found among the

[61] For another explanation of weeding (*runcatio*) see P. 18. 185. Weeds for the purpose of this study are considered to be plants which grow where they are not wanted.

[62] Testini, *Il frumento*, 35 used to hire women and boys (twelve to sixteen years old) for weeding. Also Scheuermeier, *Il lavoro* I, pls. 150-2, although there weeding and hoeing are combined (see below). *Mediastini* (Col. 2. 12. 7) are the only labourers mentioned besides ploughmen on a 200-*iugera* arable farm.

[63] Botanical names are taken from André, *Lexique*, s.vv.

[64] 37. 2. For the definition of *seges*, V. 1. 29. 1: '*Seges* refers to ploughed land which has been sown, while *arvum* is ploughed land that has not yet been sown.'

[65] Branches (*rami* might also refer to weeds large enough to have 'branches') and brambles could make a particularly effective barrier, as Caesar observes (*BG* 2. 17. 4). For other types of hedges and fences see V. 1. 14. That grain fields were fenced is clear from the passing reference in Col. 2. 21. 2; cf. 5. 12. 4. Fences and hedges, besides helping to shelter crops from the wind, are used mainly to keep out intruders, human or animal. On an intensive arable farm which depended for its success on manure from animals, well-regulated and fenced fields are the sign of careful management.

[66] Cervesato, *Latina Tellus*, 95. Note that Columella describes weeds which grow up *after the harvest* as *sentes* (6. 3. 1), a word applicable to *rubi*, *rovi* and *sterpi*.

new cereal crop? Certainly to the modern mind they seem rather too large and robust to have already invaded the young crop by late winter or early spring, especially after the care given to the maintenance of a clean fallow the year before. Yet on the other hand, it is only since the use of weed-killer (often sprayed from light aircraft) that wheat fields in both Italy and England have assumed an unvariegated, almost artificial, appearance. Wheat entwined with weeds is a thing of the past. Where now can we see Autumn?

> Drowned with the fume of poppies, while thy hook
> Spares the next swath and all its twinèd flowers.

While Varro simply refers collectively to weeds as *herba* (1. 30), the most succinct (and impressive) list of weeds which could infest the cereal crop is that of Virgil (*Georgics* 1. 150–5): *carduus, lappae, triboli, lolium, avena* (also mentioned by Cato 37. 5). Pliny adds *orobanche, aegilops, area* (18. 153-5), and *ononis* (21. 98).[67]

As an explanation of what appears to be an increase in weeds over the period,[68] it could be that greater transport and commerce in grain, as well as experimentation with different varieties, facilitated the diffusion of weeds (which travelled mixed in with the cereals) and thus augmented their number in any one area. Attractive as that hypothesis is for the present study, the literary evidence cannot be made to support it, for the usual negative reasons of silence and selection. Darnel was known in Cato's time but was not mentioned by him;[69] Varro names no specific weed; examples in Columella are rare; Pliny's list may be a result rather of the encyclopaedic nature of his work (as the transcription of Theophrastus might suggest) than of a real increase in number and diffusion.

The few recent finds of weed seeds from archaeological excavations may begin to provide some test of such a theory. The presence of ten species in the fourth and early third centuries B.C. at Metapontum indicates a considerable level of weed infestation of arable crops, even before the Roman period. Moreover, the presence of *Galium* there, at Aquileia, La Befa (near Siena), Matrice and San Giovanni, demonstrates diffusion and adaptability of that one species (which still infests cereal crops in the Mediterranean) during the period under particular consideration in this study. The existence of annual weeds, such as *Chenopodium*, which could be eliminated by the practice of fallowing, might indicate an increasing suppression of the fallow in favour of continuous cultivation of cereals or rotation of cereals with legumes. The presence of a quantity of legume species, along with this weed at Metapontum and San Giovanni, suggests the latter

---

[67] *Carduus* (*Centaurea solstitialis* L.) 'thistle'; *lappa* (*Arctium lappa* L.) 'burdock'; *tribolus* (*Tribulus terrestris* L.) 'caltrop'; *lolium* (*Lolium temulentum* L.) 'darnel'; *avena* (*Avena fatua* L.) 'wild oat'; *orobanche* (*Cuscuta Europea* L.) 'dodder'; *aegilops* (*Aegilops ovata* L.) a species of grass; *aera* (transcription of αἶρα, Theophrastus, *HP* 1. 5. 2) = *lolium*; *ononis* (*Ononis antiquorum* L.) 'rest-harrow'.

[68] The previous list is not complete or thorough; it includes only the obvious examples. Add: 'a white grass similar to *panicum*' (P. 18. 153), perhaps the modern graminaceous weed known as *Panicum Crus-galli* L.; 'an axe-leafed plant' especially noxious to lentils (P. 18. 155).

[69] Ennius, *Var.* 31, 'where the farmer sees darnel (and oats) growing among the wheat'.

explanation.[70] Yet the further likelihood, that what are now considered weeds were valued in their own right, should not be omitted from consideration (see below). Moreover, the presence of the *Polygonaceae* species might even indicate *cultivation* of the only cereal which does not belong to the graminaceous family. It is called *grano saraceno* in Italian and is still to be seen in mountainous zones, particularly in the Alps, where its short growth cycle allows it to be sown, like millet, to supplement other cereals or to replace them in case of failure.[71] The presence of a sample of *Polygonaceae* at Matrice, in the uplands of Molise, might be thus interpreted.

*Orobanche* is also interesting (P. 18. 155). The term comprises two species of parasitic weed and illustrates legume cultivation. The one type (*Cuscuta europea* L.) entwines itself around, and obtains nourishment from, legumes as they grow. Pliny notes it as a particular menace for vetch and chickpea (18. 155). The other, in modern times a greater danger, is *Orobanche crenata* L. which draws its sustenance from the roots of legumes. Pliny (22. 162) observes that it affects vetches and legumes in general. One method of avoiding it, according to modern advice, is to sow deeply, 10–15 cm (for comparison, wheat is not sown deeper than 3–5 cm). Columella stressed the importance of a deep sowing of beans; the reason is not given but can be assumed to accord with the modern instructions. Moreover, Columella asserts from his own experience ('nos . . . comperimus', 2. 10. 11) based on traditional lore, that if bean seeds are soaked in 'chemicals' before sowing, the plants are less likely to be infested by weevils (*curculio*) later on. This other menace is almost certainly the modern dreaded *tonchio*, and the prophylactic advice is the same. Other references to legume infestations and cures,[72] equally recognizable in modern terms, indicate the careful attention given to legume cultivation in Roman Italy (see pp. 105–16). Again, whether this means that legumes became more widespread over the period would be difficult to prove from the literary evidence.

Despite some evidence for cultivated oats (p. 14), it is clear that in the Roman period oats were better known in their wild form as a weed. More robust than the cultivated species, it would seem from the literary sources (archaeological evidence is still lacking) that *avena fatua* was common. Cato recommended that the seeds be stripped before they mature (37. 5); valuable advice, since once interred only some of the oat seeds germinate in the same or the following year, 'the rest remaining dormant for two or more years, and then germinating.'[73] One year's infestation thus leaves an unwanted legacy for the future. Not surprisingly then, Pliny nominated them as 'the first of all forms of disease in cereals' (18. 149). This emphasis could imply that wild oats had become more diffuse and problematic since Cato's period. Again, one has hopes from archaeology.

---

[70] Metapontum: Carter, Costantini et al., 'Population and Agriculture', fig. 16.4; San Giovanni: Costantini, 'Piante coltivate e piante spontanee'; Aquileia: Castelletti, 'Resti macroscopici di vegetali da Aquileia'; La Befa: J. J. Dobbins, *The Excavation of the Roman Villa at La Befa, Italy*, B.A.R. Int. Series 162 (1983), 48; Matrice: Lloyd, *Interim Report*.

[71] *Enciclopedia Agraria Italiana*, s.v. *Grano Saraceno*.

[72] Cf. the axe-leaved plant noxious to lentils (P. 18. 155) and the insects, slugs and snails which infest vetch (18. 156). Weeds and infestation: Tassinari, *Manuale*, 528–9.

[73] Peterson, *Wheat*, 256.

Weeds could be utilized, once pulled, for fencing or animal litter (Col. 11. 2. 19; Cato 37. 2). Yet alimentary and medical uses cannot be overlooked. Darnel seeds, for example, could be ground and applied to sores (Celsus 5. 12), or used for fattening African hens according to the tenets of *pastio villatica* (V. 3. 9. 20); or *orobanche*, if pulled when young and tender, could be eaten raw or boiled (P. 22. 162). It is most important to stress that, like other wild plants, it need not only have been eaten by *rustici*, as recent works have argued.[74]

The earliest time to weed is recognized by a stage in the crop's growth. When the plant begins to 'bush out' above the surface its root system is already well developed and is able to resist displacement by movement of the soil caused by weeding, as well as to profit from the removal of competition for the soil's nutrients. Since the speed of growth depends once again on cereal variety, soil type and micro-climate, it is difficult to fix calendar dates. This undoubtedly explains the diversity of dates offered by the agronomists. Cato refers to winter weeding of the grain crop (37. 5), Varro suggests after the vernal equinox (1. 30), and Pliny from mid-February to mid-March (18. 241). Columella, however, recommends two widely separate times: the second half of January (11. 2. 7) and the first half of May (11. 2. 40). Elsewhere he states that weeding should take place either before or soon after the flowering of the grain (2. 11. 9), which seems to refer to the recommended May weeding time.[75] Columella is therefore envisaging two weedings of the crop. Pliny also refers to a stage in the plant's growth, 'when the crop has begun to make a joint' ('cum seges in articulum exiit', 18. 185). This occurred within some twenty days after the spring equinox (Col. 2. 11. 9). It is undoubtedly to be interpreted as the commencement of the 'jointing' or 'stem-extension' stage, when the stalks (culms) which will bear the ear grow upwards, marking the completion of the tillering stage. From the above, it appears that there were three times when weeding was carried out: in winter (Cato and Columella), when the plant had begun to tiller; in the middle of spring (Varro and Pliny), when the tillering is completed and the culms lengthen; in May (Columella), at the final stage of the plant's growth, before the ripening period.

Winter weeding would have been typical of the warm southern and coastal

---

[74] Utilization of other weeds: thistles as human and animal food (P. 19. 54; for the artichoke variety, see P. 19. 154); the flower can be used to curdle milk (Col. 7. 8. 1); the caper, which can spread like a weed in fallow ground if not tended (Col. 11. 3. 54); brambles, besides being used for fencing, provided fruit (Prop. 3. 13. 28; Calp., *Ecl.* 4. 31), which use is indicated by the recovery of blackberry seeds at San Giovanni (Small, 'The Environment of San Giovanni', 210); *bromos* (= *avena*) for medical plaster (P. 21. 161); darnel seeds thrown on hot coals for a type of riot dispersal technique (P. 18. 156); poppies as a drug, poppy seed for confectionery (cf. Cels. 3. 18. 12; Cato 79), as a bleaching agent (P. 8. 195). Both J. M. Frayn, *Subsistence Farming in Roman Italy* (1979), 57–72 and J. K. Evans, 'Plebs Rustica: The Peasantry of Classical Italy II. The Peasant Economy', *American Journal of Ancient History* 5 (1980), 134–73, mislead when they argue that wild plants were only peasant food. We can be certain instead that they were used by all levels of society, and it is not therefore unlikely, as occurs today, that such uncultivated plants were sold at local markets. It is noteworthy in this context that Cato explicitly states that the *owner* should have the right to the wild asparagus and other edible plants which grow in the leased pasture land (149. 2). (This passage is cited by both Frayn and Evans as evidence that *rustici* ate such foods.)

[75] This is deduced as follows: wheats ripen between thirty and eighty days after the flowering period, depending on the relevant mixture of heat and moisture. Assuming an average of fifty-five days and given that the harvesting of the grain in warm coastal areas, known to Columella (11. 2. 54), occurred in the middle or early July (see p. 66), the weeding in May can be seen to coincide with that recommended either side of the flowering period.

areas, which experienced mild winters that encouraged a rapid growth of both weeds and cereals. A May weeding time, either just before or after the flowering period, which would be difficult and time-consuming given the by then considerable growth of the cereal crops, surely reflects the careful attention typical of the Columellan-type estate which produced for the market. As remarked earlier (p. 46 n. 21) ridged fields would facilitate the operation. In general it is clear that some weeding was carried out only once, while on other, more intensive farms it was viewed as a more or less continuous process during which the fields were gone over two or even three times. Weeds would have been a constant menace, at least until the crop grew enough to be able to dominate them itself.

Celsus, in a discussion of the cultivation of beans, had apparently stated his preference against weeding altogether, motivated by the desire to reap two crops, beans and 'hay'. Columella inveighs against such ingenuity: it was a mark of a poor farmer; he himself hoed (which in this case was combined with weeding—see below) the bean crop three times (2. 11. 6-7). Both his and modern advice report that careful cultivation produces a much better yield than the more common(?) neglect.[76] Celsus, perhaps, sought to make a virtue from necessity. Despite the possible risk in encountering weeds poisonous to cattle,[77] I have heard similar advice to that of Celsus at reaping time in a peasant community.[78] The weed growth among the wheat was harvested and fed as fodder together with the straw. In this case it was not that the negative effect of weeds growing among the wheat was not recognized, nor was it even that no attempt initially was made to hoe or weed, it was simply that on land which had been poorly ploughed and sown with unsorted and uncleaned seed, weeds luxuriated. Thus on the peasant farm weeds were accepted as a fact of life; and while cereal yields were thereby poorer than on a more intensive estate, the weeds were all the more used as part of the farm economy, as food or medicine as noted above, or as animal fodder. On this reasoning, the fact that Cato utilized weeds only as bedding for animals indicates the intensive nature of his estate (37. 2).

Weeding was performed by hand, hoeing required the use of a *sarculum*. It is equally clear, however, that some cereal and legume crops were only hoed, and this must mean that weeding and hoeing were then combined.[79] Unfortunately there is no easy explanation of the criteria in these cases which regulated the sometimes differing recommendations of the agronomists.[80] It is best to conclude that labour times and methods varied according to the region and to the type of farm.

The intensive estate producing for the market would provide the most careful cultivations for the crops it sold. It is in this context that the remark of Varro should be understood that the successful practice of hoeing twice or thrice was the result of willingness to improve agricultural methods by experiment (1. 18. 8). The aim of producing the highest yield through repeated hoeing is also emphasized

[76] Grimaldi, *Coltivazioni erbacee*, 121 f.

[77] Cf. Pliny's 'white grass similar to Italian millet (*panicum*) that springs up all over the fields and is fatal to cattle' (18. 153).

[78] Letino at 1,000 m above the upper Volturno valley between Venafrum and Bovianum (18 July 1981).

[79] e.g. for beans (Col. 2. 11. 7).

[80] Pliny advises weeding for barley (18. 184), Columella does not (2. 12. 2); the reverse is true in the case of hoeing beans (P. 18. 185; Col. 2. 11. 7).

by Columella, referring to his own experience in the case of beans:

> Cultivated thus [sc. hoed three times] they not only multiply their yield but also produce little pod so that when shelled and cleaned they are almost equally as voluminous as before shelling, so little is the amount diminished by the removal of their outer coverings. (2. 11. 7)

As regards times for hoeing, more clearly even than for weeding, it is shown that the reliable guides are climatic factors, types of soil and the stage of the plant's growth, an indication as always of ubiquity and diversity of practice (Col. 2. 11. 3–4).

### Grazing of the Growing Crop

This is not a common practice in Italy today, and for that reason, as well as to further understanding of agricultural diversity in Roman Italy, it merits comment. It has not been satisfactorily explained elsewhere.

Grazing the young crop in the leaf was a way of curbing excessive vegetative growth in the early stages ('luxuria segetum . . . in herba', P. 18. 161). Virgil clearly refers to the future danger of lodging that this was designed to prevent ('ne gravidis procumbat culmus aristis', *Georgics* 1. 111). Too much nitrogen or a mild winter can cause a rapid early growth of leaves, which divert nutrients from the later culms and conceal the base of the culms from light; these then become weakened to the extent that, when the plant is fully developed, it is less able to withstand wind or rain. Modern preventative measures include balanced fertilization and the selection of breeds with short culms and a less precocious growth rate.

In the Roman period one corrective was grazing. This had to occur before the jointing period so as not to destroy the ear, as Pliny clearly states (18. 161). Depending on the fertility of the soil, the mildness of the climate and the type of cereal, grazing might take place several times ('quidem vel saepius', ibid.) during the winter and early spring. This practice strengthens the plant's resistance to lodging, does not decrease the yield, and provides a highly nutritious pasture. Nevertheless, the flock has to be well tended to prevent it from completely devouring the young crop. It is not clear whether precocious grains were used, or early sowings practised, *on purpose* to integrate arable and livestock farming, although this occurs in some areas of the world today.[81] It seems instead to have been a purely corrective measure, although its benefit to livestock was clearly recognized. Unfortunately there is no indication as to the localities in which this sort of cultivation was typical. White briefly referred to it as 'essential to wheat growing in Italy south of the Apennines',[82] and whereas I have observed the practice on the Tavoliere, there is evidence from the sixteenth century that such

---

[81] W. H. Leonard, J. H. Martin, *Cereal Crops* (1963), 344: 'Approximately 65% of the winter wheat acreage is pastured . . . Wheat is a highly nutritive pasture crop because the young plants contain nearly as much protein as does alfalfa hay.'

[82] White, *Roman Farming*, 180.

grazing also took place near Brescia in the north.[83] Geographical precision is therefore not possible. It is perhaps better to note that before development of short-straw varieties of wheat and the practice of careful fertilizer-balance, the danger of lodging was greater, and grazing of the young crop more common, than today. Yet since it is not a practice mentioned by Cato, Varro and Columella, its ubiquity is questionable.

On Puglian cereal estates of the last century the device of 'pruning' or 'clipping' (*cimatura*) with a small sickle was resorted to (besides pasturing) when the mildness of the winter had caused a too rapid and excessive vegetative growth.[84] This was an extremely labour-intensive method and is not mentioned by the Roman agronomists. If their advice on sowing times has been correctly interpreted, they sought to avoid the problem by sowing late in the year. Instead of the laborious manual *cimatura*, the progressive Puglian farmer, to the jeers of his workforce and neighbours, introduced a form of flexible harrow (*erpice a catena*), which hoed, weeded and 'pruned' simultaneously.[85] As noted above, Pliny informs us that in some fertile areas the young crop is 'combed in the blade' ('ubertas pectinari segetem in herba cogat', 18. 186) with an iron-toothed harrow. 'Even then', he continues, 'the crop can still be grazed and then has to be stirred with the hoe.' There can be no doubt from this description that the primary object of the harrow was to clip or prune the crop (and thus *pectinare* must here be equivalent to the Italian *cimare*).[86] Weeding might also have been accomplished by the harrow, yet since grazing followed, hoeing was a separate, later operation. The use of the harrow in this case was not therefore seen as a labour-saving device, unlike the Puglian example.

[83] C. Tarello, *Ricordo d'agricoltura*, ed. M. Berengo (1975), under the alphabetic headings B and M (*Biade morbide, Morbido delle biade*), 41, 62–3, explains both the Plinian and Virgilian passages from his own experience.

[84] Testini, *Il frumento*, 37.

[85] Ibid., 38.

[86] i.e., equivalent in effect to grazing. This is certainly how Tarello takes it: the toothed harrow could be used instead of grazing against the danger of lodging. Pliny's point is that in some areas the vegetative growth was so great that both methods could be employed.

F

# CHAPTER IV: HARVEST, STORAGE AND YIELDS

## HARVEST

Summer was harvest time (V. 1. 27. 3). More precisely, most farmers began reaping between the summer solstice and the rising of the Dog Star, a period of twenty-seven days from about 21 June (V. 1. 32. 1). In temperate coastal regions ('locis temperatis et maritimis') the harvest was completed during the second half of July, as Columella attests (11. 2. 54); and in August, within thirty days of reaping, the straw which had been left in the field was cut and gathered into heaps (ibid. 6. 3. 1). The correlation between the dates given by Varro and Columella thus appears reasonably close. More importantly, their remarks reveal that the harvest period was a drawn-out one (given the manual reaping method) and varied with the region. Climate, topography and the type of grain were the influential factors.[1]

Cereals ripened earlier in hot areas, and therefore reaping began there first, followed in turn by warm and cold localities (Col. 2. 7. 2).[2] Thus, for example, wheat in the plains of Apulia would be reaped earlier than that in the mountains to the west and the north, and reapers would be able to work in the plains and then return to their smaller farms, if they owned one, to reap their own wheat. Varro speaks of the hiring of labour for the harvest, and this may be how some small farmers made extra money (1. 17. 3).[3]

Harvesting could also be staggered on individual farms. Pliny the Younger notes that on his Tuscan estate the grain on the slopes ripened later than that of the valley floor (*Ep.* 5. 6. 9). Moreover, if various types of wheat were grown on the same estate, it would have been possible to harvest them in order of ripening. Barley reached maturity before wheat and had to be reaped quickly to avoid 'shedding' (Col. 11. 2. 50; 2. 9. 15; P. 18. 80).[4] However, the wheat prized by rich consumers, *siligo*, provided problems for the farmer because it never ripened evenly and its ear was fragile when ripe (P. 18. 91).

These days, machines which combine the operations of reaping and threshing permit the farmer to delay the harvest until the last moment. Manual reaping, however, takes much longer and all the dangers such as attacks by birds and other

---

[1] As for the modern harvesting times, secure dates are impossible due to annual and regional variability. I can only report from autopsy (summer 1981). On the coastal plains of Latium the harvest was completed by the last week of June. In the Sabine hills above Rieti, reaping was still being carried out three weeks later. Further south in the mountains (between 700 and 1,000 m) above Saepinum and above the already mentioned site near Ruoti, reaping by hand was in many places *beginning* in the last week of July. On the Tavoliere, harvesting had been completed in early June. Ripening may have been a few days earlier than 'usual' because of hot weather in May and June. Cf. Grimaldi, *Coltivazioni erbacee*, 32.

[2] It should be noted that Columella, after stressing the variations in reaping times caused by climatic factors, warns the reader that his following remarks

will pertain to temperate regions only (ibid.).

[3] In the early part of the present century nomadic reapers from the Monti Lepini and Ernici and from the Abruzzi found work on the grain farms of the flat land of the Campagna: Cervesato, *Latina Tellus*, 105. For other comparative evidence of what is a common practice in Italy and elsewhere around the Mediterranean: Braudel, *The Mediterranean and the Mediterranean World* I, 47. Varro mentions the hiring of extra labour at harvest time (1. 17. 2), but there is no direct evidence for nomadic reapers in Roman Italy. Vespasian's great-grandfather led a group of labourers each year from Umbria to the Sabine country 'ad culturam agrorum'; this does not necessarily refer to reaping (Suet., *Vesp*. 1. 4). It might, for example, refer to clearing fallow land (p. 59).

[4] Cf. Percival, *The Wheat Plant*, 311.

creatures, parching by the sun, flattening by wind and rain, are accentuated. In order to minimize the hazard it would have been important to know exactly when to reap.

One common and practical test was according to colour and texture. When the crop as a whole took on a golden yellow hue and before the seed hardened and was still *rubicundus*, it was ready for reaping (Col. 2. 20. 2). In the days of universal hand reaping, the optimum time was the stage before full ripeness, at the so-called *maturazione gialla*, when the whole plant loses its chlorophyll and as a result turns yellow. The seed at this stage is still pulpy and unhardened.[5] This tallies precisely with Columella's description (ibid.). The idea was to begin reaping some time before complete ripeness because of the time-consuming methods. Waiting for the full-ripe stage when the rachis becomes brittle would have considerably increased the danger of loss of seed. Pliny's advice to reap early was oracular (18. 298).

As maturity approaches, the roots die and all goodness is gradually drained from the rest of the plant by the seed. If the crop is harvested before complete maturity, the stalk is less fragile because it still has its nutrients, and so hand reaping is easier. Yet at the same time, although it is reaped somewhat early, the seed can continue to extract the stalk's nutrition as though it were still in the ground. For this reason the cut crop should not be threshed immediately; it should be left to complete its drying and ripening in the sun.[6]

### Reaping Methods and Implements

Varro describes three reaping methods (1. 50. 1–3):

(1) In Umbria grain was cut close to the ground with a *falx*.[7] The ears were removed almost immediately and taken in baskets to the threshing floor. The straw was left in the field and later stacked.

(2) In Picenum the straw was left standing to be cut later and only the ears were reaped by means of a curved wooden instrument with a serrated blade attached at one end.

(3) Near Rome and in many other localities the straw was cut half-way up the stalk with the ear attached and both were threshed together. Although no tool is specifically mentioned, a *falx* can probably be assumed. The remaining straw was left standing in the field to be cut later. It is to be observed that methods (1) and (2) would not allow the seed to increase in size after reaping, although threshing would have been quicker and easier because of the absence of straw.

Columella (2. 20. 3), without specifying particular regions, describes two methods which correspond to Varro's (2) and (3). Ears only were removed and the straw left standing; the implements were *mergae* or *pectines*. This method, he notes, was easy only in a thinly grown crop, and the reference is to a farm, whether large or small, with poor soil, but probably not to an intensive cereal farm. Otherwise many people cut the culms in the middle with *falces veruculatae*,

---

[5] Tassinari, *Manuale*, 465.

[6] Columella observes that the increase in the size of the seed under these conditions was an established fact (2. 20. 2; cf. 12. 52. 18). For a controlled experiment to prove it: Cinelli, 'La mietitura', 1 ff. The pheno-menon was noted (although it could not be explained) and used to advantage by cereal farmers in Puglia last century, Testini, *Il frumento*, 40 f.

[7] For all the reaping tools mentioned in this section see White, *Agricultural Implements*.

*rostratae* or *denticulatae*. The remaining straw was cut and gathered within thirty days of the reaping (6. 3. 1; 11. 2. 54).

Pliny sets forth five methods (18. 296), two of which are localized to Gaul and need not concern us here. The other three are: cutting the straw halfway up with a *falx* and then the removal of the ears with two *mergae*; reaping at ground level; the simple plucking up of the plant (*evellere*).

It might be that in Varro's Umbrian method, once the crop had been reaped with a *falx*, the ears were removed with *mergae*, since from Pliny it is clear that the use of *mergae* (and perhaps *pectines*) existed side by side with that of the *falx*. Varro, however, nowhere mentions *mergae*. For the removal of only ears of wheat, whether the crop was standing or already cut, the *falx* is not a particularly appropriate implement, since wheat stalks never attain an even height; an instrument with a stripping action would be more convenient, if that is how *mergae* are to be interpreted.[8] If ears only were taken to the threshing floor, the threshing operation would have taken less time. Another point to notice is that several of the methods show that the crop was harvested twice, as it were. First the ears, or the ears and half of the stalks, were reaped, secondly, the remaining straw was cut. Cato is silent on reaping, but among the equipment for the oliveyard are five *falces stramentariae* (10. 3). These could have been especially designed for the later cutting of the straw.

Once again, the diversity of both practice and implement is remarkable, perhaps due at least partially to irrational local custom,[9] although the explanations offered here below arise from economic and agricultural considerations. The very diversity again emphasizes the diffusion of cereal cultivation in Roman Italy as well as the different forms it took. While the agronomists, especially Varro and Columella, indicate their preferences for an intensive form of cultivation, they clearly refer to other modes of cereal farming.

Some clues are provided by Pliny's further observations (18. 297): for thatching houses it is necessary to preserve the entire length of the straw; where there is shortage of hay, chaff is extracted from the straw for fodder;[10] panic straw is not used for thatching, that of millet is burned in the field, barley straw is good cattle feed (18. 297). He had earlier also considered the straw of *siligo* to be good and straight (18. 91), although no special use was indicated for it.

It is apparently as a consequence of these indications that White makes his analysis of *Varro's* different reaping methods:

> Analysis of the evidence makes it clear that these differences depended mainly on the use to which the straw was to be put. In northern Italy there was no shortage of hay or indeed of fodder generally, so the straw could be used for thatching, and was

---

[8] Ibid., 110 ff.

[9] Note the interesting observation of Hopfen and Biesalski, *Small Farm Implements*, 30, on certain local farmers who refused to use hoes which had no holes in their blades, without being able to explain why. The grandfather of the village blacksmith then explained that he had begun to manufacture hoes with holes merely as a trade mark.

[10] The Loeb translation 'where there is a shortage of hay, they require chaff for litter' is nonsensical, since chaff is never used as cattle litter. The sense of the passage is that hay is the best fodder but where it is scarce, chaff is used. Further on (18. 300), Pliny notes that where there is even a shortage of chaff, straw is used as fodder. Note Col. 7. 1. 1 on chaff as a secondary but common fodder in nearly all regions of Italy. I thus translate 'where hay is scarce, they obtain chaff from the straw'.

therefore left standing to dry. But in central and southern Italy, both grazing and litter for stock were scarce, so the corn was cut halfway up leaving useful litter after threshing, and stubble for the herds to graze in.[11]

This alignment of reaping methods with livestock needs has value, subject to certain qualifications and additions. Yet the geographical determinism cannot be accepted, not only because it negates the diversity of the agricultural reality, but also because it is not in the least implied by Varro. Varro's 'Rome and many other regions' (1. 50. 2) cannot be reduced to 'central and southern Italy'.

Firstly, *pace* White, when wheat was reaped halfway up the stalk, the stubble which remained in the field was cut later and stacked, not left as pasturage. That is clear from Varro (1. 50. 3) and Columella (6. 3. 1; 11. 2. 54). White implies that it was left in the field as pasturage. As has already been noted, animals rarely eat stubble but rather the grass and edible weeds which grow up among it. The fact that some farmers bothered to return to the field to collect the remaining straw demonstrates that it had some use. Others, however, had no further use for it and so burned the stubble left after harvesting. Although the agronomists do not recommend this, the practice is mentioned by Pliny (18. 300; cf. Virgil, *Georgics* 1. 85) as a method of either fertilizing the soil or destroying weeds. That it was common enough is implied by its appearance in the Lex Aquilia and in the 'Farmer's Calendar'.[12] A small farmer who had no facilities for the storing of straw and few, if any, animals to feed it to, would have had no interest in returning to the field after the reaping to collect the straw. After, perhaps, allowing his ass and his few sheep to graze the grass, he would have set fire to the stubble with the hope of ameliorating the soil's condition and of ridding the land of weeds. As a poor man, he may not even have had an iron sickle but instead, since his crop was thin (cf. Col. 2. 20. 3), he would simply have used reaping boards to strip the ears.[13] His ass, as Columella claimed, would have been content with chaff after the ears had been threshed (7. 1. 1). Thus he left the straw long before he burnt it; he was unlikely to have used it for thatching, at least not every year.

Zeal for the collection of straw would have been shown rather by the farmer who had a particular interest in stall-kept animals. The primary use of straw was and is for litter and consequently for manure. 'He who has good litter has good manure', is proverbial in Italy. Such a farmer would not usually have difficulty providing more succulent fodder than straw for his animals, for most of the year,

---

[11] White, *Roman Farming*, 182.

[12] *Dig.* 9. 2. 30. 3 (*ad legem Aquiliam*); note also the case where a hired reaper cuts the crop before it is ripe, ibid., 27. 25. 'Farmer's Calendar' (found in Rome and thus perhaps relating only to the local region): *CIL* 6.2305 (August, ll. 14–15). It is true that in this way the soil is fertilized to a certain temporary extent and weeds are removed. See Oliva, *Il frumento nella montagna*, 14 and Delano Smith, *Western Mediterranean Europe*, 294. The references to burning off in Lucan (9. 182 f.) and in Silius Italicus (*Punica* 7. 364 f.) concern grazing land rather than wheat fields. The old grass is burned to stimulate new growth.

[13] Experimental reaping of wild wheat in Turkey showed that ears could be simply and adequately stripped by hand. This is not mentioned in the literary evidence for Roman Italy, although it cannot be ruled out, especially in a thinly growing crop: J. R. Harlan, 'A Wild Wheat Harvest in Turkey', *Archaeology* 20 (1967), 197–200. See also Reynolds, *Iron Age Farm*, 64, who refers to hand stripping as a contemporary practice in Spain. Another method in poor soil is uprooting of the plant, noted by Pliny (18. 26). For a discussion of this see V. L. Bohrer, 'On the Relation of Harvest Methods to Early Agriculture in the Near East', *Economic Botany* 26 (1972), 145–54.

especially on an arable estate where legume and fodder crops were grown. However, on less well-integrated estates, if fodder did become scarce over the winter period, then it would be necessary to have in stock straw which was as nutritious as possible. In general, straw is poor animal fodder with much less protein value than hay. As Columella observed, over-ripe hay is no better than straw for fodder (2. 18. 1). If straw *has* to be supplied as fodder, it should derive from an early-reaped crop and then be chopped up and mixed with salt (P. 18. 300).[14] Cato, who describes the same process of increasing the palatibility of straw by the addition of salt, recommends the choice of that straw which is *herbosissima* (54. 2). This could conceivably mean that straw which had grass and edible weeds mixed with it, a practice not unknown in Italy today (p. 64).[15] On the other hand, it could refer to that straw which, coming from a crop with a good quantity of vegetative growth cut before it was fully ripe, has retained some of its freshness and nutrition. The procuring of fodder in this way may have been an important reason for beginning the harvest early. In this case, the practice of cutting the straw first and then removing the ears straightaway afterwards may well have been motivated as much by the desire to allow the straw to retain as much of its nutrition as possible as by the advantage of an easier threshing. To preserve the straw's vigour and nutrition, some farmers who had difficulty in providing other fodder, were prepared to forego the benefit of an increase in the size of the seed, perhaps supported by the consideration that an increased size did not necessarily mean a qualitative increase (P. 18. 298). Yet, as is clear from the rations recommended for oxen by Columella, estates better provided with forage crops might utilize chaff for fodder but not straw.[16] Instead straw would be used as litter for all the animals of the farm, as well as for other purposes (see below).

The serrated sickle (*falx denticulata*) mentioned by Columella is used today, especially in the south of Italy where *durum* wheat is widely cultivated. This wheat has a tougher culm than soft wheat and is cut more easily with the slight sawing action of the serrated sickle.[17] It is likely enough that such a reason dictated the adoption of the *falx denticulata* in the Roman period. The special sickle in use apparently in Picenum (V. 1. 50. 2) has never been adequately explained. From Varro's description it appears to correspond in shape readily enough to a type of Bronze Age pulling sickle, which has been found commonly in Europe (including Italy but mainly in northern Europe), where it survived well into the Roman period.[18] (See Fig. 4a.)

One difficulty with identification is that sickles hitherto found in Italian excavations have been poorly described and almost never drawn or photographed. They are often recorded merely as *falcetti di ferro*, *falci* or *falcini*, and attempts

---

[14] Peterson, *Wheat*, 327–8 for the value of straw as fodder. Its use is still much advised in Italy. Treatment with sodium hydroxide improves palatability (like the agronomists' salt): I. Rabino et al., 'La paglia nell'alimentazione del bestiame', *L'Italia Agricola* 118 (1981), 27–147.

[15] See also the interesting observations of Bohrer, 'On the Relation of Harvest Methods', 145–54, that in India last century wild vetch was allowed to grow among the cereal crop, and then it and the entwined straw were fed to cattle. In time of famine, the grain of the vetch was utilized as human food, its leaves and stalks as fodder.

[16] For the different rations recommended by both Cato and Columella, see conveniently White, *Roman Farming*, appendix C, 219–20.

[17] Grimaldi, *Coltivazioni erbacee*, 33.

[18] Rees, *Agricultural Implements*, 442 ff.

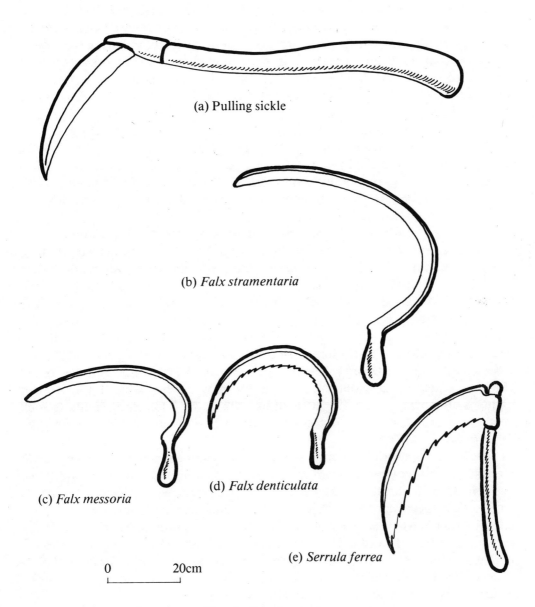

(a) Pulling sickle

(b) *Falx stramentaria*

(c) *Falx messoria*

(d) *Falx denticulata*

(e) *Serrula ferrea*

0          20cm

Fig. 4. Reaping tools.

The special sickle apparently used in Picenum (V. 1. 50. 2) might have been shaped like the pulling sickle (*a*) commonly found in northern Europe and North Italy, and then fitted with a serrated blade. Otherwise it might have looked like (*e*). Type (*c*) was the most usual reaping tool; (*d*) was especially useful for *durum* wheat with its tougher culm; (*b*), with its larger arc, permitted a rapid harvesting of the straw left standing in the field after the ears had been reaped.

at dating are rare.[19] One feature which does seem clearly indicated by such terms is that there was a considerable variation in size. No doubt this can reflect local differences in manufacture and design, but where different sizes occur in the same archaeological context, it is legitimate to imagine specialized uses on the same farm. For example, cereals, because of the fragility of their ears, would require greater care and a smaller sickle for reaping than that required during the cutting of forage crops. Or again, some cereals, for example *siligo*, were more fragile than others and might have been reaped with smaller, more specialized sickles. The later cutting of the straw, as suggested above, could have been carried out more quickly with a larger sickle.

Various sickles, then, could belong on the same farm, notably the larger farm which specialized in arable culture. The small farmer on the other hand, if he owned a sickle, was more likely to use it for a variety of different tasks, reaping cereals, collecting grass for his ass or uncultivated plants for himself by the wayside, as can be seen often enough in the remote parts of Italy today (e.g. the Agro Casentino; see Introduction, xiv).

Again, a reinforcement of the argument developed in this work would be the observation that the lists of equipment provided by Cato contain very limited reference to reaping tools for the grain which was grown on his model farms (10–11). By Varro's period the number of reaping tools and methods had considerably increased, and this could indicate a development of cereal and legume cultivation. For the usual reasons, however, this cannot be proven from the literary evidence. One group of Etruscan agricultural implements in the Archaeological Museum of Florence includes sickles of various sizes and shapes. If all were from one site and earlier than, or contemporary with, Cato, they might vitiate this idea of development. Yet as for most such pieces, unfortunately, dating is unknown and sources difficult to track down.[20] Closer attention to such detail is required from archaeologists, and better evidence will certainly be forthcoming in the future.

To resume an earlier point, it could be that reaping methods were dictated to a certain extent by weed growth. In fields where weeds had not been effectively controlled, the closer the cereal crop was reaped to the ear, the fewer the weeds able to find their way to the threshing floor and eventually into the food. On intensive estates where weeding had been thorough, the crop would be cut halfway up with little risk of weed infiltration. There would always be weeds lower down, but these would not trouble cattle if cut along with the straw used for litter. This is deduced from Columella's remarks on the advantages of collecting the straw which had been left standing in the field:

[19] See for example various entries in *Notizie degli Scavi di Antichità*: 1950, 223, 224, *falci di ferro* in an undated tomb at Libarna; 1951, 101, *falcetto di ferro*, 49 cm chord length from a tomb near Saepinum; 1955, 194, wrongly(?) described as a *roncola*, from Gualdo Tadino in Umbria, uncertain date; 1966, 149, *falce* (undated) from Metaponto; 1971, 453, 457, two *falcetti di ferro*, one 36 cm, the other 23 cm, from Amendolara near Sybaris, from the seventh to sixth centuries B.C. The sickles had disintegrated but had left an unmistakable shape in the dust. That the material was iron must therefore be an assumption.

Ibid. 1972, 81, *falcino di ferro* in a tomb at Volterra. The same tomb contained an *as* dating to no earlier than the latter half of the second century B.C. (The above list does not pretend to be exhaustive.)

[20] G. Vitali, 'Attrezzi agricoli nel Museo Archeologico di Firenze', *Studi Etruschi* 5 (1931), 427–31. It is perhaps better to argue that Cato's treatise was more geographically circumscribed than those of later writers and thus reflected less diversity; or, perhaps, reaping sickles were owned by tenants who took charge of cereal cultivation (cf. Cato 136).

The fields are thus freed from weeds [*sentes*, Columella's general term for weeds], which if they are cut back in summer . . . usually die off at the roots, and also the straw which is put down as litter produces very large amounts of dung. (Col. 6. 3. 1)

Thanks to the clear exposition of White, one earlier question has been resolved: cereals were harvested by sickles, not by scythes, in Roman Italy.[21] Scythes were, however, used for mowing hay, especially, it can be assumed, on the intensive arable estates integrated with livestock.[22] Since it can easily be shown that cereals are reaped quicker and with less labour by adopting scythes rather than sickles, the question arises why use of the scythe was not extended to cereals in the Roman period, especially on those estates that were producing cereals for the market.

A recent study of harvest technology in England has shown that change from one tool to another is governed by a whole series of factors, not just economic and technical, but cultural and social as well.[23] There is no suggestion of a debate in the Roman sources on the pros and cons of the introduction of the scythe against the sickle, but certain factors can be identified which would have militated against any such technological change. For example, for effective employment of the scythe the ground had to be level (Col. 2. 17. 4). This would mean that the common rocky terrain, hillslopes or ridged land would have been difficult to reap with a scythe, and certainly could be reaped no quicker than with a sickle. Even when performed on flat meadow land, scything left an untidy, ragged look, which caused an uneven secondary growth (V. 1. 49. 1; P. 18. 259), and the field had to be 'tidied up' with the sickle. Transposed to the grain field an untidy scything would have resulted in a wastage of grain and straw, not compensated by theoretical savings in labour costs; it would as well perhaps have offended the aesthetic sense of those 'who worshipped at the shrines of even stubbles, tidy symmetrical sheaves, and clean, unlittered fields'.[24] Despite the retarding effects of tradition and custom, or of the difficulty in retraining the workforce, it was finally the shortage of labour and resulting escalation of costs that achieved technological change in nineteenth-century England. But again it must be emphasized here that for the Roman period under discussion there is no compelling evidence of a significant decline in agricultural labour in Italy. Moreover, for what it is worth, a labour calculation for mowing provided by Pliny does not indicate that, with an Italian scythe at least, the speed of harvesting would have been much increased.[25]

## Threshing

'And this is the crowning reward of the farmer—to gather the seed which he had entrusted to the earth' (Col. 2. 20. 6). In order to experience this pleasure to the full the threshing had to be done well. Threshing floors (*areae*), as described by the agronomists, range from the very elaborate, requiring considerable capital outlay, to the less permanent and simpler type. This variety suggests again the

[21] White, *Agricultural Implements*, 78 ff.
[22] Col. 2. 17. 4; V. 1. 49. 1; P. 18. 259.
[23] E. J. T. Collins, 'Harvest Technology and Labour Supply in Britain, 1790–1870', *Economic History Review* 22 (1969), 453–73.
[24] Ibid., 463.
[25] One labourer could harvest one *iugerum* of hay each day (18. 262). See further pp. 124; 139.

widespread practice of cereal growing and further emphasizes that the agronomists were describing not only one system of farming. A peasant farmer would
have used the most basic type of threshing floor, hardly more than a bare patch of
hardened earth, whereas an estate specializing in cereal culture would have been
furnished with a much more elaborate construction. Yet the differences need not
necessarily correspond to rich and poor. They also reflect the agricultural
composition of an estate as well as its wealth. A large farm mainly devoted to
arboriculture, for example, would have required a relatively simple threshing
floor.

The size, according to Varro, and, it can be inferred, the elaborateness of the
threshing floor, should correspond to the yield of the crop (1. 51. 1). Some
farmers build up the floor with stones ('muniunt lapide'), while others also pave
it.[26] Such constructions would have been permanent, testifying to the importance
of arable culture in an estate's economy. Pliny, however, asserts that it was more
common simply to smooth over a piece of ground and to smear it with diluted cow
dung to lay the dust (18. 195). Another simple design was to choose part of a
meadow which, after being hardened by a preliminary threshing of beans (cf.
n. 30 below), would be ready for grain (Col. 2. 19. 2). Yet in every case it was
necessary to have a hard-packed surface to prevent small stones and loose earth
from dirtying the grain, to insure against loss of wheat through cracked earth, and
to stop up the holes of mice and ants. A coating of *amurca* (oil lees) would
discourage insects and weeds (Cato 91).

In Italy today, the threshing floors are often of beaten earth and have to be
cleared of weeds each year before being packed down again with mud and straw.[27]
Since such threshing floors 'return to nature' within a short time, it is hardly
surprising that they do not appear in excavation reports. Often also, especially in
the past, it was not the type of feature to cause much archaeological interest. The
*area* of the villa of San Giovanni di Ruoti probably lies beneath the *aia* of the
modern settlement, superbly situated to catch the wind essential for the winnowing process (V. 1. 51. 1).[28] The so-called 'Villa Pompeiana della Pisanella' on the
lower slopes of Vesuvius had obviously been concerned with arable cultivation on
some scale.[29] The threshing floor was large (*c.*120m²), built up above ground level
and paved in *opus signinum*. The floor seems to have been on a slight incline,
perhaps to allow any rainwater to drain off as quickly as possible, as Varro
advised (1. 51. 1), into the cistern found along one of its sides. Sited on the slope
of Vesuvius, it would have received the winnowing breezes, and positioned next to

---

[26] The 'building up' of the threshing floor would
have been particularly necessary when it was sited on
sloping ground. It might be commonly thus located in
order to catch breezes necessary for winnowing (see
p. 78 below).

[27] H. Rasmussen, 'Grain Harvest and Threshing in
Calabria', *Tools and Tillage* 1 (1968–71), 93–104;
careful packing of mud and straw was then followed
by a threshing with beans to harden the surface
further. That Columella used chaff, not straw, for this
purpose (2. 19. 1) perhaps indicates (*a*) there was
enough better fodder on the farm, (*b*) all straw was
used for litter.

[28] The threshing floor of Pl. III, 2 is similarly sited.

[29] The fullest excavation report of this villa appears
in A. Pasqui, 'La villa Pompeiana della Pisanella
presso Boscoreale', *Monumenti Antichi* 7 (1897),
397 ff. See also White, *Roman Farming*, 423 ff. For
two possible small, circular threshing floors see M. A.
Cotton, G. P. R. Métraux, *The San Rocco Villa at
Francolise* (1985), 13, Fig. 3. For the view that the
estate (which might have included the smaller site of
Posto) was under cereals and olives, Pavolini, 'Review
of M. A. Cotton, *The Late Republican Villa at Posto,
Francolise*', 371–5.

the villa, it would have been easily visible to the owner or procurator, as Columella advised (1. 6. 23). Its rectangular shape did not comply with Varro's preference for a circular design (1. 51. 1); but the stating of a preference in itself suggests differences, and Columella's description of bean threshing seems to refer to a rectangular or oblong floor (2. 10. 13).[30] The capacious room leading directly on to the threshing floor, where quantities of what appeared to be cereal and legume remains (but no detailed examination was made) were found, was interpreted as a *nubilarium*. This building, recommended by Columella and Varro (Col. 1. 6. 24; V. 1. 13. 5), which had to be large enough to house all the harvested crops waiting to be threshed, served as a protection against rain.[31] The excavator's interpretation does not seem unreasonable, and if accepted, helps to confirm the picture of a considerable capital outlay for the purposes of cereal and legume cultivation at this villa. One of the advantages of a *nubilarium* would have been that once the crop had been harvested it could be protected while it was being systematically threshed. The cereal and legume remains discovered in the Pompeian villa's *nubilarium* suggest that the threshing on that estate had not yet been completed by 26 August.

Even though Varro says it was most common to bring half the stalk and ear to the floor to be threshed together, his discussion of threshing only deals with ears already separated from their stalks (1. 52). This may suggest that on the well-furnished grain farm which Varro describes (it has a permanent, solidly constructed threshing floor and used animals and sledges for the threshing), the important advantages of having nutritious straw were recognized.

Two processes have to be carried out before the grain is ready for storing. Firstly, separation of the seed from the ear and the straw, if any, and secondly, separation of the seed from the chaff. The type of grain would affect the threshing procedure. Husked grains have only their straw and beard removed (P. 18. 298). If only the ears of emmer wheat were brought from the field, then they could be stored straight away. This is clear from Varro: 'emmer, which you have stored in the ear at harvest time and wish to prepare for food, should be brought out in winter so that it can be ground in the mill and parched' (1. 63; 1. 69. 1). That is, emmer wheat, if during the reaping process its ears had been removed from the culms, required no threshing. This, without doubt, would have been another of the great advantages of emmer wheat for the peasant. Not only could it have succeeded on poor soils, and have resisted infestation by insects and fungi, it might also be 'eaten straight from the field', without either threshing or winnowing. As a husked grain, before milling or converting it into porridge, it had to be roasted and then pounded to remove its husk. From Varro's remarks it seems that the pounding and roasting operation would also include the removal of the

---

[30] 'Through the middle of the longest length of the floor' ('per longissimum eius mediumque spatium') suggests movement of threshers down the centre of a rectangular floor. Threshing floors these days are of all shapes, since it is often necessary to conform with the lie of the land.

[31] Could this be another indication of a wetter summer climate? The presence of a *nubilarium* would further signify large-scale cereal production. Smaller harvests could be threshed more quickly and run less risk of being damaged by rain, thus rendering uneconomical the construction of a special shed.

husked grains from the ear.[32] The inconvenience of this operation for the peasant would have been far outweighed by the other manifold advantages of the husked grain. It is clear too from the large number of mortars found in bakeries at Pompeii that urban dwellers also ate husked wheats (emmer, perhaps also barley).[33]

To return to Varro and the first process of separation of the grain from the ear, two methods are described:

(1) Animals (*iumenta*) are yoked to a *tribulum* (cognate with *tero*, to 'grind'). The *tribulum* may be a board with stones or metal on its underside; on top is the driver or a heavy weight, to maintain grinding power. Alternatively, it may be a type of 'Punic' cart with small wheels and spiked axle. The latter, Varro notes, is used in Hither Spain and other places, and we might infer that the sledge variety was used especially in Italy, since elsewhere Varro states that it was one of the implements that could be made on the farm (1. 22. 1).[34]

(2) A flock or herd (*grex*), again of *iumenta*, is driven round and prodded with sticks, and the seeds are liberated from the ear by their hoofs.

Unlike Varro, Columella includes the threshing of ears still attached to the straw. The threshing sledge was particularly good for this because it easily broke up the straw (2. 20. 4).[35] (Conversely, if the straw needed to be kept long for any reason—e.g. for thatching— this system would not be adopted.) The *iumenta* could be either horses or oxen; the former were better, according to Columella (ibid.). If only the ears of the grain arrive on the threshing floor, they are best threshed with sticks. This is one of the advantages of this method of reaping, as Columella implies. Simple equipment can be used and, moreover, having been stored in the granary in the ear, the grain can be taken out and threshed during the winter (ibid.). This would relieve some of the labour pressure at a very busy period of the year and give the labourers work in the slacker winter season. Instead of using sticks to thresh this grain, *pecudes* could be used. This more general term for animals might indicate that on some farms asses or mules, rather than oxen or horses, were used. The storing of grain in the ear, and its later threshing with simple tools or by means of the ubiquitous ass, may reflect rather the practice of farmers who were either peasants chancing their hand at the cultivation of bread wheat, or who had possibly worked as gleaners on a larger estate, or who as richer men concerned with growing only enough wheat to feed the *familia*, owned

---

[32] Emmer wheat is thus 'threshed' simply by a mortar and pestle and would have usually then been converted straight into a type of porridge. For comparative evidence see Harlan, 'A Wild Wheat Harvest in Turkey', 197-200. His comment, 'Modern, free-threshing wheats had, of course, largely replaced emmer in Pliny's time', is incorrect (cf. p. 10 n. 27).

[33] Moritz, *Grain Mills*, 23 ff. This might reflect lower-class diet in towns and a not unimportant market for the cereal producer (p. 144 below).

[34] At Montorio nei Frentani near Larino I saw a *tribulum* as described by Varro (a plank with roughened metal on its underside). This can be added

to White's list of 'survivals', *Agricultural Implements*, 156. Hitherto *tribula* have not been reported in Italy. See Scheuermeier, *Il lavoro* I, pls. 228-31 for various threshing devices including a possible 'Punic cart'.

[35] Besides a *tribulum* Columella refers also to a *trahea*, both of which efficiently break up the straw. The identity of this second implement puzzles commentators, cf. White, *Agricultural Implements*, 154 ff. It may well have been just a general 'drag', perhaps similar to the block of stone which, drawn by a yoke of oxen, was noted at Ruoti in Basilicata (August 1981).

neither oxen nor horses.[36] Those farmers, on the other hand, who owned large extents of arable land and who chose to farm it intensively, would have been able to use the many teams of oxen or horses which their land could support to thresh the grain. Further down the scale Columella appears to recognize those whose land supported *pauca iuga* (a 200-*iugera* arable farm supported two *iuga*, 2. 12. 7), yet who were still concerned to produce cereals and legumes in some quantity. These farmers especially would have used a *tribulum* (Col. 2. 20. 4).

To summarize so far, there is again evidence of considerable diversity, according to scale and mode of agriculture. On large arable farms (at least over 200 *iugera*) teams of oxen or, preferably, horses were used for threshing. The mention of horses calls for comment. They were not used for other agricultural tasks (V. 2. 7. 15), and so the type of estate envisaged was one which could provide sufficient forage for the breeding and maintenance of horses for purposes extraneous to the needs of the farm. In other words, horses were not essential to the arable estate as oxen were, and an estate which could utilize the 'luxury' of horses to thresh the grain must have ranked among the largest Roman arable estates, such as the later *domus cultae* of the Campagna.[37] Next down the scale were those estates which could dispose of enough oxen, but not horses, to trample the grain with their hooves. Smaller estates, with only a 'few teams of oxen' (which indicates that the size of the estates would not have been sufficient to support agriculturally inessential animals like horses), utilized a *tribulum* or a *trahea*, which would to a certain extent compensate for the lack of a greater number of animals. White misses the point when he asserts that the *tribulum* 'was an obvious improvement on ancient methods of treading out of the grain with animals'.[38] Columella (2. 20. 4) clearly states that such a device is used only when a sufficient number of animals was not available. That is, in his view, the *tribulum* was not an *improvement*; rather, it was second best. In the Molisan community of Montorio nei Frentani, the *tribulum* was considered a better threshing implement than a mere block of stone, and the mark of a more prosperous farm. There might have been a similar difference between the use of the *tribulum* and *trahea*, although Columella observes that both perform their task well ('either of which very easily breaks up the straw', 2. 20. 4). There was certainly, however, a difference between the farm which used such threshing devices and that which perhaps used merely the ubiquitous ass or mule. This was no doubt a small farm which did not use oxen for ploughing. On an even poorer scale, perhaps, were those who stored and then threshed their ears of wheat with sticks as was necessary during the year. It is not unlikely that such people were those who had been let in to the rich man's fields, after the harvest, to collect the fallen ears of wheat, a custom noted by Rasmussen.[39] One practice, common enough in Italy today but of which there is no indication in the ancient sources, is the collective use by

---

[36] Small amounts of grain enough for family needs are still threshed by the domestic mule or ass on peasant farms in the south of Italy. The alternative for the small cultivator, namely storage and then beating out with sticks as needed during the year, is shown by Scheuermeier, *Il lavoro* I, pls. 215–20.

[37] For a photograph of horses being used for the threshing at a *domus culta* which specialized in cereals, sheep and horse breeding, see Cervesato, *Latina Tellus*, facing p. 112.

[38] White, *Agricultural Implements*, 155.

[39] Rasmussen, 'Harvest in Calabria', 97. Cf. p. 138 n. 20 below.

several farmers of threshing facilities (floor and animals), which are hired out by a richer proprietor once his own harvest has been completed.

The second threshing process, namely the separation of the seed from the chaff, is winnowing or 'wind-grading'. The chaff consists of the husks of the threshed grain. Naked wheats have husks, but the point is that their husks are removable by normal threshing and winnowing, whereas those of husked grains are not. The chaff will already have been dislodged from around the seed by threshing. Winnowing removes it altogether. The grain, as Varro clearly describes (1. 52. 2), is thrown into the air when there is a breeze blowing, and the seed, being heavier, falls to the floor, while the chaff floats off. To toss the grain mixed with its chaff into the air, light wooden spades were used, called *ventilabra*. Another implement (*vallus*), made at least partially from osiers (V. 1. 23. 5), could also be used. In function and purpose it appears to have been exactly the same as the *ventilabrum*. It was probably a wooden fork with osiers woven between the prongs.[40] If there had been no sign of wind for several days, Columella advised the use of a *vannus* (2. 20. 5). The most natural way of interpreting its design and function is to understand it as a sieve-like instrument with a fine mesh. The grain and chaff mixture would be shaken back and forth until all the chaff had been dispersed, leaving the clean seed still in the sieve.[41] On the intensive cereal farm where the product was to be stored 'for some years' (Col. 2. 20. 6), a second winnowing was recommended so as to reduce the possibility of impurities and weevil infection.[42]

Chaff, however, was not discarded. It was used 'in most parts of the world as fodder' (*pabula iumentorum*) (P. 18. 99). Only if there was a shortage of chaff would straw need to be used for fodder. This reinforces the earlier argument that the main single use of the carefully collected straw was for litter and thence manure.

Other uses of the by-products of cereals should not be underestimated. They are usually forgotten. I do no more than merely list some of them. Chaff in the construction of threshing floors (Col. 2. 19. 1) and granary walls (V. 1. 57. 2), as well as for bricks in general (Cato 14. 3). Straw for packing and storage (V. 1. 59. 1, 3); for unproductive olive trees (Cato 93); for protecting newly grafted plants (Cato 40. 4); for covering seedlings and new shoots in nurseries (V. 1. 45. 2; Col. 5. 6. 6); the moisture-retention property of straw was put to good effect in nurseries without irrigation (Col. 11. 3. 48); straw for thatching (P. 18. 97); for filling mattresses (P. 18. 14).

[40] As observed by Rasmussen, 103. Wooden forks (without osiers) are used also for shifting the grain and straw during the threshing process. For the various threshing and winnowing implements still used today and undoubtedly the same as or similar to those of the Roman period, see Pl. III, 2.

[41] The sieve interpretation derives from autopsy near Ruoti (August 1981). But cf. White, *Agricultural Implements*, 32 f. and id., *Farm Equipment*, 75 f.

[42] The reading *reteri* (Col. 2. 20. 6) cannot stand. *Repurgari* or *repoliri*, as various editors have sug-

gested, provides the required sense. Before storage in wetter climates, the grain might be dried in special ovens: cf. P. Morris, *Agricultural Buildings in Roman Britain*, B.A.R. British Series 70 (1979), 5–22. But in Italy of the present day drying is left to the sun. That there is no mention of grain-drying ovens in the ancient sources (Frayn, *Subsistence Farming*, 109 confuses references to parching emmer with grain-drying (Ovid, *Fasti* 2. 521 ff.; P. 18. 7 f.)) might help the supposition that summers were no wetter in the Roman period than today.

## STORAGE

The interest exhibited in the construction of capacious and solid granaries by Varro, Columella and Pliny is a clear indication of the existence of large arable farms which needed to store considerable quantities of cereals and legumes in good condition, to be able to take advantage of market prices, as well of course as to provide for the subsistence of the estate's workforce, and for sowing in the following year. Yet, as we might now expect, the agronomists' discussion of this topic also reveals the diversity of storage practice (mainly in Italy, but also in some of the provinces of the empire).

A second winnowing was advised only if the grain was to be stored for more than one year; otherwise, if it was all to be consumed during the coming year, one winnowing would suffice (Col. 2. 20. 6). This juxtaposition neatly expresses the difference between the two basic emphases of cereal cultivation, profit and subsistence. The main concern of the owner who expects to store his grain for some length of time, Columella continues, was to avoid infestation by weevils. The threat from these insects should not be undervalued. In normal years losses through weevil infestation may have been of the order of 10 per cent; occasionally, more serious outbreaks may have caused famine.[43]

Wheat is most liable of all cereals and legumes to weevil attack, according to Pliny (18. 304). He was talking about *triticum*, not husked grains which were less prone to infestation. To prevent the problem, grain should be sprinkled with olive lees (*amurca*) or other 'pesticides', and the walls and floors of the granary should be lined with hard-packed clay or marble cement. As weevils breed in warm places, the granary should have vents open to cold, dry winds, and the grain should be cool and free from moisture before storing. Yet it is clear from the agronomists themselves that even with the most elaborate precautions, infestation was hard to avoid. If weevils did strike, Varro (1. 63) suggested that the infested wheat should be hauled out and purified, while Columella (1. 6. 17) counselled inaction with the rationale that the insects inhabited only the top layer.

A small farmer who relied on his cereal crop for subsistence rather than profit might perhaps have suffered less than a large proprietor, who marketed his crop. This would not only be because the grain he stored, for one year only, was husked, but also because the principal grain pest, *Sitophilus granarius* L., being flightless, depends for its diffusion on movement by man. Immunity was therefore more likely where there was least transportation of grain.

One effective method of grain storage, as was noted by the agronomists, was in underground pits (V. 1. 57. 2; P. 18. 307; Col. 1. 6. 16). Unfortunately, according to Columella, the subsoil of Italy was too moist to permit conservation of grain in that way. Yet in Puglia on the Tavoliere from the Middle Ages until today, grain has been stored in pits under the central *piazze* of the towns.[44]

[43] P. C. Buckland, 'Cereal Production, Storage and Population: a Caveat' in *The Effect of Man on the Landscape: the Lowland Zone*, ed. J. G. Evans and S. Limbrey, CBA Research Rep. 21 (1978), 43 ff.

[44] Colamonico, *Memoria illustrativa della Puglia*, 103. Continued existence, source: Stefano Zezza, an estate owner at Cerignola. Note that the author of the *Bellum Africanum* (65) referred to underground storage of cereals as 'an African custom'. For medieval grain storage in pits elsewhere in Italy, see next note.

However, Varro describes Apulian granaries as situated in the fields and raised above the ground, to allow cooling not only from wall vents but also from beneath the floor (1. 57. 3). The difference between Roman and medieval practice could indicate a moister climate in the earlier period, although the need to centralize and conceal grain reserves in towns and fortified centres during the troubled medieval era might itself account for the change.

Against the idea of climatic change, one could note the occurrence of wet weather in 1334 which ruined the grain stored in pits near the Etruscan site of Vulci.[45] Andrews's argument that abandonment of such underground storage in central Italy at the end of the Middle Ages reflected a decline in grain cultivation might be correct; however, it does not explain why or when the practice was adopted in the first place. Bell-shaped pits sunk in impermeable rock near Grosseto and dated to the Roman period were interpreted by Minto, the archaeological expert of the area earlier this century, as grain stores, in contradiction of the agronomists' evidence.[46] Yet there is nothing whatsoever to compel acceptance: no cereal remains were found, nor was any attempt made to look for them, and we may assume that the interpretation offered was erroneously influenced by medieval comparative evidence. Other possible Roman underground grain pits revealed by archaeology are just as doubtful.[47] Water storage seems more probable.

There is no doubt that urban centres in the Roman period had facilities for storing grain provided by the surrounding countryside. Caesar, when he began to besiege Corfinium in early 49 B.C., sent for grain from the neighbouring *municipia*, and surely the inhabitants of Corfinium itself relied on the town's own stores (*BC* 1. 18). Little, however, is known about methods of storage in such places. Rickman describes the storeplace of the so-called Pompeian *horrea* as:

> simply an irregular shaped, but completely enclosed, area, roughly divided into sections and with a few small rooms on its south side. The whole ensemble is simple in the extreme, and shows none of the features we have come to expect from *horrea* associated with the imperial *annona*. What was true of Pompeii may also have been true of other places.[48]

The final conjecture indicates the regrettable absence of evidence: Rickman's chapter on granaries in Italy outside Rome and Ostia describes only the facilities of Trajan's harbour (Portus) and the above few remarks on Pompeii. He might have added in that context that several of the bakeries of Pompeii exhibit storage space, a not unlikely occurrence in other towns of Italy in the period.[49]

Another possibility, which has given rise to some debate and is discussed and dismissed by Rickman, is the storage of grain in urban centres in cryptoporticos.

[45] D. Andrews, 'Underground Grain Storage in Central Italy' in *Medieval Lazio. Studies in Architecture, Painting and Ceramics*, ed. D. Andrews, J. Osborne and D. Whitehouse, B.A.R. Int. Series 125 (1982), 123.

[46] *Notizie degli Scavi di Antichità* 1936, 47–8.

[47] Cf. ibid. 1943, 21; 1948, 229.

[48] G. E. Rickman, *Roman Granaries and Store Buildings* (1971), 147.

[49] Storage area in Pompeian bakeries: B. J. B. Mayeske, 'Bakers, Bakeshops and Bread: a Social and Economic Study' in *Pompeii and the Vesuvian Landscape* (1974), 42, 45.

Despite Rickman's comments, the debate continues, and I note that the tourist guide pamphlet to the excavations at Egnazia (Roman Gnatia) interprets the large cryptoportico as a grain store, without explanation. The granaries of the Roman towns of Italy (apart from Rome and Ostia) will have to await further research and exploration.[50]

In the interim it can be assumed that the estates which produced cereals and legumes for the market sold to middlemen or bakers who had storage space within the town, only when the price was favourable to themselves. Until then they would store the produce on the farm itself or perhaps transfer it to their own urban *horreum*, if they had one. The agricultural writers describe grain storage in the country, although it is not impossible that some of Pliny's examples belong equally to an urban context.

All the complexities and difficulties of grain storage are explained and discussed by Varro, Columella and Pliny. The concern expressed of course reflects the importance attached, especially, as is argued here, to the long-term conservation of large quantities (Varro speaks in units of a thousand *modii*, 1. 57. 2) of grain destined for the market. It would usually be just before the harvest of the following year that grain would be scarcest and its price highest. Inability to preserve one's stored grain until then would mean selling at an unfavourable price, doubtless to someone else's profit. Columella could envisage conserving grain for several years ('in annos', 2. 20. 6), perhaps with the hope even of profiting from famine conditions.[51]

As with threshing floors, granaries could be of different shapes, sizes and degrees of sophistication, according to the importance of cereal and legume crops to the economy of the farms, or according to the wealth of their owners. Such diversity renders the identification of granaries in the excavation of rural buildings notoriously difficult. The type that is most readily recognizable, namely that with its floor raised above ground on a series of dwarf brick piers, appears to have been introduced in non-military contexts only at the end of the period here under discussion. Otherwise, sizeable, undecorated rooms are often tentatively designated (cryptoporticos are also a candidate if a villa possessed one), but certainty is rare. One indication to look for would be width of walls, since the floor and walls of the granary, especially if the grain was stored loose and in some quantity, would have to be solidly constructed to support internal stress.[52]

Yet more commonly, perhaps, grain and legumes were stored in separate receptacles within a dry room. Columella (1. 6. 13) speaks of placing each kind of legume into a distinct 'basin' (*lacus*) of an undefined size. Otherwise earthenware containers were adopted, such as *dolia*. These could be large. At the turn of the

[50] Storage in cryptoporticos: Rickman, *Roman Granaries*, 144 ff.; R. A. Staccioli, 'Sulla destinazione e l'uso dei cryptoportici' in *Les cryptoportiques dans l'architecture romaine*, Collections de l'École Française de Rome 14 (1973), 57–75.

[51] In general, the time to sell was when the price was high, according to Varro (1. 69. 1). 'Observations made in a number of low-income countries generally indicate that prices immediately before the harvest are appreciably higher than immediately after the harvest', C. Clark and M. Haswell, *The Economics of*

*Subsistence Agriculture* (4th edn. 1970), 62. Cf. Cic., 2 *Verr*. 3. 227; Caes., *BC* 1. 48, 52. At a time of scarcity in Africa large quantities were found stored on nearby estates, not in the towns (*B.Af.* 9).

[52] Rickman, *Roman Granaries*, 293 ff. That section of the villa complex of Settefinestre identified as the granary clearly possessed very solid foundations: D. Manacorda, 'Il granaio e l'ovile' in *Settefinestre, Una villa schiavistica nell'Etruria romana*, ed. A. Carandini (1985) III, 192.

century 35 *dolia* buried up to their rims and ranging in capacity from 28 to 47 *amphorae*, with an average size of 40 *amphorae* (the equivalent of 10 hectolitres, or 120 *modii*), were found at Ostia. These were interpreted as *dolia frumentaria* (grain recipients) by the excavator, although Rickman argues for liquid storage.[53] No product remains were found and no tests have been subsequently performed on the insides of the containers. Yet the possibility that cereals were stored in *dolia* discovered in excavations should not be lightly dismissed: Cato included *dolia frumentaria* in the inventories for both vineyard and oliveyard (10. 4; 11. 1/2), and the *villa rustica* of Pisanella certainly adopted in this way some of the many *dolia* sited near the so-called *nubilarium*.[54] Columella observed that if lentils were not a major crop, they could be stored in sauce and oil jars (*vasa*, 2. 10. 17; cf. Varro on beans in jars, 1. 13. 11; 1. 57. 3). By analogy, it would be where wheat was not a very large crop on the farm, or in general on a small farm, that the grain would be stored in a dry room in jars. *Amphorae*, too, sometimes contained cereals or flour, perhaps for both transport and storage.[55] Wooden chests or barrels, large cylindrical baskets and sacks are more common than earthenware containers on small farms today. Yet such materials, had they been used widely in the Roman period, would have slender chance of appearing in the archaeological record.[56]


## YIELDS


The study so far has sought to demonstrate not only that cereal farming in Roman Italy was as diverse in practice as it was ubiquitous in extent, but also that several systems or modes of cereal culture prevailed. There were at least three broad categories:

(1) small farms growing cereals for self-subsistence;

(2) larger farms growing cereals for self-subsistence, while perhaps specializing in other crops;

(3) larger farms producing cereals for sale.

While all three would strive for a surplus to guard against lean years, only the third category would attempt to achieve the highest yields in order to obtain maximum profit. Such a farm could have cultivated the best soils, practised careful seed selection, manured its land well, paid close attention to ploughing, weeding and hoeing, and so on. There can be little doubt that the yields per unit of such an estate were far higher than those of the other two categories.

The discussion of cereal farming in Italy has often revolved around the problem of productivity, with argument centring on the exiguous evidence of yields. Such arguments, because of the paucity of evidence, seek to support this or that preconception, or, at best, remain inconclusive. In accordance with the

---

[53] Rickman, *Roman Granaries*, 75.

[54] See above, p. 74. A large *dolium granarium* was apparently found during excavation of a large villa site near La Spezia on the Ligurian coast: *Archeologia in Liguria: scavi e scoperte 1967-75*, ed. La Soprintendenza Archeologica della Liguria (1980), 71. The cereal samples from Matrice were recovered from a *dolium*: Lloyd, *Interim Report*.

[55] M. H. Callender, *Roman Amphorae* (1965), 37 ff.

[56] See Scheuermeier, *Il lavoro* I, 144, pls. 250-1. A Roman peasant might heap his grain on the floor in a secure part of his dwelling: *Moretum* 15-16.

general approach followed in this study, calculations of an average yield for the whole of Italy will not be attempted. Indeed, the value of an 'average yield' is seriously questioned. Averages tend to conceal rather than illuminate the historical reality. Diversity must be emphasized.

Despite the wide-embracing title of his book, *Rural Economy and Country Life in the Medieval West*, Duby provides little Italian information. In France, however, he reports (p. 100) that at the beginning of the fourteenth century, alluvial plains, although apparently not of exceptional fertility, yielded between 11 and 15:1; in mountain country during the same period, yields were as low as 3 or 4:1, although even in these areas on small and well-manured plots near towns a ratio of 6 or 7:1 could be achieved. Can the same sort of evidence be presented for Italy?

Before continuing, it will be as well to set out the literary evidence for yields in the Roman period and to refer to some of the important studies which discuss the subject.

> It will be your practice to adapt the quantity of seed sown to local soil conditions, since the influence of this variation is so great that the same seed yields in some places ten-fold, in another fifteen-fold, as in several parts of Etruria . . . in the country around Sybaris they say that the annual yield is one hundred-fold. (V. 1. 44. 1)

> We can scarcely remember a time when over the great part of Italy wheat returned a four-fold yield. (Col. 3. 3. 4)

The hundred-fold yield at Sybaris belongs to the realm of the exceptional, as do Pliny's anecdotes (18. 94–5). Almost certainly what is being referred to is the growth of 100 ears from a single seed, by no means impossible, but rare. Cicero (2 *Verr.* 3. 112) reports yields from the fertile region of Leontini in Sicily, strictly outside the geographical limits of this study, but perhaps comparable with the driest areas of the south. From the context of the speech it is probable that these yields were meant to sound impressive, although eminently credible, to a jury composed of Italian landowners: 8:1 in a good year, 10:1 in a very good year, at a sowing rate of 6 *modii* per *iugerum*.

White defended the Varronian yields by comparing statistics from Italy in 1959. Yet such comparative evidence is too late to be of serious use. Agriculture in the north and in the lowlands of the south and centre was by then mechanized, and regional statistics conceal the enormous differences between plains and hills.[57] Columella's estimate was so low, White argued, because it referred to an *arbustum*, where cereals had to compete with olives or vines. Yet Columella would not have based his estimate of Italian yields on intercultivation, the extent of which White overestimates (see p. 6 n. 16). Perhaps Frank's suggestion is more acceptable, namely that in a persuasive passage promoting viticulture, Columella

---

[57] White, 'Wheat Farming'. Like other scholars, he takes Varro's 10:1 to refer to Italy in general, and 15:1 to Etruria. A more natural reading, together with Varro's dislike for Italy-wide generalization, allows both yields to refer to Etruria. The spread of mechanization and differences between the plains and the hills: M. Rossi Doria, *Memoria illustrativa della carta del suolo della Basilicata* (1963), 108.

consciously played down the profits to be made from cereals.[58] De Martino interprets Columella to mean that cereals were one fourth as profitable as vines, not that they yielded four-fold, but his argument is not compelling.[59]

Although his specific aim is an estimation of the agricultural productivity of archaic Latium, Ampolo's discussion of yields, and his use of comparative data in particular, have much value for the Roman period. Oddly, however, he commends an outdated study by Barbagallo which, little more than arbitrarily, assumes an average Roman yield of 5:1.[60]

A recent and well-documented study by Evans argues that the estimates of Varro and Columella are compatible if the latter had calculated on the basis of mean annual productivity under a biennial rotation system. That is, a 4:1 yield would be the average annual ratio of a field which in reality produced 8:1 every second year. This approaches closely enough to Varro's 10:1 (Evans gives little credence to a yield of 15:1). He then applies this average yield to Campania, to show that even in rich soils, subsistence for the family of a small cultivator was difficult. However, this argument is defective, since, if the notion of an 'average' has any value, then the rich soils of Italy must have achieved yields well above it. A self-styled 'addendum' furnishes the discussion with yields of 6–7.2:1 for wheat and 8–8.7:1 for barley from the seventh-century Negev of Palestine with an annual rainfall of only 100 mm. Yet it is difficult to use this evidence to prove anything for Roman Italy.[61]

It seems better, then, to provide some comparative data along the lines proposed above. For the following table I have collected as far as possible yields of specific areas where there is also some information on the mode of cultivation. I have limited the evidence to before the Second World War, at which point yields for much of Italy begin to show a significant increase, as the last example indicates. Before the 'modern period' thus defined, we cannot, in my view, talk about any appreciable improvement in method or rise in yields since the Roman period.[62]

While the detailed comments included in the table speak for themselves, the following general observations are relevant:

(1) Averages for whole districts or for the whole country conceal the diversity of yields. Seasonal fluctuations are also concealed.

(2) Plains yield more than hills.

(3) Given Young's figures from the more fertile areas of Tuscany, there is no reason to doubt Varro's yields of 10 or 15:1 for Etruria in the Roman period.

---

[58] Frank, *Economic Survey* v, 141.

[59] F. De Martino, 'Produzione di cereali in Roma nell'età arcaica', *Parola del Passato* 187 (1979), 242–53. For some further thoughts: id., 'Ancora sulla produzione di cereali in Roma arcaica', *Parola del Passato* 217 (1984), 241–63.

[60] C. Ampolo, 'Le condizioni materiali · della produzione. Agricoltura e paesaggio agrario', *Dialoghi di Archeologia* n.s. 2 (1980), 15–46 (especially 20–4); C. Barbagallo, 'Produzione media relativa dei cereali e della vite nella Grecia, nella Sicilia e nell'Italia antica', *Rivista di Storia Antica* 8 (1904), 477–504.

[61] J. K. Evans, 'Wheat Production and its Social Consequence in the Roman World', *CQ* 31 (1981), 428–42; P. Mayerson, 'Wheat in the Roman World: an Addendum', *CQ* 34 (1984), 243–5.

[62] Thus Jones compares Roman and medieval average yields and notes that while more land might have been cleared in the latter period, *productivity* did not increase. Jones, like others, concentrates on average yields and thereby glosses over the diversity of the agricultural reality. P. Jones, 'Medieval Agrarian Society in its Prime: Italy', 377. For the most impressive collection of medieval yield figures, see now Cherubini, 'Le campagne italiane', 280–2.

(4) The *mezzadria* system was unable to economize on labour or to allow specialization, and thus was unlikely to have achieved as high or higher yields than the slave-staffed arable estates of the Roman period (cf. pp. 133–40), although it might be seen as equivalent to the average Roman peasant, or tenant, farm.

(5) Yields of species other than soft and hard wheats are not represented. Some evidence can be adduced to indicate that 'inferior cereals' yielded highly (emmer, p. 11; millet, p. 97). Disparity of yields among various cereals further vitiates the utility of an 'average yield'.

TABLE 2

### Emilia Romagna, 10th century

| Terrain | Yield |
|---|---|
| Enzola, in the plain 8 km from the Po | 3.3 + :1 |
| Reggio, on a higher river terrace of the Po | 2.8:1 |
| Vercallo, 3 km south of Canossa in the hills | 2:1 |
| Sciola di Tezzano nel Parmense in the mountains | 1.7:1 |

*Comments*: These examples come from large monastic *domus cultae* let out in small tenant blocks. Climatic and pedological conditions for cereal cultivation are more favourable in plains than in hills; this is reflected in yield rates. This difference is what regional averages conceal.

*Source*: V. Fumagalli, *Coloni e signori nell'Italia settentrionale, secoli VI–XI* (1978), 71.

### Tuscany, Arezzo, 1386–90

| Terrain | Yield |
|---|---|
| Plain of Tregozzano on northern outskirts of Arezzo | 5–11:1, usually 5-7:1 |

*Comments*: Tenant farms (*mezzadria*) practising biennial fallowing but very few legumes.

*Source*: G. Cherubini, *Signori, contadini, borghesi. Ricerche sulla società italiana del basso medioevo* (1974), 369 f. (For general remarks on the *mezzadria* system: R. Dumont, *Types of Rural Economy*, trans. D. Magnin (1957), 244 ff.)

### Tuscany, Siena, 15th–16th centuries

| Terrain | Yield |
|---|---|
| Unspecified territory of Siena | 4–5:1 |

*Comments*: This yield is an average one for the area and derives from no specified farming system.

*Source*: Cherubini, ibid.

### Lombardy, Mantua, 17th century

| Terrain | Yield |
|---|---|
| Unspecified territory of Mantua | 5:1 |

*Comments*: This yield is an average one for the area, from no specified farming system.

*Source*: Cherubini, ibid.

# CHAPTER IV

## Tuscany, Altopascio, 17th–18th centuries

| *Terrain* | *Yield* |
|---|---|
| The ducal estate of Altopascio (between Florence and Lucca) comprised ⅓ low-yielding hills and ⅔ fertile, reclaimed and drained plain land | 6.5:1 |

*Comments*: This is an average for the two centuries concerned. It thus conceals ups and downs over the period, although yields showed no increase over time (6.55:1 in 1600, 6.92:1 in 1768). The estate was divided among individual peasant families on the *mezzadria* system. Three or four years of continually-sown cereals were followed by a turning of the land with spades and sowing of a soil-enriching legume.

*Source*: F. McArdle, *Altopascio. A Study in Tuscan Rural Society 1587–1784* (1978), 95.

## Tuscany, Florence, late 18th century

| *Terrain* | *Yield* |
|---|---|
| 'The whole dutchy (of Florence) through' | 5–6:1 |
| 'In the plains' | 8:1 |
| 'In the deposits of rivers, or spots remarkably rich' | 12, 15, or even 20:1 |
| In the low hills overlooking the Arno, just upstream from Florence at Villamagna | 9–10:1 after legumes |
| | 6–7:1 after wheat |
| | 3–4:1 after wheat |

*Comments*: It is clear how the low average for the 'whole dutchy' conceals the high yields from the fertile areas. A similar diversity was no doubt true also for the Roman period. On three farms at Villamagna, where the spade was used more than the plough—'the most decisive proof that tillage is in a state of mediocrity, if not barbarism'—the rotation system was legumes, wheat, wheat, wheat; yields declined progressively with each sowing.

*Source*: A. Young, *Travels During the Years 1787, 1788 and 1789* (2nd edn. 1794) II, 157, 209–15.

## Piedmont, late 18th century

| *Terrain* | *Yield* |
|---|---|
| Chentale (modern Centallo), in the high Piedmont plain with rich, sandy loam and coarse gravel | 6:1 up to 10–11:1 |
| Savigliano (as for Chentale) | 8:1 |

*Comments*: The 6:1 yield at Chentale was 'normal' according to Young, the 10–11:1 'good'. The yield at Savigliano was described as 'a good crop'.

*Source*: Young, ibid.

## Lombardy, late 18th century

| *Terrain* | *Yield* |
|---|---|
| Codogno, in the well-watered, low plain of the Po, with loamy soils and finer gravel | 6:1 up to 12, 14, 16:1 (millet 48:1) |

*Comments*: The lower yield occurs when the fields are cultivated with the plough, the higher when cultivated with the spade—'a sure proof of miserable tillage'.

*Source*: Young, ibid.

### Veneto, late 18th century

| Terrain | Yield |
|---|---|
| Verona, vines and grain intercultivated on flat and well-watered loamy soils | 5–6:1 |
| Padua (as for Verona) | less than 7:1 |

Comments: Such 'poor' yields in both areas are attributed to 'the execrable system of encumbering their fields with pollards and vines'.

Source; Young, ibid.

### Latium, 1832–3

| Terrain | Yield |
|---|---|
| Sora, in the hills above the Sacco river plain | 3.14–5.2:1 |
| Gaeta, on the coastal plain | 5–7.5:1 |

Comments: The difference between hill and plain is again obvious.

Source: G. Porisini, *Produttività e agricoltura: i rendimenti del frumento in Italia dal 1815 al 1922* (1971), cited in Ampolo, 'Condizioni materiali', 22.

### Latium, early 19th century

| Terrain | Yield |
|---|---|
| Best soils | 10:1 |
| Good soils | 7:1 |
| Medium soils | 5:1 |
| Poor soils | 4:1 |

Source: P. M. C. de Tournon, *Études statistiques sur Rome et la partie occidentale des états romains* (2nd edn. 1855), cited in Ampolo, 22.

### Piedmont, Astigiana, 1910

| Terrain | Yield |
|---|---|
| Various soils, from sand to heavy clay | Average 18 qu. per ha. (c.13–14:1?) |

Comments: Small farms of 3–8 hectares. Legumes rare, cultivation very simple, although limited use of chemical fertilizer introduced. No seed specialization. Seed scattered, ploughed in and soil levelled with rakes. 'Despite the fact that the grain cultivation leaves much to be desired . . . the productivity of our fields is not as poor as one might at first suppose.'

Source: G. Dalmasso, 'Problemi economici di agricoltura astigiana', *Annali della Reale Accademia d'Agricoltura di Torino* 53 (1910), 145–288, at 163.

**Basilicata, early 20th century**

| Terrain | Qu. per ha. | Yield |
|---|---|---|
| The region as a whole for the following years: | | |
| 1909 | 10.3 | 8:1 |
| 1910 | 5.7 | 4:1 |
| 1911 | 8.8 | 6.5:1 |
| 1912 | 6.8 | 5:1 |
| 1913 | 10.6 | 8:1 |
| Average yields in 1930 for the three main geological zones: | | |
| Rocky mountains | 6–8 | 5–6:1 |
| Pliocene clays | 10–12 | 8–9:1 |
| Alluvial soils in valleys and coastal plains | 12–14 | 9–10:1 |

*Comments*: Despite the fact that these are average yields, the first set of figures is a useful indication of how harvests could alter considerably from year to year. This continued into recent times: in 1960 an average yield of 6.5 qu. per ha. followed a 1959 yield of 11.0 and was followed in turn by a 1961 yield of 14.1 qu. per ha.

*Source*: Rossi Doria, *Memoria illustrativa della Basilicata*, 108-9.

**1935**

| Locality | Qu. per ha. | Yield |
|---|---|---|
| Reggio Calabria | 5.5 | 4:1 |
| Viterbo | 13 | 9.5:1 |
| Siena | 13.6 | 10:1 |
| Florence | 16.3 | 12:1 |
| Lucca | 16.2 | 12:1 |
| Ascoli Piceno | 13.6 | 10:1 |
| Trieste | 16.4 | 12:1 |
| Reggio Emilia | 20.8 | 15:1 |
| Modena | 20.7 | 15:1 |
| Alessandria | 20.4 | 15:1 |
| Cuneo | 17 | 12.5:1 |

*Comments*: Average yields for the provinces of the listed towns. Used by Floridia to 'prove' (and thus possible propaganda) that yields of the Fascist period could compare with those of the late Roman republic and early empire.

*Source*: S. Floridia, *I cereali nell'economia italiana dell'alto impero romano dal I secolo a.C. al II secolo d.C.* (1940), 42-4. Another useful guide to the average yields of the provinces of Italy can be found in Naval Intelligence Division, *Italy* III, 527, Table 13 (for the year 1938).

# CHAPTER V: 'INFERIOR' CEREALS—MILLET

This chapter has appeared in *PBSR* 51 (1983), 1–15

This chapter examines the cultivation of millet in Roman Italy and seeks to demonstrate that a variety of cereals was grown for both human and animal consumption not only by the small farmer, as a precautionary measure against the probability of a bad harvest, but also by the larger arable farmer, for his own needs and for the urban market.

There exists no satisfactory account of the cultivation of millet in the classical period.[1] Jasny includes it among spring crops which he describes as being generally unsuited to the Mediterranean climate. More precisely, according to Jasny, they cannot be cultivated in the southern areas of the Mediterranean unless irrigated, but do grow in the north where rain is not limited only to the winter months. In particular, millet was confined to certain select areas such as the Po valley.[2] Jones, concerned with the agriculture of medieval Italy, and favouring the view of continuation and similarity between the Roman and medieval periods, also argues from geographical delimitation, and localizes millet to the 'moister parts of Upper Italy and Campania'.[3] Such geographical determinism, while it may be useful as a general guide to the distribution of *hard* and *soft* wheats (p. 15), is inapplicable in the case of millet. It is true that millet was cultivated in both the Po valley and Campania, but the reasons advanced by Jasny and Jones reveal ignorance of its agricultural and climatic requirements.

## GENERAL CLIMATIC AND AGRICULTURAL CONSIDERATIONS

Millet is, in fact, very resistant to drought conditions, and in areas of poor fertility and little rainfall gives a securer return than other cereals. In modern times, for example, it is the major staple crop grown on the southern fringe of the Sahara. It is not, therefore, unsuited to the driest parts of the Mediterranean. On the other hand, it is also cultivated in quantity on the Russian steppes. At the beginning of the century millet and a similar grain, *grano saraceno*, were the most widely grown cereals in the Italian and Swiss Alps.[4] Pliny the Elder referred to its cultivation in Sarmatia, Ethiopia, the Black Sea region, Gaul and Italy (18. 100 f.). It is this *diversity* of area and climate which requires explanation.

It should at once be pointed out that there are today several types of millet, and this in part explains the wide diversity in area of cultivation. While they share the important general characteristics of tolerance of drought and poverty of soil, Italian and common millets differ from other types in their somewhat greater resistance to cold. They therefore tend to be limited to more northerly latitudes, yet are cultivated in an extremely wide area, comprising central Europe, south and central Russia, northern China, the Middle East, India and Japan. Since they are the millets grown in Italy in modern times, I assume in the absence of other

---

[1] An entry by P. Orth entitled 'Hirse' in P–W 8. 1950–6 collects many of the literary references on the subject for classical antiquity.

[2] Jasny, *Wheats*, 14, 17.

[3] P. Jones, 'Medieval Agrarian Society in its Prime: Italy', 372.

[4] Scheuermeier, *Il lavoro* I, 177.

evidence that they were the types also cultivated there in the historical period, and the Latin terms *panicum* and *milium* are translated accordingly 'Italian' and 'common' millet. Archaeological evidence has certainly demonstrated the existence of common millet, but usually finds are identified only as 'millet'. Closer attention to species is a desideratum.

## CULTIVATION OF MILLET IN ITALY

If there is any difference between Italian and common millets, it is that the latter requires a slightly more fertile soil; both, however, succeed better on poorer soils than other cereals.[5] Apart from this, they have the same climatic and agricultural requirements and thus, for the purposes of this study, are treated as one crop.

Despite variable resistance to cold, no millet can germinate successfully or survive in temperatures much below 10°C. For the best yields, the soil has to be carefully worked in order to allow the very small seeds to develop rapidly. While millet can grow in poor and dry soils, experiments have demonstrated that discreet use of irrigation and fertilizer produces larger yields. One of the great advantages of millet is its short vegetation cycle of only three or four months. In the early stages of growth the crop is very susceptible to suffocation from weeds and, later, the seeds of the ripening ear are particularly liable to depredation by birds.

Because of its relative intolerance of cold it can be grown nowhere in Italy as a winter crop. However, it can be grown anywhere as a spring or summer crop. In cold regions such as the Alps it is its short growth cycle which is of advantage; on the southern coast of Sicily or on the Tavoliere of Puglia, the driest parts of Italy, its resistance to drought would be the important factor.

As regards the cultivation of millet in Italy, arguments based on geographical determinism must, therefore, be dismissed. In the right season it can be grown anywhere. Modern statistical information on cereal growing in Italy does not, unfortunately, concern itself with differentiating among the minor grains. However, a thorough survey carried out in 1930 demonstrated that while most of the country's millet grew in the north, a small amount was cultivated in every region, except perhaps Basilicata.[6]

*Comparative Archaeological and Literary Evidence*

Archaeological botanical evidence shows that, in Europe, millet was grown first in South Poland, Czechoslovakia and Yugoslavia (4400–4000 B.C.). It seems then to have spread west and south, appearing in Swiss lake settlements by 3000 B.C., and by the early Bronze Age (2000–1500 B.C.) it had become firmly established in the Po valley.[7] In the middle and late Bronze Age its presence is well attested further south, throughout Etruria as far as Lakes Bolsena and Bracciano.[8] For Iron Age Rome, use of millet seems to be demonstrated by a seed

---

[5] For the modern agricultural details of the cultivation of millet in Italy referred to here and throughout the chapter, see Tassinari, *Manuale*; United Nations, F.A.O., *Improvement and Production of Maize, Sorghum and Millets* (1972).

[6] G. Acerbo, *L'economia dei cereali nell'Italia e nel mondo* (1934), 807-15.

[7] Van Zeist, 'Aperçu'.

[8] Oliva, 'I frumenti a Belverde'; Jarman, 'Plant Remains'; Helbaek, 'Agricoltura preistorica a Luni'.

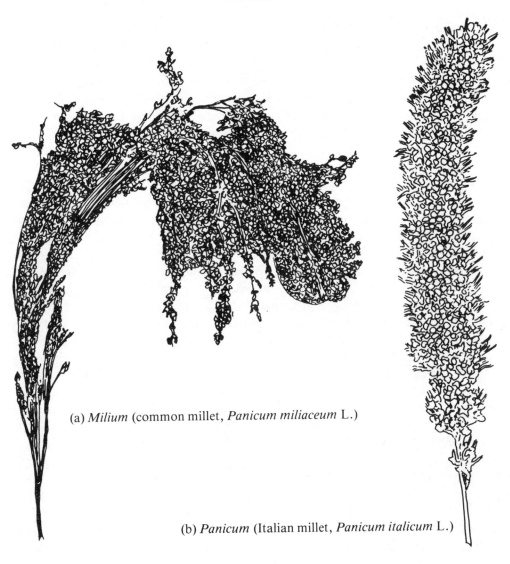

(a) *Milium* (common millet, *Panicum miliaceum* L.)

(b) *Panicum* (Italian millet, *Panicum italicum* L.)

(c) A Pompeian panel showing quail fed on barley and
*panicum*, perhaps an indication of *pastio villatica* (p. 101).

Fig. 5. Ears of Millet and Panic ((a) and (b) approx. actual size).

impression on a vase from a tomb.[9]

From these data it appears possible to trace a diffusion pattern beginning in eastern Europe, passing across the Alps and through Italy as far as Rome. However, given the difficulty of recovering millet in an archaeological context, such a conclusion would at this stage be premature. Because millet has such a small seed, flotation methods and very finely-meshed sieves are required to recover it. Many archaeological excavations have been poorly equipped in this respect. The safest conclusion would be simply that millet was cultivated in various areas in northern and central Italy before the classical period.

There is no archaeological evidence for the cultivation of millet in southern Italy for the pre-classical period. If early agricultural development of that region depended on direct transmission from the eastern Mediterranean, especially from Greece, a brief review of the evidence for millet in that country will not be out of place. There is considerable disagreement among modern commentators. Jardé dismisses the cultivation of millet in Greece and states that it was considered as food fit only for barbarians. Yet the passages he cites do not prove his case.[10] Orth asserts that millet was of little significance in Greece. Michell, however, observes that 'millet was well known and apparently widely cultivated'.[11] As regards archaeological evidence, millet has occurred at two early Neolithic sites (5500 B.C.) in Thessaly, at Argyssa and Achilleion.[12]

Yet there is a wealth of accurate detail on the subject in Theophrastus. It should be assumed that his information relates to Greece, since his practice is to specify the provenance of a plant if it is found abroad. In fact, in a discussion of the keeping qualities of various crops, including millet, in Media and other 'high countries', he concludes: καὶ ἐν τοῖς περὶ τὴν Ἑλλάδα τόποις.[13] Agreement with Michell seems preferable.

That millet has not occurred in pre-classical archaeological contexts in the south of Italy, which have, however, produced other palaeobotanical material,[14] might rather then be ascribed to the failure to employ adequate techniques for its recovery. Nevertheless, although it is true that the cultivation of millet is possible everywhere in Italy, the evidence, as it stands, for the pre-classical period refers to cultivation only in central and northern Italy.

In all the archaeological finds where millet occurred it was recovered in smaller quantities than other cereals. Since, like emmer wheat, in order to be freed from its husk it had first to be parched, its chances of being carbonized were greater than those of naked wheats; from this it can be assumed that the

---

[9] Helbaek, 'Funeral Meals'.

[10] A. Jardé, *Les céréales dans l'antiquité grecque* (1925), 4. The passages cited are: Xen., *Anab.* 7. 5. 12, 'millet-eating Thracians'; Ath., *Deipn.* 10. 447, 'the Paeonians drink παραβίη made from millet'. Jardé appears to ignore the evidence of Theophrastus (see below).

[11] Orth, 'Hirse', 1953; H. Michell, *The Economics of Ancient Greece* (1957), 51.

[12] Argyssa, see Van Zeist, 'Aperçu'; C. Renfrew, *The Emergence of Civilization. The Cyclades and the Aegean in the Third Millennium B.C.* (1972), 271. Achilleion, see M. Gimbutas, 'Achilleion: a Neolithic Mound in Thessaly. Preliminary Report on the 1973

and 1974 Excavations', *Journal of Field Archaeology* 1 (1974), 277–302.

[13] Theophr., *HP* 8. 11. 6, 'as also in many areas of Greece'. Several references to millet occur in book 8. Cf. Hesychius (lexic.), ἔλυμος σπέρμα ὃ ἔφοντες οἱ Λάκωνες ἐσθίουσιν, 'millet, a grain that Spartans eat boiled'. This is an entry to explain ἔλυμος, which occurs as fr. 398 of Aristophanes. It is unnoticed by P. Cartledge, *Sparta and Laconia, a Regional History 1300–362 B.C.* (1979), in his discussion of Laconian foodstuffs.

[14] Evett and Renfrew, 'L'agricoltura neolitica italiana'. The difficulties of identification of species are stated (p. 408); also note: the absence of a species should not be taken as significant' (ibid.).

archaeological evidence accurately reflects cultivation of millet in smaller quantities than other grains, within an overall pattern of mixed cereal cultivation. On the other hand, if the recovery and identification of millet, even on those sites where it has occurred, has been somewhat haphazard, it could be that many seeds remained unnoticed, and this would cause incorrect conclusions about the quantity ratio of cereals cultivated. It is hoped that the increasing use of sophisticated methods for seed recovery will provide a more accurate picture.

It is conceivable that in certain areas millet was the most widely grown cereal. Yet this would be difficult to deduce with certainty from archaeological evidence. Near Lucca in Tuscany, in the late medieval period, it appears from the literary evidence of official records and contracts that millet was cultivated almost to the exclusion of other cereals. While the suggested deterministic climatic or pedological reasons for this can be rejected, it may be that because bread wheat was imported by sea the need for alternative cereals would be met locally. Or, on the other hand, it may indicate a traditional food preference.[15]

In general, it can be argued that advance in agricultural technology and technique, connected especially with the supply of a growing market, leads to specialization and elimination of variety. On this view, while polyculture of cereals might be expected during the Bronze and Iron Ages in Italy, with the growth of urban centres and the development of agriculture in the late Republic and early Empire of the Roman period, the cultivation of cereals became increasingly limited to naked wheats; later, as cities and agriculture declined in the early medieval period, a variety of cereals once again became the norm, and then renewed specialization occurred in the late medieval period as cities began again to flourish. Such is the influential thesis of Sereni, who sees the first indication of a return to reliance on 'inferior' grains ('superior' cereals are naked wheats) in a letter of Cassiodorus ordering the release of millet from the granaries of Tortona and Pavia during a period of grave famine c.A.D. 535 (Cass., *Variae* 12. 27). By the thirteenth century, however, urban centres were fed almost entirely on naked wheats, according to this theory, although it is noted that rural classes continued to depend on inferior grains until much later.[16] This thesis is accepted by Jones, although he suspects that peasants had always subsisted on 'inferior' cereals.

Although, as was noted, the pre-classical evidence, indicating the cultivation of a variety of cereals, appears to support this hypothesis, studies of the medieval records make it difficult to accept the proposition of specialization and elimination of variety. For example, millet was grown extensively in the Po valley in the ninth and tenth centuries within an overall pattern of mixed cereal cultivation,[17] but retained its importance right up to the introduction and diffusion of

[15] G. Pinto, 'Coltura e produzione dei cereali in Toscana nei secoli XIII–XV' in *Civiltà ed economia agricola in Toscana nei secoli XIII–XV. Atti dell'VIII Convegno Internazionale del Centro Studi di Storia ed Arte* (1981), 221–85. See also the discussion which arises from that paper.

[16] The thesis of Sereni, *Storia del Paesaggio*, ch. 16 and 34. Moritz, *Grain Mills*, also concurs with this general hypothesis for the Roman period. See p. 10

n. 27. But note that Moritz adds (p. xxi): 'the millets, both common and Indian, were essentially a standby in times of shortage, though common millet was used for bread when better grains were not available' (Indian = Italian).

[17] I. Montanari, 'Cereali e legumi nell'alto medioevo nell'Italia del nord, secoli IX–X', *Rivista Storica Italiana* 87 (1975), 439–88.

maize in the sixteenth and especially seventeenth centuries.[18] It appears that millet continued to be important from the thirteenth to the fifteenth centuries in Tuscany west of Florence, especially in the territories of Lucca and Pisa.[19] It was cultivated, as it had been in earlier periods, in small quantities in Campania and Basilicata.[20] The cultivation of millet in the thirteenth and fourteenth centuries in Latium actually appears to have increased.[21] In general, millet seems to have been cultivated in most regions of Italy throughout the medieval era: to those already mentioned can be added Romagna and Marche (in the late sixteenth century),[22] and Puglia.[23]

Thus, while it is probable that there were fluctuations in the ratio of the various cereals cultivated, it is better to assume that the overall pattern of cereal culture in Italy had always been one of polyculture and that true specialization is only relatively modern. Further, it is almost certain that the division between town and countryside has been over-emphasized. As far as cereals are concerned the division may rather have been along economic lines: the poorer classes, both urban and rustic, would have continued to rely on 'inferior' grains.

*Roman Period*

Following on from the preceding argument, it ought to be assumed that whereas there may have been some increase of cultivation of naked wheats from the late Republic to suit upper-class urban tastes, other grains, especially emmer, barley and millet, retained their importance throughout the Roman period. There was never any real 'monoculture of naked wheat' which was then abandoned in the early Middle Ages and replaced by 'a variety of cultivated species'.[24]

It should immediately be admitted that archaeological evidence for the cultivation of millet in Roman Italy is very limited. The paucity of finds is at least partially, if not wholly, explained by the fact that only very recently have Roman sites begun to be examined with agricultural or environmental questions in mind. The previous remarks about equipment will also apply here.

Millet has been found at the Roman villa site at Matrice in Molise between Campobasso and the Roman Larinum, although it is not yet clear to which phase of the villa's six-hundred-year existence (200 B.C.-A.D. 400) the seeds belong.[25] Apart from this, a *dolium* filled with millet was discovered at the Pisanella villa near Pompeii.[26] Both these sites, it is immediately noted, are south of Rome.

Given that there is no reason to accept the usually stated deterministic limitations of geography or climate, Columella's statement that in many regions *coloni* are sustained by millet (2. 9. 17) need not be taken, as the Loeb translator

[18] L. Messedaglia, *Per la storia dell'agricoltura e dell'alimentazione* (1932), 48.

[19] Pinto, 'Coltura e produzione dei cereali'.

[20] Acerbo, *L'economia dei cereali*, 377.

[21] P. Toubert, *Les structures du Latium médiéval: le Latium méridional et la Sabine du IXème siècle à la fin du XIIème siècle* (1973), 244 ff.; A. Cortonesi, 'Colture pratiche agrarie e allevamento nel Lazio bassomedioevale', *Archivio della Società Romana di Storia Patria* 101 (1978), 109.

[22] J. Delumeau, *Vie économique et sociale de Rome dans la seconde moitié du XVIème siècle* (1959), 537.

[23] R. Licinio, 'L'organizzazione del territorio fra XIII e XIV secolo', in *La Puglia tra medioevo ed età moderna*, ed. D. Blasi et al. (1981), 209.

[24] Montanari, 'Cereali e legumi', 476.

[25] Lloyd, 'Interim Report'.

[26] Pasqui, 'La Villa Pompeiana della Pisanella', 405 ff.

suggests, to refer to countries outside Italy.[27] All the agricultural writers refer to the cultivation of millet and, unless they specifically state otherwise, their statements should always be interpreted as applying to Italy.

There is some difference of opinion among the Roman agronomists as to what type of soil was suitable for millet. Columella (ibid.) observes that it does well in a light, loose soil, or even in sand, provided that it is irrigated or the climate moist, but not in dry or chalky soil. Cato recommends rich soil in areas where fogs are prevalent (6. 1); that is, soil which would normally be used for wheat were it free from fog. Pliny, while noting that in general summer crops flourish in irrigated land, marks out millet as an exception. Instead, it should receive very little water, for otherwise it runs to leaf.[28] Polybius had recorded the abundance of millet in the Po valley (2. 15.1–2), and Strabo, perhaps drawing on Polybius' account,[29] states that millet flourished there because of plentiful water (5. 1. 12).

The best yields of millet occur when there is some moisture, but excessive moisture is to be avoided. There can be little doubt that if it was grown in wet conditions in the Po valley, as Strabo suggests, then its yield in grain would suffer. Helbaek, comparing the imprint of the millet seed from Iron Age Rome with millet seeds of the Bronze Age in the Po valley, notes that the former is considerably larger and explains that this may have been due to improved agricultural techniques and to cultivation in drier soil. The wet soil around the Bronze Age *palafitte* would have been thoroughly unsuited to millet.[30] On the other hand, if the land were drained and rational irrigation practised, as was increasingly the case in the Roman period, good millet grain yields would have been produced.[31] While the grain may have been smaller and, in yield, less than that grown on more adapted soils, as Helbaek suggested, the amount of leaf and stalk produced by the millet in the wet conditions of the Po valley was probably considerable. It may thus have been equally important as animal forage. White is almost certainly incorrect when he states that in the Roman period millet was not used for animal fodder, and appears to have overlooked Cato 54. 4, where *panicum* is included in a list of green forage crops. However, there is no basis for Frank's assertion that millet was generally sown for hay.[32]

The discrepancy of opinion of the ancient sources might indicate that millet

[27] 'Inter frumenta etiam panicum ac milium ponenda sunt . . . nam multis regionibus cibariis eorum coloni sustinentur' ('among the grains should also be counted millet and panic . . . since in many localities peasants subsist on food made from them'), (Col. 2. 9. 17). The choice of the term *regionibus* rather than *provinciis* also indicates the Italian context. Ash, the translator, adds an explanatory footnote quoting the various regions outside Italy where millet was cultivated according to Pliny (18. 100–1).

[28] P. 18. 101. However, there is textual difficulty here, and it seems that Pliny has excerpted a line from Theophrastus (*HP* 8. 7. 3), where it is stated that with too much water millet loses its leaf. It is not impossible that Pliny was correcting Theophrastus.

[29] G. E. F. Chilver, *Cisalpine Gaul: a Social and Economic History from 49 B.C. to the Death of Trajan* (1941), 133.

[30] Helbaek, 'Funeral Meals'.

[31] Brunt, *Italian Manpower*, 173 ff. In the Po valley the rainfall maxima occur in the autumn and spring and, until recently, often caused the river to flood, sometimes washing away the autumn-sown crops. In such a situation millet could be used as an emergency crop (p. 21 above). With Roman attention to drainage works in order to lessen the danger of flooding it may be that millet gave ground to other cereals. It is known that autumn-sown cereals were cultivated there in abundance in the Roman period (Brunt, 178).

[32] White, *Roman Farming*, 137; Frank, *Economic Survey* v, 143.

was grown on marginal land or in areas not suitable for wheat: sandy or wet soil or places prone to fog. It may also reflect the adaptability of millet and its widespread diffusion. That it reflects ignorance is to be doubted, since Columella's instructions for its cultivation, which include a very thorough harrowing and close attention to weeding (2. 9. 18; 11. 2. 75), and Pliny's observation on the danger of attack by birds (18. 53; 160), demonstrate an accurate understanding of the agricultural reality as outlined above.

It is clear from Pliny that millet was sown both in spring and, perhaps more commonly, in summer (18. 49, 60, 96 *aestiva*; 18. 50 *verna*). Both sowings are in theory possible because of the rapid growth cycle. Seneca, pedantically and erroneously providing another example of what he terms Virgil's lack of agricultural knowledge, reports from autopsy the sowing of millet at Liternum in Campania in the second half of June (*Ep. Mor.* 86. 16). Virgil had referred to millet as a spring-grown crop (*Georgics* 1. 215–16). Columella, correctly stating that millet requires a warm temperature, observes that it cannot be sown before spring and advises a *prima satio* in late March or in April (2. 9. 18; 11. 2. 33). A reference elsewhere to the harvesting of millet in the second half of September indicates that he does not exclude a second or summer sowing (11. 2. 72).

Speed of growth and tolerance of conditions recommended millet as an emergency crop in the event of other cereals, perhaps particularly winter ones, failing or yielding poorly. This prophylactic use seems clear from Strabo, who remarks that in the Po valley millet was a sure protector against famine when other crops failed (5. 1. 12). Although in a year of extremely bad harvests, even millet could fail, as happened in the Veneto in *c.*A.D. 535 (Cass., *Variae* 12. 26). On one occasion in the early history of Rome, a shipment of millet and emmer wheat down the Tiber from the grain-producing regions of central Etruria temporarily saved the city from starvation (Dion. Hal. 7. 12. 3). This is the only literary reference from the Roman period to the cultivation of millet in Etruria. Yet given that in both the pre-classical age and the medieval period it is well attested there, the reference is taken here to suggest a continuation of such cultivation throughout the Roman period. In times of plenty the people of late medieval Pistoia preferred bread wheat, but in lean years those who succeeded in bringing millet from the country were rewarded as much as those who supplied wheat.[33]

Besides the brief growth cycle, another advantage is the small volume of sowing seed required. As Columella remarks, 'they [sc. millets] do not burden the farmer's budget with heavy expense, since about four *sextarii* are sufficient for a *iugerum*' (2. 9. 18; at 11. 2. 75 he recommends four or five *sextarii*).

Modern estimates of sowing quantities vary between 5 and 40 kg per hectare; the more fertile the soil, the lighter the sowing. The Roman authorities, while they discuss the relationship between soil fertility and sowing rates for wheat, do not do so for millet. Columella's advice of four to five *sextarii* per *iugerum* is equivalent to 6(+) kg per hectare, satisfactory, according to modern estimates, for

---

[33] On the credibility of the early annalists see Brunt, *Italian Manpower*, 704 f. and E. Gjerstadt, *Early Rome* 5, *Acta Inst. Rom. Regni Sueciae* (1973), 191. Even if they reported what could have happened rather than what did, they are likely to have remained within the bounds of contemporary credibility. Moreover, they might have been guilty of retrospection: all the better in this case. Medieval Pistoia: D. Herlihy, *Medieval and Renaissance Pistoia, the Social History of an Italian Town 1200–1430* (1967), 123–4.

fertile soils.[34] It cannot necessarily be concluded from this that Columella sowed millet in good soil. Regarding sowing quantities of wheat, Varro recommended a thicker sowing on *rich* ground (V. 1. 44. 1). Likewise in Puglia towards the end of the last century the common practice was to sow rich land heavily because 'like a strong ass it could carry more'.[35] Both Columella and Pliny, however, recommend more wheat seed for poorer soil, as is the modern practice (Col. 2. 9. 1; P. 18. 198).

In modern times the ratio of sowing amount to yield is of the order of 1:50. After allowing for the disadvantages of too thick and uneven a sowing, given the ancient method of broadcasting the seed by hand compared with the modern systematic technique of planting in evenly spaced rows, it can yet be assumed that ancient yields were far from negligible, especially when, as was likely in a subsist or perish situation, careful attention was afforded the crop as it grew.[36]

However, one should not imagine that millet was grown only when it was realized that other cereals had failed. It is more likely that a variety of cereals was always grown as a precautionary measure by the small farmer.

From a study of cereal cultivation in the Po valley in the early medieval period the picture of polyculture of cereals emerged, in which, interestingly, tenants grew a variety of cereals, and while rendering bread wheats to their land-lords, consumed the inferior grains themselves.[37] It is possible that Columella's *coloni* did the same (2. 9. 17).[38] In this case it would be the landlord who suffered in a year of poor harvest, since bread wheats were more likely to fail than inferior grains. Yet in reality, if there was a poor wheat harvest, it can be supposed that the landlord took the millet. It is to be noted that not infrequently the medieval rents also included millet besides the superior grains, which might suggest either that the landlord ate it himself or sold it. One idea, already countered, namely that it was common to sow a mixture of grains in the same field as a conscious precautionary measure, should be abandoned. Mixtures of grain do occur, but as the result of careless seed selection compounded over the years, not of a rational decision.[39]

Another important advantage of millet was the length of time it could be stored without deterioration: twice that of wheat in certain situations (V. 1. 57. 2/3), because it is a husked grain (P. 18. 304). This, which would also apply to emmer

---

[34] 4 *sextarii* = ¼ *modius*. (Wheat was sown at 4 or 5 *modii* per *iugerum*.) 1 *modius* = 8.75 litres; 1 litre of millet = 0.7 kg; 1 *modius* of millet = 6.125 kg; ¼ *modius* of millet = 1.53 kg; sowing rate per *iugerum* 1.53 kg; per hectare 6 kg (approx.).

[35] Testini, *Il frumento*, 12 f. Cf. p. 57 above.

[36] It is stated in the *Geoponica* (a tenth-century A.D. compilation of Hellenistic agricultural knowledge) (2. 4) that a sowing of 4 *sextarii* produces a yield of 40 *sextarii*: that is a ratio of 1:10 (Orth, 'Hirse', 1956). Pliny, in reference to a marvellous new variety of millet recently brought from India, asserts that one

(sown) grain produces 3 *sextarii*. That would mean, if taken literally, a yield ratio of 1:225,000 and cannot be credited. (1,000 seeds weigh approx. 5 g.) Note the yield of millet recorded in Table 2, p. 86, for eighteenth-century Lombardy, 48:1.

[37] Montanari, 'Cereali e legumi', 450 and *passim*.

[38] In this case perhaps meaning 'tenants' rather than 'peasant cultivators'.

[39] Ampolo, 'Condizioni materiali', 18 and Montanari, 'Cereali e legumi', 476 presume, like most historians, that mixture was a conscious anti-famine measure.

wheat, would have been a distinct advantage for the small farmer who did not have sophisticated granaries. He would, of course, not be interested in keeping the grain for much more than a year, but within that year conservation of husked grain would involve less risk than conservation of naked wheat. Millet's long-keeping power was also, no doubt, of importance in cities where a certain quantity of millet might be stored as a precaution against lean years or other difficulties. Marseilles, when under siege to Caesar's forces during the Civil War, sustained its populace from stores of stale *panicum* and mouldy barley (*BC* 2. 22).

In a severe case of famine in North Italy in the first half of the sixth century, as already noted (p. 93), Tortona and Pavia were requested to open their granaries of millet to the people. This is arguably what often happened throughout the Roman period in the Po valley, and cannot be given the particular significance urged by Sereni. The unusual point about that one case is that a Prefect of Rome concerned himself with it; normally the matter would be left to local officials or entrepreneurs.

In *tenera* soil (fertile and easily worked) such as in Campania, millet, because of its short growth cycle, could be inserted into a rotation system as a summer crop between the reaping of barley and the sowing of turnips (P. 18. 191; cf. Strabo 5. 4. 3). Cato's juxtaposition of turnips and millet in rich, foggy areas might imply rotation (6. 1), as perhaps also does Seneca's observation that in late June near Liternum beans were being harvested and millet sown (*Ep. Mor.* 86.16). There was another school of thought, however, which argued that millet exhausted the soil, which then had to be repaired by manuring (Col. 2. 13. 3); and that it exhausted vines and fruit trees if intercultivated in an *arbustum* (P. 18. 101). Certainly millet is not a soil-improver and would need to be followed by manuring or a fallow period; yet that it exhausts the soil more than other cereal crops is probably wrong,[40] although Italian agriculturalists still maintain the view that other crops may suffer in their initial growth stages if they follow on from millet.[41]

Nevertheless, it seems clear that in parts of Campania and in other especially favoured soils millet was grown as a summer crop in rotation. In such cases the motive was hardly a precautionary one. It was surely profitable, if the soil, the resources of the farm, and the market possibilities permitted, to exploit the land to the full. Such, obviously, was the situation on the famous plain of Campania. There millet was converted into a white porridge or a sweet bread (P. 18. 100). As such it may have been enjoyed by even the most refined palates and have found a specialist but lucrative market among the summer residents of the coast or as an export to Rome. Columella appreciated millet porridge with milk: 'a food not to be despised even in time of plenty' (Col. 2. 9. 19).[42]

### VARIOUS USES OF MILLET IN THE ROMAN PERIOD

*Food*

That millet was a widespread food, especially but not exclusively among the lower classes, is deducible from the following considerations. Pliny states that

[40] White, *Roman Farming*, 137.
[41] *Enciclopedia agraria italiana* (1972), s.v. *Miglio*.
[42] This implies (*a*) that as milk porridge millet was eaten by men of Columella's class, and (*b*) that it was usually a food in times of scarcity.

legumes were mixed with grain to make bread (18. 117). Legumes of all kinds, including cattle fodder (and even wild herbs, Caesar, *BC* 3. 48), were apparently used, although the most common were beans. The most usual cereal in such admixtures was Italian millet (P. 18. 117). Pliny observes that legumes were employed in order to increase the weight and therefore the sale price of bread (ibid.). Since the bread was for sale, an urban situation can safely be assumed, not only perhaps that at Rome. Beans and Italian millet were eaten in some mixed form (bread is not specified) in the Po valley, and since this is a general statement of Pliny's (18. 101), it may refer to both urban and rural dwellers alike. In the Po valley and near Lucca in Tuscany during the early medieval period such a mixture was eaten by the poor in general, without any obvious distinction between city and country.[43] Paulinus, bishop of Nola, writing in the early fifth century A.D., describes it as monastic fare (23. 7), and it may be that a similar frugal combination had been one way of consuming Campanian millet in an earlier period.

With regard to Italy in general, Pliny notes that barley porridge *à la Grecque* was eaten in Italy with the special additional ingredient of millet (18. 74). Barley, however, in bread or porridge form, was probably in the main rustic food, and like millet important in times of scarcity (Col. 2. 9. 14). It was also eaten by the slave household (Col. 2. 9. 16).[44]

While *panicum* was combined with legumes to make bread, millet was converted into bread without admixture, in Campania as has been seen, as also perhaps elsewhere (P. 18. 54): 'panis multifariam et a milio fit'.[45]

Being non-glutinous it produces a heavy, flat bread, as Pliny observes, and also swells up more than any other cereal when made into porridge (18. 55). This would have made it a good appetite-satisfier, particularly serviceable in staving off hunger. Yet millet bread, if eaten hot, had a pleasant flavour, according to Columella. As such, therefore, it may have been especially eaten by the affluent in both urban and rural areas. In eighteenth-century Lombardy, street vendors sold hot millet bread as a delicacy; when it became cold it was considered unpalatable and ground up to make *gnocchi*.[46]

As regards its nutritional value, millet is richer in carbohydrates but poorer in digestible proteins than other cereals. In a healthy diet it would thus have to be balanced by a protein-rich food. Such a balance could, for example, be achieved by shepherds who would supplement their millet-based diet with cheese, as is recorded in the region of Brescia in the mid-sixteenth century.[47] Varro does not discuss the diet of slave herdsmen, although he notes that their dogs eat meat, which is characterized as human food (2. 9. 8). Pregnant bitches should eat barley bread, and it may be implied in the context that their masters do also (2. 9. 11).

---

[43] Montanari, 'Cereali e legumi', 483.

[44] It is to be observed that neither barley nor millet appears in Cato's slave rations (Cato 56). That cannot be taken to show that slaves ate neither millet nor barley. The danger of such an argument is exemplified by Lynn White's use of the absence of beans in Cato's slave diet to confirm his theory that legumes only became important in the Middle Ages. See pp. 104–11.

[45] *multifariam* means that there were several varieties of millet bread. The *et*, 'even', should not be seen as an indication of rarity so much as upper-class or Pliny's own sensibility (cf. *et pabulo*, 18. 117). Columella also mentions bread made from millet (2. 9. 19).

[46] Messedaglia, *Storia dell'agricoltura e dell'alimentazione*, 49.

[47] Ibid., 51 f.

More interestingly for this discussion, Ovid asserts that millet was offered to Pales at the shepherds' festival (*Parilia*) (*Fasti* 4. 743).

Even at Rome where the dole presumably consisted of naked wheat, the poorer classes, if they had to eke out their ration of wheat with purchases, probably relied heavily on inferior, less expensive grains. Local cultivation of millet, apparent in Iron Age and medieval Latium, ought also then to be assumed for the Roman period. Cultivation would have been carried out not only by the subsistence peasant but also by the larger arable farmer producing for the urban market. There may have been some importation of millet to Rome from Campania, central Etruria, and possibly the Po valley where, according to Polybius (2. 15. 1–2), there was a surplus production (ὑπερβάλλουσα δαφίλεια).[48] Yet, of course, exports from all these regions need not have gone only to Rome.[49] Martial's friend as *pragmaticus* at Rome apparently sold *frumentum*, *tisana* (barley), millet and beans, but as a country/suburban dweller had to buy them (12. 72). The joke is open to interpretation, but the point about variety of grains is made.[50]

### Leaven

When mixed with wine-must, millet acted as a leaven for bread (P. 18. 102). A possible example of this is the *dolium* full of millet found in the so-called wine cellar of the Pisanella villa near Boscoreale at Pompeii. Certainly, this was how the excavator interpreted the discovery. On the other hand, since other cereals were also found in *dolia* in the wine cellar, it is perhaps better to assume that the bulk of the cereals produced on the farm was stored in the granary, while an amount for current use was transferred to more accessible *dolia*. That grain was kept in *dolia* is clear from Cato (p. 82 above). Further, such a use of millet was rare in Pliny's time, the most common method of leavening bread being to preserve some of the previous day's dough (P. 18. 104).

### Birdseed

In Italy of the present day, what little millet is grown is mainly for birdseed and green forage, and its cultivation is confined largely to parts of Piedmont, Lombardy and Venetia, although individual small-scale production is still quite widespread. That it was also used as birdseed in Roman times is clear from Columella (book 8 *passim*), particularly for farmyard hens and pigeons. Poultry-

---

[48] Yet while the waterways of Cisalpine Gaul may have allowed an active internal commerce in cereals, such trade with the rest of Italy, especially the west coast, was almost certainly very limited (Brunt, *Italian Manpower*, 183–4); ὑπερβάλλουσα may therefore rather refer to the exuberance of the vegetation, important, as suggested above, for animal fodder.

[49] Not all the Mediterranean's surplus went to Rome. There is no doubt that Rome's needs stimulated trade in all products, but grain commerce would have been diffused throughout the west and east Mediterranean, merchants taking advantage of temporary shortages or famines wherever they occurred. Caesar's *Bellum Civile* and the *Bellum Afri-*

*canum* give the impression that cargo ships (*naves onerariae*), sometimes with a specific cargo of grain, were often met with (cf. *BC* 1. 36, Massilia; 3. 23, Brundisium; 3. 96, Thessalian coast; *B.Af.* 34, near Thapsus). In the late sixteenth century the Tuscan Maremma supplied not only Tuscan cities, Genoa, and Rome, 'mais encore à Marseille, Montpellier et naturellement à la cour d'Avignon (Delumeau, *Vie économique et sociale de Rome*, 536).

[50] The *pragmaticus* was probably partly paid in kind. But when he retired and bought some unproductive property in the suburbs of Rome he had to buy his staple foods.

keeping can be considered to have been fairly ubiquitous in rural areas, except perhaps among the poorest inhabitants like the gardener and one-time owner of Lucius the ass (Apul., *Metam*. 9. 32). In Italy most peasants these days have one or more hens which wander around the house and yard. According to Varro, the keeping of hens in the yard and pigeons on the roof had always been a feature of the traditional country villa (3. 3. 6). Maintenance of hens for eggs was one of the duties of the *vilica* (Cato 143. 3). However, it is clear from Columella (8. 4. 1) that millet was only one of a variety of foods for hens, and so even if it can legitimately be assumed that poultry-keeping was ubiquitous, the feeding of millet obviously was not. Other recommended hen food included barley, grape pulp after pressing, chickpeas and chaff. In practice poultry is thrown all manner of scraps, and is often allowed to range free, to supplement the necessary cereal-based diet. In the Columellan passage referred to, neither peasant nor the typical villa owner, but instead a specialized poultry breeder who has to purchase feed, is being envisaged. This is a valuable insight into the rural economy in the vicinity of urban centres. There undoubtedly existed people who bred hens for eggs or meat either within or not far without the city limits, to supply the urban market.[51] Such breeders would buy feed directly or through middlemen from cereal producers. A breeder of wild boars for city tables like Seius, the nonpareil of the *pastio villatica* system, would even purchase acorns (V. 3. 2. 12). Of the recommended feed for hens, it appears that the millets were the most expensive and would be the first to be replaced by cheaper substitutes if the price was too high (Col., ibid.). Pigeons were also fed on millet, their diet not differing greatly from that of hens (Col. 8. 3. 6; V. 3. 7. 8). Not only typical of country estates, they were also kept in the city (V. 3. 7. 8). Since profits could be large (V. 2 *pr*. 5; 3. 7. 10–11), the best food was no doubt sought after. A commerce which included the sale and purchase of cereals and legumes and perhaps also of pigeon manure, as well as the construction of clay dovecotes (*fictilia columbaria*, V. 3. 7. 11), may have been considerable.

*Fodder*

As regards fodder for quadrupeds, the most highly-esteemed chaff for oxen was that from millet, according to Columella (6. 3. 3). Presumably it was sifted from the flour once the grain had been parched and pounded. This may imply either that the flour was sold, or that the farm personnel, *coloni* and slaves, ate it in bread and porridge, although mixed with milk it could also provide nourishment for young calves (Col. 6. 24. 5). Millet cut or pastured green provides excellent animal forage, and since Cato includes *panicum* in a list of green fodder (54. 4), it can safely be concluded that the reference is to the crop cut green.[52] In this case, the more leaf and stalk the better and, as was suggested above, millet as cattle fodder may have been especially important in the Po valley, where abundant water would have caused copious leaf growth. More generally, the word *penus* was commonly understood to refer to wine, wheat, oil, lentils and beans, but it could be pointed out that it also included millet, acorns and barley (Gellius 4. 1. 8).

[51] The *gallinari* of Pompeii who were powerful enough to hope for election of one of their number to a local magistracy are probably to be thus identified: *CIL* 4. 241, 373.

[52] *Panicum* as animal forage: while all millets provide excellent green fodder, that of Italian millet is considered the best, F.A.O., *Improvement and Production of Maize, Sorghum and Millets*, 19.

This may reflect a distinction between human and animal food, or even between that of the upper and lower classes. That there was some similar distinction in the early third century A.D. is indicated by Ulpian's reference to the throwing of *frumentum* and *milium* into the river as being actionable under the Lex Aquilia de damno (*Dig*. 9. 2. 27. 19). In the Edict of Diocletian (1. 4, 5) millet is listed among other food grains (notably as either pounded or whole, which suggests that it could be purchased in the form of flour), at a price slightly lower than barley or rye and at half the price of wheat (*frumentum*).

## Medicine

Not negligible, perhaps, was the amount of millet used for medical and veterinary purposes (P. 22. 30; Col. 6. 12. 4). Diocles of Athens (fourth century B.C.) had called Italian millet the 'honey of crops', and Celsus, who listed types of bread in order of *firmitas*, places wheat bread first, followed by bread made from millet and then barley bread (2. 18. 4).

## Conclusion

Other references would only confirm what appears to be a clear enough situation. It should be assumed that a variety of cereals was grown in Italy throughout the Roman period. The main types were naked wheat, barley, emmer and millet (V., *LL* 5. 106). It is expected that archaeology will increasingly confirm this hypothesis.

The short growth period of millet, its tolerance of soil and climatic conditions (apart from cold temperatures), simplicity of reaping (Col. 2. 9. 18), and resistance in storage, would have recommended millet to the small farmer, who might also have used it to make a type of 'wine' (P. 14. 101), although not, apparently, for thatching or fencing (P. 18. 296).[53] As a rotational crop on especially fertile land, or in soil which could be manured on those estates where there was a predominant combination of arable and livestock, it might furnish food, fodder and birdseed for the estate itself and for the urban market.

---

[53] Not that millet straw is unsuitable for thatching or fencing, for which it is used commonly in Africa (F.A.O., *Improvement and Production of Maize,* *Sorghum and Millets*, 18). In the absence of other evidence, however, Pliny's statement should be accepted.

# CHAPTER VI: LEGUMES

It is clear from the palaeobotanical evidence from the Near East that legumes, especially the pea, lentil and bitter vetch, were domesticated at the same time as, or shortly after, cereals. They then spread across the Mediterranean region.[1] The near simultaneity of domestication suggests some physically instinctual understanding of the nutritional importance of the combination of cereal and legumes.

Legumes attract a species of soil bacteria to their roots. Cells of the roots divide, form nodules and house the bacteria which converts atmospheric nitrogen into a form of nitrogen absorbable by the plant, which in turn manufactures amino-acids essential for the human diet. Amino-acids are the base of proteins and three of them, lysine, metheonine and tryptophan, are either completely absent or present only in part in the various domesticated cereals. As a generalization, cereals supply the carbohydrates and legumes the proteins. What is true for men is also largely true for animals, and it is therefore to be emphasized that legumes are also important as animal fodder.

Legumes also maintain and improve soil fertility. The process of conversion of atmospheric nitrogen means that the plant does not have to draw on the nitrogen reserves of the soil as do cereals. Moreover, during the plant's growth cycle root nodules disintegrate and supply nitrogen to the soil. However, the efficacy and amount of nitrogen enrichment depends on cultivation practice. For example, the soil should be kept well aerated to permit the percolation of atmospheric nitrogen. If the whole crop is harvested, roots as well, the soil enrichment will not be as great as when the whole crop is ploughed under as green manure.

## THE ARGUMENT

According to Lynn White, it was the introduction of the three-field rotation system in the tenth century A.D. which not only revolutionized agriculture but also raised the quality of life.[2] The triennial rotation system is as follows:

|         | Year 1      | Year 2      | Year 3      |
|---------|-------------|-------------|-------------|
| Field 1 | autumn crop | spring crop | fallow      |
| Field 2 | spring crop | fallow      | autumn crop |
| Field 3 | fallow      | autumn crop | spring crop |

The Roman system, as commonly conceived, was a two-field, biennial rotation:

[1] D. Zohary and M. Hopf, 'Domestication of Pulses in the Old World', *Science* 182 (1973), 887–94. See also W. R. Aykroyd and J. Doughty, *Legumes in Human Nutrition*, F.A.O. Food and Nutrition Series 12 (1964), 3–11. Legumes receive a very limited treatment in White, *Roman Farming*, 189–91.

[2] L. White, *Medieval Technology and Social Change* (1962), 69 ff. For following comments on beans, ibid., 75 f.; on legumes as garden crops, id., 'The Vitality of the Tenth Century', *Medievalia et Humanistica* 9 (1955), 26–9; cf. F. J. Green, 'Iron Age, Roman and Saxon Crops: the Archaeological Evidence from Wessex' in *The Environment of Man*, ed. M. Jones and G. Dimbleby, 141.

|          | *Year 1*     | *Year 2*     |
|----------|--------------|--------------|
| Field 1  | autumn crop  | fallow       |
| Field 2  | fallow       | autumn crop  |

Under the two-field system, legumes had little importance, since the autumn crop was invariably a cereal. 'Under the three-field rotation the autumn-planting was largely carbohydrates, but the spring-planting held a large amount of vegetable proteins . . . by the end of the 11th century these latter loomed as large as cereals.' 'In the full sense of the vernacular, the Middle Ages, from the tenth century onward, were full of beans.' In earlier periods, according to this theory, legumes had been grown mainly in gardens.

One apparent inconsistency in the argument should be noted. Incompatible with the remark that cereals and legumes began to be grown in equal quantities is White's earlier statement that oats were one of the major spring crops. The growing of oats is necessary to the assumed widespread use of the horse in the new arable agriculture. Thus the spring sowing would have been divided between oats and legumes, and the latter could never have been grown in the same quantity as cereals. Doubts can be expressed about the imagined wholesale introduction of triennial rotation in the tenth century (p. 117 n. 1), but more germane to the discussion here is an examination of earlier evidence, in order to test the thesis that legumes had remained a marginal crop. As for the suggestion that the widespread cultivation of legumes increased the vitality of the medieval population, it should be said immediately that the optimum combination of legumes and cereals depends on the type of cereal and is never a combination of equal quantities. Emmer wheat, for example, has more than twice the protein content of modern bread wheat and is deficient in only one amino-acid.[3] Thus to be 'full of beans' in the vernacular is not necessary in the literal sense.

Firm conclusions from botanical evidence from archaeological sites are impossible. The factors which caused preservation and carbonization of seeds are accidental, and the temptation to establish from such data rotation systems or the quantities in which individual crops were cultivated, should be resisted. However, what *is* permissible and valuable is a general survey of various sites, since this can demonstrate trends.

Whereas the pea, lentil and bitter vetch appear regularly in the earliest sites in the ancient Near East and Greece, and the chickpea, although less common, was not chronologically far behind, the broad bean (*vicia faba*) appeared considerably later (2900–2700 B.C.). This last, it would appear, had spread throughout the Iberian peninsula by 2500 B.C., but only reached Italy via Switzerland in the Bronze Age.[4] It then spread rapidly throughout Italy and has been found in an Iron Age site at Monte Irsi in the south of Basilicata.[5] Alternatively, there might have been a dichotomous diffusion pattern as was suggested for millet, although evidence for this seems to be limited to one possible bean specimen from the very

[3] Reynolds, *Iron Age Farm*, 64.

[4] Van Zeist, 'Aperçu'. General comments on the archaeological recovery of legumes: R. W. Dennel, 'The Interpretation of Plant Remains: Bulgaria' in *Papers in Economic Prehistory*, ed. E. Higgs (1972),

149–59. The diffusionist argument for the establishment of crops is now questioned: cf. Barker, *Prehistoric Farming in Europe*, 250 ff.

[5] Hjelmqvist, 'Economic Plants'.

early site of Passo di Corvo in Puglia (4000 B.C.). In the present state of evidence we should beware of any rigid classification of early diffusion patterns.

## BROAD BEANS

The argument rather to be developed here is that the broad bean had become the most widespread legume in Italy by the Roman period. A recent review of the faunal and botanical evidence for central and northern Italy for the Neolithic, Bronze and Iron Ages appears to demonstrate that legumes became more common in the middle and late Bronze and Iron Ages, and that of those identified, the broad bean occurs most often.[6] The little botanical evidence so far collected suggests the presence of the broad bean throughout the Roman period. Finds have been made at the villa of Settefinestre near Orbetello in Tuscany (late Republic to late second century A.D.), at the villa of San Giovanni near Potenza in Basilicata (early to late Imperial period), from Imperial Rome, and at Aquileia; and Pompeii has yielded some twenty-six to twenty-nine separate samples.[7] This seems sufficient evidence to conclude that this legume was widely diffused in Italy in the period under discussion.

A comparison of the sizes of the bean samples from the Bronze Age to the Roman period, wherever this is possible, appears to indicate that beans became larger over time. Perhaps this was due to improved agricultural techniques. However, such a hypothesis, although quite conceivable on general grounds, will require further archaeological attestation before commanding acceptance.[8]

Nor, as stated above, can any quantity ratio or rotational practice of beans and cereals be deduced from the archaeological evidence. It would be improper to conclude from the Monte Irsi data, for example, where far more beans than any other crop, including cereals, were found, that beans were the most widely-cultivated crop on that site. However, since beans are the most common *legume* found on Bronze and Iron Age sites, their predominance among *legumes* in those periods can be reasonably assumed, since there is no special reason connected with their preparation for consumption which would have caused their carbonization and not the carbonization of other legumes. Yet since for the Roman period, from the little evidence which has been recovered, a greater variety of legumes appears to have been cultivated than in earlier periods, it is unsafe to argue from the archaeological evidence alone that beans continued to predominate. Nonetheless, other considerations, taken together with the botanical evidence, seem to point to such a conclusion.

Isidore of Seville, in his brief chapter on legumes, remarks that the bean was the first legume used by men for food (17. 4. 3). Its antiquity, attested by the archaeological record, is indicated by its religious use and the superstitions connected with it (P. 18. 118). The tradition allowed Ovid to characterize the agriculture of old Latium as a combination of only emmer and beans (*Fasti* 6. 180).

[6] Forni, 'Origini delle strutture agrarie nell'Italia preromana'; for a find of beans in a tomb in the forum of 'archaic Rome', *Notizie degli Scavi* 1905, 193.

[7] Respectively: Jones, 'I resti vegetali'; Small, 'The Environment of San Giovanni'; for the rest see the good survey of Hjelmqvist, 'Economic Plants'. Now also from the early third century at Metapontum: Carter, Costantini et al., 'Population and Agriculture', fig. 16. 4.

[8] Hjelmqvist, 'Economic Plants'.

It was a popular food, and an anxious father from Canusium could warn his sons against aspiration to presumably local magistracy, where their inheritance would be squandered on largesse of beans, chickpeas and lupins (Hor., *Sat.* 2. 3. 182–3).[9] Martial, exploiting the *topos* of the humble dinner, offers a menu of beans, peas, chickpeas and lupins, as well as the perhaps not so humble eggs, fish and sausage (5. 78). Elsewhere he refers to *faba fabrorum* ('builders' beans'), perhaps accurately matching food to level of society, despite the play on words (10. 48. 16). Beans are what a richer man might send to a client (10. 14; 7. 53). However, if it is correct to assume that the recipes which occur in Apicius are reflections of an upper-class diet, it can be concluded that beans were not only poor food (5. 3 (197–9, 202)). Perhaps the only people not to eat them were some priests (*flamines*) and Pythagoreans (P. 18. 118–19). That they were included in meals offered to the dead, as stated by Pliny (ibid.), is proved by archaeological evidence, at least for Iron Age Rome.[10]

Pliny opens his long account of the bean with the assertion that it holds the highest place among legumes since it is used in crushed form (*lomentum*) in the baking of bread (18. 117). Although it is implied that beans were the most common vegetable-mix, it is noted that all other legumes were combined with cereals to make bread, even animal fodder (ibid.), and, in times of necessity, even wild plants (Caes., *BC* 3. 48). Vases (*urcei*), which contained *lomentum* perhaps for this purpose, have been found at Pompeii (cf. *CIL* 4. 5738). Since the beneficial effects of a mixed diet of cereals and legumes depend on the near simultaneity of ingestion of both, bean-bread was healthy food.

How many people ate bread made of such a mixture is unknowable, and guesses will vary according to whether one believes that in Roman times inferior breads had almost disappeared as specialization in naked wheats increased, or that naked wheats and pure breads were rare. Certainly Pliny does not imply that bread made from cereals and legumes was unusual. Nevertheless, it appears that Cato's agricultural slaves ate bread but no beans, and this observation is naturally used by White as proof of his thesis.[11]

Given the weight of the archaeological and literary evidence, it could be argued that the lack of beans in the Catonian slave diet is an exception. It could also be that Cato omitted a specific mention of beans, since his treatise was neither complete in content nor systematic in form. It is to be noted that he envisages the cultivation of beans (136); bean chaff is oxen fodder (27; 54. 2); and a pestle for pounding beans is included in the oliveyard's equipment (10. 5). Since it has been assumed that beans were eaten by all levels of society, it would be odd if slaves were rigorously excluded. However, information on slave diet is slight. While there are several references to *alimenta* in the *Digest*, specification appears to be limited to wine and *frumentum* (cf. 34. 1. 9. 1). In a legacy of water rights, legumes are mentioned, but it is very doubtful that they can be taken to refer to the slave's diet (34. 1. 14. 3). On the other hand, *frumentum* is an imprecise term

---

[9] It is possible that magistracies at Rome are being referred to, but the point remains.

[10] Helbaek, 'Funeral Meals'. One speculative explanation for the rejection of beans by Pythagoras is that he suffered from the disease favism: Aykroyd and Doughty, *Legumes*, 66.

[11] L. White, *Medieval Technology*, 76; Cato 66; Jasny, *Wheats*, 55, who interprets *triticum* here as emmer wheat (cf. P. 18. 98); cf. Moritz, *Grain Mills*, 221 nn. O and P.

which can include legumes (P. 18. 49–50). Moreover, when Cato states that the slaves should receive quantities of *triticum*, this could also comprise legumes, as is clear from Pliny (18. 50). Thus, if Cato was using the term in its widest sense, it may account for the apparent exclusion of legumes from the slave diet.

That beans were predominantly a field rather than a garden crop is clear from an examination of the literary sources. Garden crops included cabbage, salad plants, herbs (*Moretum* 6 ff.; Apul., *Metam.* 9. 32). Beans do not appear among Pliny's exhaustive list of kitchen-garden products (19. 61–175; cf. V., *LL* 5. 103). At a meal, garden plants appear as hors d'œuvres, whereas beans are served as part of the main course (Martial 10. 48; 5. 78). Beans and lupins are mentioned by Columella in his tenth book 'on gardening', written in verse (in lieu of Virgil), but from the context it seems that they were not grown in the garden but were only cooked together with certain garden plants (10. 113–15). The other major garden crop, and one which could provide profit if cultivated near an urban market, was of course flowers (Col. 10. 308).[12]

On the other hand, 'white beans' (*fabuli albi*) are included among garden herbs employed for veterinary purposes, and it may be that they came from the garden (Cato 70). Apicius refers to *fabaciae virides* which probably means fresh beans (5. 6 (210–11)). The Edict of Diocletian includes fresh beans among garden products sold by the *sextarius* measure, whereas dry beans, sold by the *modius* (= 16 *sextarii*), are listed with cereals (6. 38; 1. 9). It ought, therefore, to be assumed that beans were also grown by market gardeners to be eaten fresh,[13] while the beans eaten out of season, which had been stored whole or crushed as *lomentum*, were field crops, and accounted for the bulk of beans consumed.

Whereas a certain production of fresh beans in gardens can de deduced, literary evidence for beans as a field crop is plain. On this score at least, the argument of White is clearly refuted. There is not the least doubt that the legumes grown for both human and animal consumption were field crops, and of these, beans were probably the most usual. In a contract for leasing arable land, cereals and beans are the crops mentioned (Cato 136). There are many other passages which imply a close connection between the cultivation of beans and cereals. For example, both beans and wheat prefer dry soil, and sowing amounts of cereals and beans are given together (V. 1. 23. 5; 1. 44. 1). Beans can follow a grain crop on continually cropped *restibilis* land (Col. 2. 10. 6); and on farms too small to allow half their land each year to remain unproductive under the biennial system, a rotation of emmer wheat followed by beans was proposed (P. 18. 187). That large and small farmers both grew beans is to be further concluded from Columella's reiteration of the saw of *veteres rustici* (a *rusticus* being understood here as a small farmer; 2. 10. 9). That beans were the most commonly grown legume may also be inferred from such formulations as 'beans and other legumes' (cf. V. 1. 57. 3).

Beans were also animal fodder. The extent to which they were so employed varied with the type of farm. On an estate where forage crops could be grown in some abundance, a list of such crops might not include beans (V. 1. 23. 1). In an

---

[12] Cf. Cic., *Fam.* 16. 18; Cato 8. 2; V. 1. 16. 3.

[13] Evidence for bean cultivation in vineyards within Pompeii perhaps indicates such market gardening, Jashemski, *The Gardens of Pompeii*, 47, 210, 242.

Carbonized legumes found in a store-room in a villa at nearby Torre Annunziata (ibid., 320 ff.) do not prove garden production.

earlier age when fewer fodder crops were known, bean stalks, pods and chaff would have been fed to oxen and other animals.[14] It would be better to say for the late Republic/early Empire at least, that on farms where space allocated to crops purely for forage might compromise human subsistence, a crop such as beans which could serve both man and beast would be preferred. The alternative in such situations might be to intercultivate a crop of hay among the beans, but this expedient could be rejected by a larger arable farmer who was interested in a well-weeded crop of beans in order to achieve the maximum yield for the market (Col. 2. 11. 6–7).

The actual beans themselves, there is no doubt, were too valuable as human food to be fed to animals. The only exceptions would be made by livestock breeders during crucial periods of the reproduction cycle such as during mating and at birth;[15] or occasionally, if the cost was not too great, in order to vary the working oxen's diet (Col. 6. 35). Thus, on a farm which could afford to make a distinction between forage and food crops, beans would lose their importance as a prime fodder crop. Nevertheless, their stalks and pods would still no doubt have been fed (P. 18. 120; Col. 11. 2. 50); and any surplus could be utilized as compost (Cato 37. 2). The other case in which beans would be used as animal fodder would be when a bean crop, destined to be ploughed under as green manure before bearing pods, was pastured (assumed from Cato 27).

That the larger arable farm intent on supplying the urban market with cereals could also find a lucrative market for beans is to be assumed from earlier observations on the widespread consumption of beans. In such a context it becomes easier to understand remarks about the high cost of beans near towns which prohibit their being ordinarily fed to animals (Col. 6. 3. 5; 7. 3. 22). Commercial activity in beans is clear at Herculaneum where the excavation of a shop has revealed *dolia* full of beans and chickpeas.[16]

From the agricultural point of view, there is nothing that would exclude cultivation of the bean from any region of Italy. Since it can withstand temperatures as low as –5°C, it can be sown in most areas of Italy in the autumn. Where winters are severe it is planted in the spring. Such seems to have been the case in the Po valley, as Pliny asserts in approval of Virgil (18. 120). It would also have been the case at high altitudes throughout Italy. At San Giovanni, near Potenza, where winter temperatures of –15°C are not uncommon, while the wheats found there could have been autumn-sown because of their greater resistance to the cold, the beans were definitely spring-sown. However, although autumn or spring plantings were most commonly divided along climatic lines, in the more temperate areas there was clearly an element of choice, although it was well known that a spring bean crop yielded less (Col. 2. 10. 9).

In modern times, in order to accelerate the germination of beans grown in market gardens for eating fresh, seeds are soaked for one or two days before sowing. Virgil perhaps alludes to a similar practice when he notes that beans are

---

[14] For the development of fodder crops from Cato to Columella, see the argument of White, *Roman Farming*, 202 ff.

[15] Cf. V. 2. 4. 6, 2. 4. 17 (pigs); Col. 6. 24. 5 (calves), 6. 30. 1 (horses), 7. 3. 22, 7. 4. 2 (sheep),

7. 9. 9 (pigs). V. 2. 1. 17 as variety in diet.

[16] A. Maiuri, *Ercolano* (1955), 402. For other indications of commerce in beans: Petr., *Sat.* 76. 7; *ILS* 3851, 7494.

soaked in nitre and oil lees to increase yield and speed of growth (*Georgics* 1. 195-6). Columella, however, interprets this specifically as a protection against infestation from weevils after the new beans have reached maturity (2. 10. 11). In this case there is no doubt that he is envisaging the harvesting of beans for dry storage and not for eating fresh. For in the latter case the beans, as soon as they matured, would be plucked; in the former they would be left to dry in the pods in the field until the whole crop was ready for harvesting.

Concerning soil, beans have the same requirements as wheat. Fertile, well-drained soils suit best, but they can adapt to most types. Thus they grew wild in many places (P. 18. 121). Such adaptability would have aided widespread diffusion; wherever cereals were grown, beans could also be found. If placed in a rotation system with wheat, Columella advised a heavy manuring of beans (2. 10. 6). This would have produced an excellent crop of beans and have left the soil in optimum condition for the next crop. However, on a smaller farm, where fallowing was impractical and manure almost certainly scarce, Pliny's advice of a rotation of emmer and beans (18. 187) was eminently reasonable. Small amounts of manure are sufficient in such a rotation; the beans themselves enrich the soil, and a tolerable harvest of both the cereal and legume crop will be maintained. Columella, on the other hand, was interested in the maximum yield. His reference to 'ridging' the soil in preparation for beans is a reminder that they were to be sown on the best cereal land (2. 10. 5).

Another factor which undoubtedly contributed to their widespread diffusion was ease of cultivation. Like vetch they could be simply scattered on unbroken soil and ploughed under (P. 18. 181; cf. Col. 2. 10. 6). In garden cultivation, the more time-consuming and labour-intensive method of planting in holes or individual rows might be expected, but there is no firm indication of this in the Roman sources, since the word *serere* (general, like our 'sow') is used. Columella, who speaks exclusively of field cultivation, uses *iacere* ('broadcast', 2. 10. 5). As for cultivation during the growth cycle, it appears that many did not bother, and even encouraged the growth of grass as eventual animal fodder. Yet a farmer intent on the best yields could recommend as many as three hoeings/weedings (Col. 2. 11. 6-7). Those who did not weed did so at their own risk; empty bean pods choked by weeds were the symbol of a bad harvest (Calp. Sic. 4. 115-16). There is, in fact, one particular weed called *orobanche*, which is a parasite of the bean and is to be feared. Its dangers and necessary precautions against it were known to the agronomists, as discussed on p. 61. Hoeing, besides aerating the soil, is useful for the percolation of atmospheric nitrogen.

There is no doubt that the more attention given the bean while it grows the better its harvest will be. However, it is clear from the Roman sources, as can be seen these days, especially in certain regions in the south of Italy (four-fifths of the beans cultivated in Italy are grown in the south, including Sicily), that often little care was bestowed either at sowing time or during the growth cycle. On the other hand, some farmers obviously practised more intensive methods of cultivation, including soaking before sowing, careful preparation of soil, and several weedings, all of which would have contributed to produce a larger plant, more beans and more animal fodder. As has been mentioned earlier, the apparently *laissez-faire* method of cultivation has been seen as a sign of 'extensive' farming and the decline of slavery. If there is some truth in the theory, it is only partial, since there can be several reasons for not applying intensive methods. Here the only point to be emphasized is that the type of cultivator who did use intensive methods was likely to have included the farmer producing for the urban market.

Beans have a shorter vegetational cycle than wheat and are therefore harvested earlier, in late June or before (Col. 11. 2. 50; Sen., *Ep. Mor.* 86. 16). This is important in Italy, in regions where summers are hot, since the bean does not withstand high temperatures and drought. It seems clear that the beans were harvested by hand without the aid of a sickle. All legumes were 'pulled' (*vellere*), according to Varro (1. 23. 2; 1. 32. 2), and Columella uses the same term (2. 10. 12), which almost certainly means roots and all. This is one of the methods still in use today.[17] Since beans on the same plant do not ripen all at the same time, it might be expected that they were plucked individually if grown as a garden crop. Such an operation would also be carried out by hand and could be described in such phrases as *manibus ducere* (Col. 2. 11. 6), although since Columella appears to refer to beans only as a field crop for dry storage, it is more likely that this phrase is to be understood as equivalent to *vellere*. However, both Pliny and Seneca use the term *metere*, and Columella appears elsewhere to refer to the practice of ploughing up the soil which has roots of the legume crop still in it (2. 13. 2). As occurs in the present day, there may have been two methods of reaping the field crop: (1) pulling out by hand and (2) cutting the crop close to the ground with a *falx*.

It was perhaps on those farms where maximum yields were sought, that the roots were left in the ground or returned to the ground if pulled up during reaping, which thereby ensured the greatest possible nitrogen and humus enrichment. Where grass was grown for hay among the bean crop, the beans were surely pulled out by hand rather than cut with a sickle, since the idea was to reap the hay separately afterwards. On such a farm it is perhaps doubtful that the bean roots were later returned to the soil. This was then perhaps a further disadvantageous result of less intensive methods.

Columella's calculation that it takes one man one day to reap one *iugerum* of beans (2. 12. 2) is a clear indication that he was not concerned with harvesting beans for eating fresh. It would mean waiting until almost all the beans had ripened, in which case many would be already dry. When he refers to more than one harvest (11. 2. 50), it is thus unlikely that he means returning to the same plants again, as the beans lower down ripen (as would be the case in market gardening), but to the fact that, since he had mentioned two possible sowing times, there were also two possible reaping times (2. 10. 8; 11. 2. 85).

As for threshing (which would naturally only apply to a field crop destined for dry storage), it was less complicated than that of wheat. It could be carried out by human trampling, if animals were not available, and by beating with sticks and forks. Winnowing could be done without having to wait for a suitable wind (Col. 2. 10. 12–14). Elsewhere valuable indication is given of the commonness of bean cultivation on a farm larger than a peasant holding (it has some pasture land (*pratum*), but is not oriented towards intensive arable culture, since it does not possess a permanent threshing floor); a piece of pasture is selected and beans are

---

[17] Grimaldi, *Coltivazioni erbacee*, 122.

threshed there in order to harden the ground for the ensuing threshing of wheat (Col. 2. 19. 2). It could be at this stage that the beans recovered in rural excavation became carbonized: before threshing the wheat, the floor would be swept clean of the remains of beans, which might then be left to burn in a smouldering fire.[18]

As a consequence of all these considerations, White's thesis that beans were unimportant in the Roman period can be discarded. Because of their ease of cultivation, of threshing and reaping, and of their adaptability to soil and climate, they were widely grown in Roman Italy. Furthermore, from the literary evidence it seems possible to identify the cultivation of beans on various types of farms, from the subsistent peasant to the large-scale arable farmer who produced for the urban market.

How much arable land was under beans at any one time in Roman Italy seems impossible to answer. Under the medieval triennial rotation, one-third of the land would be under spring crops, but as already noted, these would include oats as well as legumes. Then again, the ratio of cereals to legumes would vary according to the type of estate. One other way of approaching the problem would be to note that to obtain the optimum dietary effect of a cereals/legume combination, the ratio should be about 6:1 respectively.[19] We might not, therefore, expect a greater cultivation ratio. An inscription from Macedonia records a consignment of alimentary supplies to the army of four hundred *medimni* of wheat, one hundred of barley and sixty of beans.[20] If the barley was for men rather than horses, the ratio of cereals to beans would be 8:1. It is just possible that this reflects an average cultivation ratio of cereals to beans.

Some modern statistics are of interest here. Between 1920 and 1930 the ratio of land under grain (of all kinds, including rice and maize) to that under dry legumes in Italy was approximately 6:1. In 1970 to 1975 the ratio was 9:1. (The actual production ratio altered much more dramatically, from 11:1 to 45:1 approximately.) These figures represent both a decline in area under legumes and a far greater attention paid to the improvement of cereal yields.[21]

Decreasing legumes are the result of a combination of factors of which an important one is the general rise in affluence of Italians since the Second World War. Legumes, the 'poor man's meat', have been increasingly replaced by the real thing. Of course, the above statistics regard the country only as a whole. It continues to be the case that in the less prosperous south legumes make up a larger part of the diet than in the north. But even in the most depressed areas meat is eaten now more regularly than a generation ago.[22]

It could be that increased wealth in the period *c.*200 B.C.–A.D. 100 resulted in a similar decline in the consumption of dried legumes. Signs of dietary distinctions along economic lines were noted above. Yet caution must be exercised here, since the rich remained in the extreme minority.

---

[18] An idea adopted from Reynolds, *Iron Age Farm*, 58.

[19] Even less, if the main cereal was emmer (n. 3 above).

[20] R. W. Davies, 'The Roman Military Diet', *Britannia* 2 (1971), 125 n. 29.

[21] *Sommario di statistiche storiche dell'Italia 1861–1975*, Istituto Centrale di Statistica (1976), 74 ff., Table 56.

[22] Aykroyd and Doughty, *Legumes*, 33–4; F. Gross, *Il Paese. Values and Social Change in an Italian Village* (1973), 132 f.

Fewer dried legumes in the modern period have been matched by an increasing cultivation of fresh broad beans, french beans and peas. This surely is another sign of affluence, perhaps also a concomitant of growing urbanization. It seems to be a trend also noticeable for the Roman period as the following discussion of peas and *phaseoli* seeks to indicate.

## PEAS AND *PHASEOLI*

Of all Italian legumes grown in modern times for human consumption, the bean continues to retain the prime position. It is by far the most widely cultivated. The other main legumes include the french (or kidney) bean, the pea, the chickpea, lentil and lupin. In this list, the only newcomer is the french bean which has assumed importance since its discovery in America. Its European near-equivalent, which was cultivated in Roman and medieval times, is called in Italian *fagiolo dall'occhio* because of its characteristic black spot. In Latin it was termed *phaseolus*, and is little cultivated today.

The french bean fears cold, great heat, wind and rain. In Italy it is, therefore, only a spring crop, or sometimes also a summer crop if irrigated. Because of its lack of resistance to wind and rain it is not much grown anywhere in the Apennines and, in fact, its cultivation is limited almost entirely to the plains. It would seem, however, from Columella that the *phaseolus* was an autumn-sown crop, and so it might have been more resistant than the french bean (2. 10. 4; 11. 2. 72). Indeed, from his account, it is the pea which seems the more delicate of the two plants, whereas now the roles are reversed. The pea is more resistant to cold, wind and rain but does especially well in places which receive the sun, as Pliny correctly observes (18. 123). Columella refers to it also as an autumn-sown crop; in modern times it is sown in autumn or spring in the south and in spring or summer in the (colder) north. Pliny, it is to be noted, limits it to spring throughout Italy (18. 123).

It may be doubted whether either the pea or the *phaseolus* was widely grown. References to their cultivation are scarce. Archaeology has revealed no evidence for the latter in Italy, although the former is occasionally represented.[23] If the *phaseolus* was like its American relative, more fastidious than Columella implies, that could be one explanation for its limited diffusion. The pea may have been more widely cultivated, given its slightly greater climatic resistance and its correctly-recognized soil-enriching qualities (Col. 2. 13. 1). These days its leaves, stalks and pods are useful animal fodder.[24] That there is no mention of its use as such by the Roman sources, which appear to include every possible type of forage, might confirm the suspicion that it was not widely grown.

That peas were a field crop is clear from their inclusion in book 2 of Columella (as argued in the case of the broad bean). As such it would have belonged to the dwarf variety, which is self-supporting. In gardens today a climbing variety is cultivated which, trained on trellises or canes, produces more peas to a given unit

[23] Bronze Age sites in the north: Forni, 'Origini delle strutture agrarie'; Bronze Age site in central Tuscany, an example of field pea: Oliva, 'I frumenti a Belverde'; pea (garden?, field?) from San Giovanni, Roman (Empire) villa near Potenza: Small, 'The Environment of San Giovanni'. Also at the villa of Settefinestre: Jones, 'I resti vegetali'.

[24] Tassinari, *Manuale*, 541. For a list of all animal fodder referred to by the Roman authors: White, *Roman Farming*, 213 ff.

of land than the field variety. That such a system was practised in the Roman period is made very plain by Pliny: 'peas climb if they have a prop' (18. 57). It seems clear, then, that the pea was also cultivated in gardens, as might have been expected. The doorkeeper in the *Satyricon* shelling peas into a silver dish (which incidentally demonstrates consumption by the rich) had probably taken them from the garden (28. 8). However, it is rather strange that only dried peas appear in what remains of the Edict of Diocletian (1. 13, 14). From the several recipes left by Apicius it can be concluded that peas were eaten by the upper classes, although whether they were fresh or dried cannot be known, since in either case they were boiled before eating (5. 3 (197–9, 202)).

The *phaseolus*, on the other hand, was clearly eaten fresh according to the Edict (6. 39), and Columella refers to it as a garden crop (10. 377; 12. 9. 1). Apicius has less use for it than the pea, but references to it in fresh, and perhaps also dry, form are recorded (5. 8 (212)). It appears with peas in the list of dried foods in Diocletian's Edict (1. 13, 14, 21). Neither is remarked on as popular food. Their specialist market might have been slightly widened by sale to pigeon-breeders (V. 3. 7. 8).

## LUPINS

These appear from the literary sources to have been in considerably greater circulation than peas or *phaseoli*. The archaeological evidence is as yet scanty. There has been only one find of lupins, as far as I know, and that somewhat doubtful.[25]

In the absence of any secure archaeological evidence to date, it seems overbold to suggest that cultivation of the lupin was widespread in Roman Italy. Pliny places it high on his list of legumes because it produced food for both man and beast (18. 133). Its excellent qualities as green manure ploughed or dug under in arable land or vineyard were recognized by all agricultural writers.[26] Columella, who treats lupins first in his section on legumes, before even the bean, observes that 'it requires the least labour, costs least, and of all sown crops is most beneficial to the land' (2. 10. 1). As such it would have been a crop available to both large and small farmers.

There are no climatic or agricultural impediments to the cultivation of lupins in Italy. A robust plant, it can thrive in most soils, even those with a gravelly or acidic composition. It resists heat and drought. Its only limiting factor is susceptibility to cold in the first part of its vegetational cycle. Thus it has to be planted early in the autumn in high regions or in northern Italy. This is emphasized by Columella (2. 10. 2). It does not need manuring, requires almost no cultivation, suffocates weeds and, once reaped and threshed, the seed can be adequately stored in a smoky place such as a kitchen.[27]

[25] At Castiglioncello near Livorno a 'Roman' tomb (no date) contained a small ceramic receptacle with an egg and some lupin seeds. This appears to be evidence for the use of lupins in funeral meals (see below), *Notizie degli Scavi* 1952, 29.

[26] Cato 37. 2; V. 1. 23. 3; Col. 11.2.60; P. 17.54–6. One reason why it was used as such in vineyards was because manure was felt to taint the flavour of the wine. Columella's uncle thought so, and the point is emphasized by the fourteenth-century Bolognese agronomist De Crescenzi (Col. 2. 15. 3; De Crescenzi 3. 14).

[27] Cf. especially Col. 2. 10. 1–3; P. 18. 133-5.

Therefore, there is no need to reject the possibility of ubiquitous culture of the lupin. The uses to which it was put perhaps divided along economic lines. The large farmer used it for green manure and fodder; on the small farm it was grown mainly as human food.

In the first case—the large farm—it could be pastured green as fodder before seeding (it also formed part of the mixed green feed called *farrago*, V. 1. 31. 5), or it could be cut and dried, or the seeds fed. That lupin *seeds* are referred to in Columella's recommended diet for oxen (6. 3. 4) is obvious from the fact that they are soaked (see below). Lupin stalks and leaves are not the most nutritious of cattle feeds, but since the plant produces a large quantity of such material, it can be used to satisfy hunger; otherwise it could be spread as stable litter (Cato 37. 2). Lupin seeds, however, are high quality feed.[28]

It is only in Columella and Pliny that the lupin is referred to also as human food. It was especially useful in times of scarcity (Col. 2. 11._1). It would have been the small farmer with few or no animals, and therefore with little or no manure, who grew lupins, not as animal forage, but for himself as a precautionary measure against a year of bad harvests. The robust lupin would survive when the bean could not. It would also have had the benefit of helping to correct the fertilizer deficiency. Columella refers to the lupin as fertilizer where the farmer is destitute of manure (2. 15. 5). Almost certainly the small farmer is envisaged. A caricature of the poor peasant describes him as reaping lupins and eating them, or another legume, in place of bread, and grinding cheap barley (Calp. Sic. 3. 82–5). Oil could also be made from lupin seeds, and it is clear from the literary sources that several substitutes for olive oil were used, especially for cooking, and no doubt also for lamps. In Italy today, for ordinary cooking *olio di semi* is used, olive oil for condiment. It is a question of availability and price, perhaps also of taste.[29]

It is probable that lupins were a consistent item of diet also for the poorer urban classes. The relevant passages of Martial and Horace have already been mentioned. With a *dipondium* (2 asses) one might buy sufficient lupins and chickpeas for a meal for two persons (Petronius, *Sat.* 14).[30] The antiquity of their cultivation is indicated by their use in funeral meals (ibid. 66) and offerings to the dead (cf. Calp. Sic. 3. 82 and perhaps also Tibullus 1. 5. 53–4). This might explain the earlier-mentioned tomb find from Livorno, although examination of botanical remains from tombs of Iron Age Rome did not reveal any lupins.[31]

Before consumption by either animal or man, lupins have to be soaked or, preferably, boiled in water, in order to expel the bitter and, in some varieties, mildly poisonous substance contained in the seed. This means that to avoid harm cattle have to be kept out of the crop grown for seed, although perhaps instinctively they would shun it. The need to soak lupins explains the presence of the lupin

[28] Of all legumes they have the highest raw protein content.

[29] It is important to remember that cultivation of the olive is limited by climate (and therefore also altitude). At sites such as the Matrice villa or the San Giovanni villa, the olive grows only with difficulty. Substitutes, and other oil-producing plants: lupin (P. 15. 30); plane tree berries (P. 15. 29); cornel berries (Col. 12: 10. 3); radishes; and, of course, lard. For the last two, see Davies, 'Roman Military Diet', 124 f.

[30] Cf. Duncan-Jones, *Economy of the Roman Empire*, 245.

[31] Helbaek, 'Funeral Meals'.

vat (*labrum*) in Cato's equipment lists for both vineyard and oliveyard (10; 11. 3). Varro is explicit (1. 13. 3; cf. Col. 11. 2. 10). Such a use has been suggested for one or both the so-called *lacus* (circular pits measuring about one metre across and half a metre deep), excavated outside the small Roman farm on the edge of the Luceria centuriation grid on the Tavoliere.[32] This interpretation is a possible but neglected one for the many odd pits or single large earthenware receptacles, resembling *dolia*, found outside excavated buildings.

The boiling process accounts for Martial's *tepens* (5. 78. 21; cf. Col. 10. 115). These days in the towns, lupin seeds seen floating in buckets of lightly salted water are sold in small quantities to passers-by. At this stage they have already been boiled and can be eaten immediately. That they might have been sold in some similar way in the Roman period is suggested by their inclusion in Diocletian's Price Edict as dry or cooked. When cooked they were sold in much smaller quantities than when sold dry (1. 19, 20). The lupins bought in the street market described in the *Satyricon*—a particularly instructive scene, where everything and anything is sold, and both urban and rural dwellers are present—were probably already boiled and ready to eat (Petronius 12–14).

Street vendors of lupins were perhaps not in the same commercial category as the *duumvir* of Pompeii who was a *lupinarius* (*CIL* 4. 3423, 3483).[33] Such a man would perhaps have grown lupins on his own country estate and have purchased them from other estates to supply the urban market. It is another reminder of the profits to be made from the products of an arable farm.

## LENTILS AND CHICKPEAS

These were the other major field-grown legumes of importance to the Roman diet. Their cultivation was well known to, and accurately described by, the Roman agronomists. Lentils occur at the Roman villas of Settefinestre and San Giovanni. One example of the chickpea is recorded at Pompeii and one from the Iron Age settlement at Monte Irsi,[34] while, as mentioned above, a substantial quantity has been found in a shop in Herculaneum.

The lentil is a very nutritious legume and is adapted to many different soils and climates. In modern Italy much of it comes from Puglia and Sicily, where it is sown as an autumn and winter crop. Where winters are colder—it is cultivated in many places in the Apennines, where it has a smaller seed and is more flavoursome than the lowland lentil—it is sown in spring and summer.[35] Such variation in sowing times is permitted by its short growth cycle of three to four months. Columella speaks of two sowing times (2. 10. 15), in autumn and spring, and Varro refers to a summer sowing (1. 32. 2), but one should keep in mind that its short growth cycle would permit cultivation at almost any time of the year in favourable regions. Thus it could for example be included among those

[32] G. B. D. Jones, personal communication.
[33] Cf. also *CIL* 4. 2657, lupins stored/transported in an amphora.
[34] Settefinestre: Jones, 'I resti vegetali'; San Giovanni: Small, 'The Environment of San Giovanni'; a find of 'carbonized lentils' from 'the pre-Roman period' at Egnazia in Puglia: *Notizie degli Scavi* 1965,

296 ff. Chickpeas: Hjelmqvist, 'Economic Plants'. Both chickpeas and lentils appear in the third-century levels at Metapontum: Carter, Costantini et al., 'Population and Agriculture', fig. 16. 4.
[35] The smaller variety is perhaps to be identified as Columella's *lenticula* (2. 7. 1; 2. 11. 10; 8. 8. 6).

unspecified three-month crops to be sown if time and space permitted (Col. 2. 12. 9). The remarks made about the possibilities arising from the short growth period of millet will be generally relevant here.

The lentil occurs in modern rotations with cereals, where it precedes the grain crop, but does not return to the same ground for four years.[36] This, and the fact that, although it is eaten throughout the whole of Italy, it is not eaten as often as cereals and beans, means that it can be seen growing in most areas, but usually only in small quantities. Such was probably the situation also in the Roman period. Its ease of cultivation and its adaptability favoured widespread diffusion and would not have excluded the small farmer. Near cities, as has been argued, a certain cultivation for sale should be imagined on the larger arable estates. On such an estate, to achieve the best yields, dried manure might be mixed with the sown seeds (Col. 2. 10. 15). It is to be noted that Columella envisages both small- and large-scale production: 'It should be stored in the granary if the amount is rather large, or in olive-jars and salt-fish jars if there is not much' (2. 10. 16).

The chickpea prefers a warm climate and is more fastidious than the lentil as regards soil. It might not then be surprising that evidence of the *cicercula* (chickling vetch), a more robust plant, treated by Columella along with *cicer* (2. 10. 19–20), has been found in excavation of Iron Age Rome, whereas the chickpea has been identified only in the south at the Iron Age site of Monte Irsi and, possibly, also at Pompeii.[37] Nevertheless, the chickpea can be grown throughout Italy as long as it is sown in spring, at least in colder regions. Its actual area of cultivation, however, was possibly more limited than that of the lentil, especially since it was considered harmful to land, as it is in many parts of Italy today.[38]

Records indicate that lentils and chickpeas were shipped in sizeable quantities from Alexandria.[39] Pliny, Martial and Virgil all mention lentils from Alexandria, and this is much more easily explained now that it is clear that they were imported. In such a context it can perhaps be assumed that the ballast of lentils in the ship which brought Augustus' Egyptian obelisk to Rome found a market (P. 16. 202). Lanciani reports the discovery of several bushels of lentils in the *Horrea Galbana* at Rome.[40] Amphorae which carried chickpeas and lentils occur at Pompeii.[41] Such a trade in these legumes, crops that do especially well in warm, dry climates, might well have been connected with the importation of Alexandrian grain, as seems clear from the records found near Pompeii.

As can be argued in the case of grain, importation does not exclude local cultivation. Rome depended on supplies of grain and legumes from Italy; they were as necessary to the capital's smooth functioning as supplies from anywhere else. The evidence of the importation of lentils and chickpeas demonstrates only the demand, mainly at Rome, for supplies beyond the means of local production.

[36] Tassinari, *Manuale*, 543.

[37] Iron Age Rome: Helbaek, 'Funeral Meals'. Monte Irsi and Pompeii: Hjelmqvist, 'Economic Plants'.

[38] Foliage of the chickpea provides reasonable forage and is used as such today in Italy. That there is no mention of this in the Roman sources perhaps strengthens the idea that it was not grown in large quantities. The *cicera* mentioned by Columella among forage crops (2. 10. 24) I assume to be a variety of Lathyrus (*Lathyrus cicera* L.). For forage crops see the following chapter.

[39] Wax tablets found near Pompeii which record business deals: Casson, 'Rome's Grain Trade', 33.

[40] R. Lanciani, *Ancient Rome* (1888), 250.

[41] Callender, *Roman Amphorae*, 37–40. For trade in legumes in a later period: Braudel, *The Mediterranean and the Mediterranean World* I, 423, 571.

# CHAPTER VII: ANIMALS AND ARABLE

As has been consistently argued, the Roman agricultural writers do not describe just one type of agricultural system. To state this does not mean only that they discuss vineyards as well as oliveyards and cereal cultivation, but that in a discussion of each such topic, they recognize different systems of cultivation. Thereby the complexity of the Roman rural economy and agriculture is revealed. This observation is extremely important and provides a fundamental key to the understanding of the agricultural writers.

This chapter begins by demonstrating the hitherto unrealized diversity of rotation patterns in Roman Italy and then continues to examine how these were influenced by the need to integrate livestock with arable cultivation. In my view this 'integration' increased over the period as the demand for cereals and legumes intensified. The question of transhumance is then referred to with the object of indicating that large-scale seasonal movement of flocks was not as common as is usually thought. The all-important result of keeping animals—manure—is discussed at the end of the chapter.

## ROTATION

### Diversity

As was observed earlier, orthodoxy will have it that the Roman system of agriculture was characterized by a two-field, biennial rotation of autumn crop, fallow, autumn crop, fallow. The Greeks and Etruscans in Italy are credited with the great advance from the more primitive systems of slash-and-burn and long-fallow. Nevertheless, it was only with the Roman conquest of Italy, and of Nature herself as Goethe remarked, that the biennial system was established everywhere. The next step, that of the three-field rotation, had to wait for several centuries. The tenth century was the magic one according to Lynn White. Duby, however, was not so sure: 'It is safest to conjecture that there was considerable variation in the crop rotation in use'.[1]

This more hesitant point of view is surely right. It is also correct for the Roman period. It should not, however, be accepted only as a result of prudence. It is what ought to be expected from the outset. In Roman Italy there was a diversity of contemporary agricultural systems, ranging from the Ligurian tribes to the superbly managed estates of Tremellius Scrofa. Yet we should not expect diversity only from region to region; it appeared within the same region, from farm to farm and even, particularly with regard to patterns of rotation, within the same farm.

This recognition outmodes the debate as to whether the Romans fallowed their land in alternate years or whether they practised a rotation system akin to the triennial.[2] Such a debate remains trapped within the orthodox classifications; the

[1] Duby, *Rural Economy and Country Life*, 24. L. White: cf. p. 103 n. 2 above. Establishment of the biennial system: Sereni, *Storia del paesaggio*, 44 f.

[2] Brunt, Review of *Roman Farming*, 156 f. collects most of the source material on rotation and is more cautious than White, whose full thoughts on the subject appear in 'Fallowing, Crop Rotation, and Crop Yields in Roman Times', *Agricultural History* 44 (1970), 281–90. C. Parain, 'The Evolution of Agricultural Technique', 135 argues from geographical

real picture is more complex, more fluid. It will be demonstrated here that there
existed not only annual fallowing *and* suppression of the fallow, but *also* long-
fallowing, normally considered to be a primitive technique.

A good starting place to consider the different Roman systems of rotation is
Pliny (18. 187, 191). Six types can be identified.

(1) Emmer wheat one year, soil-enriching legumes the next.

(2) In *tenera* soils like Campania, barley, millet and turnips one year,
followed by wheat (*triticum*) or barley.

(3) Emmer followed by fallowing over winter and then a spring sowing of
beans.

(4) Extremely rich soil can bear two successive grain (*frumentum*) crops and
then one legume crop in the third year.[3]

(5) In a thin soil, one year of grain (*frumentum*) is followed by two years of
fallow.[4]

(6) Grain (*frumentum*) should be sown only in land that has lain fallow in
the previous year.

From Varro two additions can be made. *Vervactum* is defined as land which
*sometimes* (*interdum*) lies fallow between crops (1. 44. 2). There is thus a seventh
type: intermittent fallow.[5] The other situation is the bringing under cultivation of
new land ('in rudi terra', ibid.).

Example (1), as the context shows, applied especially to the small cultivator
with little land. Example (2) seems to have been limited to Campania and other
areas with particularly fertile and easily-worked soil and favourable climatic
conditions. Yet here I want to concentrate more specifically on the larger estate
which, throughout the country, produced cereals for the market.

Columella was one of those who maintained that wheat should be sown only
in land which had borne no crop in the preceding year (2. 10. 7). Elsewhere it
appears that emmer and *siligo* should be sown only in land which was alternately
fallowed (2. 9. 4). Barley could, however, be followed by another crop if the soil
was manured (2. 9. 15; cf. Cato 35). It may be then that *triticum*, in the strict sense
of hard wheat (*triticum durum*), could also be followed by another crop.

Nevertheless, although Columella stated his *preference* for the system of
fallowing cereal land, other rotation systems are clearly described in his text. For
example, he characterized the large farms of his period as *amplissima veterata*
(1. 3. 10). This perhaps refers to large farms on which considerable tracts were 'let
go' on a long fallow. However, although this is quite conceivable, the context has
a moralistic tone, and we should beware exaggeration. In another passage it is
asserted that a well-manured field of turnips or navews is an excellent preparation

---

and climatic determinism that suppression of
fallowing was only 'a happy exception' because of the
lack of fertile soils, the need to practice dry farming
and the failure of spring-sown crops in peninsular
Italy. These objections have been treated above.

[3] This is not a certain interpretation. *Tertio* is taken
to imply that wheat was grown for two consecutive
years. One other occasion in which *tertio* is used by
itself in Pliny refers to a spring sowing (18. 49–50).
But it would seem scarcely credible that the wheat

crop could be mature enough to be harvested by the
spring to allow a spring legume-sowing.

[4] 'Two years of fallow' ('in annum tertium cesset').

[5] Latin terms for fallow are confusing in that they
each appear to have more than one meaning. This will
in turn suggest multiplicity of system. *Novalis* means
either (1) new land or (2) fallow land; *vervactum*, (1)
worked fallow land, (2) intermittently fallowed land;
*veteratum*, (perhaps) old fallow land. Various
occurrences are discussed below.

for good yields of grain (2. 10. 24: *segetes*; 2. 17. 4: *frumentum*). Columella also notes that some used beans, as he recommended lupins, as preparatory crops (2. 10. 7; 2. 10. 1; 2. 15. 5). Elsewhere in the text reference is made to 'three-month crops' (2. 12. 6), and Columella's comments on spring-sown cereals have already been discussed on pp. 43 f.

There are, besides, several references to *restibilis* land. There is no ambiguity about this term: it means land which is sown each year, although perhaps not usually with the same crop (cf. V. 3. 16. 33; *LL* 5. 39). The list of crops which can be sown on *restibilis* land comprises broad beans, peas, *phaseoli*, vetch, bitter vetch, fenugreek, *farrago* and oats.[6] One thing is immediately obvious: forage crops are in the majority. This is especially true if it is accepted, as argued earlier, that peas and *phaseoli* were less commonly grown than other legumes.

## Fodder Crops to Suppress the Fallow

Legumes for human consumption, particularly broad beans, no doubt suppressed the fallow where and when demand for them was great enough; yet here discussion centres on fodder crops which were increasingly used in order to feed cattle and enrich the soil, both with the result of greater arable production. Again, of course, only that arable estate which produced for the market is being considered.

That vetch was commonly grown can be argued briefly along the usual lines. Agriculturally it is suited to all soils except wet ones; climatically it is very robust. It produces good quantities of valuable forage with very little outlay of capital or energy. It is sown after one ploughing only, although it can even be sown on untilled ground and then ploughed in (Col. 2. 10. 29; P. 18. 137, 181). It has two or three main sowing times, autumn and late winter/early spring, which adapt it to a variety of climatic or rotational regimes. It enriched the soil but did not itself require manure. It could be grazed green, cut and used as dry forage, be ploughed under as green manure, or its seeds fed to poultry and young calves; its chaff too was prized. Vetch was also an associated component of *farrago* and meadow pasture, and could be grown with lupins.[7]

Wide adaptability, ease of cultivation and many uses, if they do not attest, at least strongly indicate widespread cultivation. That it was the most common forage crop is suggested by the archaeological record from the Middle Neolithic to the Roman period under discussion. In earlier eras it and a similar species, *Lathyrus*, occur where they would appear to be the only forage crops, in contexts of mixed cereal and legume cultivation.[8]

---

[6] For the correct interpretation of V. 3. 16. 33, Brunt, Review of *Roman Farming*, 156. Listed crops: *farrago* and oats are treated together (Col. 2. 10. 31–2). Vetch et al.—all fodder crops (Col. 2. 10. 24)—are understood as crops sown on *restibilis* land from the clear indications of Col. 2. 12. 3–4.

[7] Mainly common vetch (*Vicia sativa* L.) but also bitter vetch (*Vicia ervilia* L.; *ervum*). Hjelmqvist, 'Economic Plants', 276 f. states that bitter vetch was human food, certainly in the prehistoric period, possibly in the Roman period. Both vetches appear in the Edict of Diocletian, among human foods, although

the agricultural writers treat them only as forage. It is probably best to conclude that on the small farm vetch served as both food and fodder, but on the intensive arable farm at least, crops for human and animal consumption were segregated. Occasionally vetch is heard of as famine food: Philostr., *Vita Apoll.* 1. 15 (Aspendus) and cf. p. 70 n. 15.

[8] Forni, 'Origini delle strutture agrarie'; Oliva, 'I frumenti a Belverde', 347 mentions a find of vetch at Casa Carletti (near Pienza); Helbaek, 'Agricoltura preistorica a Luni', bitter vetch and *Lathyrus cicera* L. (the *cicera*—a forage crop—cf. Col. 2. 10. 23). Bitter

Literary evidence, which is expected to be increasingly borne out by archaeology, suggests that a greater variety of fodder crops was cultivated in the Roman period, a development visible even from Cato to Columella, as White has argued.[9] It is probable, however, that vetch (and related species) remained predominant, although even the 'miraculous' crops like lucerne may have seen a slow but steady diffusion; it turned up, for example, in the latest period (mid-fifth to mid-sixth centuries A.D.) of a villa in the highlands of Basilicata.[10] Yet attestation of its presence in the early third century at Metapontum warns against over-simplified notions of diffusion over time from the literary sources. We must await further archaeological evidence.

For the present, however, it is argued here that forage crops were increasingly used to suppress the fallow. The archaeological evidence, of course, is unable to show whether vetch or any other forage crop was used in a rotation system without fallow. Nevertheless, it will fit the model of the intensive arable farm which produced cereals and legumes for sale, where it should be imagined that the relationship between arable farming and animal raising was fully realized and put into practice (cf. *Dig.* 33. 7. 8 *pr.* and further below). Adequate forage was absolutely crucial on such an estate (cf. Col. 6 *pr.* 2). For example, as Columella states, if there is sufficient fodder a cow can reproduce once a year, if not, only once every second year (6. 24. 4). The more forage, the better the conditions of the work animals; and the greater the number of animals, the larger the quantity of manure for the crops which need it, especially cereals and beans.

However, it is not likely, even on the most intensively managed arable estates, that *no* land was fallowed. Fallowing, suppression of the fallow and long-fallowing were all practised on such a farm. The ideal estate, according to Columella, should have many animals fed both from the cultivated *and* uncultivated land (1. 2. 5).

*Long-Fallow*

Certain land might be fallowed for a considerable length of time and used as pasture. The relationship of cultivated to uncultivated land would always be a changing one. It can be imagined that from year to year parts of the uncultivated land would be brought under cultivation, or other parts let go. Obviously, the most fertile arable land would always be under cultivation. The amount of less fertile land utilized would depend, among other things, on market potential and size of the estate. If the urban demand for staple foods rose, then more arable land would be brought under cultivation and correspondingly less land allowed

vetch and *Lathyrus* sp. at Metapontum (early third century B.C.): Carter, Costantini et al., 'Population and Agriculture', fig. 16. 4.

[9] White, *Roman Farming*, 212.
[10] For ready comparison between Cato's and Columella's oxen rations, ibid., 219 f. Even Columella's rations, it will be objected, still demonstrate reliance on fodder such as grape-pressings: White, 282. Variety, however, must be carefully distinguished from scarcity. A mare or ox can be filled with hay, but variety is necessary and the more the better (cf.

V. 2. 1. 17). It is clear from the agronomists that leaves and grape-mash were delectable (V. 1. 15; Col. 6. 3. 5). As always, various possibilities are considered by the agronomists, which shows that some estates cultivated more forage crops than others (Col. 6. 3. 2–8). 'In some districts chaff is the only resource' (Col. 6. 3. 3). The villa excavation in Basilicata (Small, 'The Environment of San Giovanni') has so far produced beans, peas, lentils, vetch, oats (cultivated) and lucerne. For this as a reflection of animal husbandry, see p. 10. Lloyd, *Interim Report*, 8 notes the find of 'several pulses, including vetch'.

for pasturage.[11] It would be in such a situation that forage crops would be grown and the fallow suppressed.

In more mountainous and remote areas (which, in terms of distance, need not be very far from even the most intensively cultivated regions, given the geography of Italy), it can be assumed that more primitive rotation systems such as slash-and-burn (Italian *debbio*) continued to exist in the Roman period. (They still occur sporadically today.[12]) The small trees and undergrowth were cut down and burned, and in the area thus cleared and fertilized with the ash, cereals were cultivated for several consecutive years. The area was then abandoned to a long-fallow of perhaps ten or twenty years, while other parts of the forest were utilized.

Such a system requires access to an extensive area of forest land but can be put into effect with little labour and good results as regards crop yields. The fertility of wooded land brought under cultivation was common knowledge in the Roman period (Col. 2. 1. 3; P. 17. 39). Yet it was not only those who subsisted in the mountains and areas remote from Roman influence who used this method of rotation; large and intensive farms might also have had areas under woodland (useful for the supply of timber/firewood near towns, as well as for pasture), which were brought under cultivation by a similar method. This seems clear from Columella (2. 1. 3–6; 2. 2. 11). Yet on such a farm the original (climax) woodland would disappear completely, for it was there that the large trees would be cut down and uprooted (Col. 2. 2. 11). These would have been in forests in fertile plains, valleys, or hills on the estate, rather than in rugged mountain country (for other remarks on deforestation, see p. 8 n. 22).

Lupins, according to Columella, can be sown on 'unploughed fallow' (*crudis novalibus*) in September before the autumn equinox, or at the beginning of October (2. 10. 2). It is difficult to make sense of *crudis* here unless a long-fallow is understood.[13] One of the Plinian rotation systems was a two-year fallow, and it is possible that a similar case is being described by Columella. It could equally refer to fallow ground older than two years. Whatever the situation, it is clear that the lupins were sown on land which was unworked, and overgrown with grass, shrubs, briers and ferns. One of the advantages of the lupin was that it could succeed if scattered on land in such a condition (P. 18. 134). The return to cultivation of long-fallow is further described by Pliny (18. 45–7).

*Novalis* land still retained its original meaning in this context. Forest land freshly cleared for arable cultivation was called *novalis* (P. 17. 39–40). Such land would either be virginal forest land or for all intents and purposes new, if it had been let go under a very long fallow and little used for pasture. As the practice of shortening the fallow became more common, the technical terms for fallow land became seemingly more confused. In Pliny's time, *novalis* could also apply to land fallowed for only one year, whereas *vervactum* might mean land fallowed only over the winter (18. 176; for *novalis* in this later sense cf. V. 1. 29. 1).

---

11 Cf. the similar general observations of B. H. Slicher Van Bath, *The Agrarian History of Western Europe AD 500-1850* (1963), 61 f.

12 E. Sereni, *Comunità rurali nell'Italia antica* (1955), 194 ff.; id., *Terra nuova e buoi rossi* (1981), 3–100, for Calabria and elsewhere in Italy. However, recently very strict legislation has been introduced in order to conserve forest land.

13 'Difficult' because, if the land was only fallowed for one year, it would already have been ploughed at least once (depending on soil consistency) by the beginning of October (pp. 25–7).

However, it should again be emphasized that short-fallowing, suppression of the fallow and long-fallowing could exist on the same farm. The various coexistent systems would account for what appears at first glance to be confusion of the technical terms.

The reasons for long-fallowing were various. Columella merely subsumes them under two heads: deliberate and accidental (2. 1. 3). The one considered here is the fluctuating relationship between grazing land and arable cultivation. Cattle graze in 'cultivated land and scrub' (*culta et dumeta*, Col. 1. 2. 5). Land which can be described as *dumeta* is surely that which had at one stage been exploited for arable cultivation but is now under long-fallow. At a later stage it would again be brought under cultivation. The shifting balance (if it can be plotted) of pasture, wood and arable land is one of the keys to the understanding of Italian agriculture, rural settlement, demographic fluctuation and economy in all periods. It should certainly not be seen simply as a progressive reduction of forest since the prehistoric period. The number of Roman sites now under thick wood provides a rapid corrective to such a simplistic, yet often asserted, model.

## Pasture

There are two words for pasture land in Latin and they must be carefully distinguished. *Pascuum* can be translated 'rough grazing'; *pratum*, 'meadow'. The latter is an area of the estate carefully selected and tended; the former would comprise an area under long-fallow. The care of long-fallow utilized as *pascuum* was relatively simple and included aspects of the *debbio* system. In Columella's words:

> The care of *pascuum* is easy; in order that the grass may grow more abundantly, it is usually burnt in the last part of summer. This makes the fodder more tender when it grows again, since the hard briers are burnt, and it keeps down the bushes which would grow to a great height. (6. 23. 2; cf. Sil. Ital. 7. 365)

It is important to realize that a part of the home farm is here described and not an area of *ager desertus* grazed by transhumant flocks. The large arable farm would have any or all three of the following forage facilities: cultivated fodder crops, meadow land, rough grazing.

There were two types of *pratum*: dry and irrigated. Both provided green-grazing or cut-forage in the form of hay. Grazing took place between autumn and spring (Cato 149. 1; V. 1. 37. 5). Meadows of both sorts were closed to animals and cut at the beginning of June (P. 18. 258), and at least one more time after that (Cato 5. 8). If the meadows were irrigated they could be cut three times; in certain special cases even dry meadows might yield up to four cuttings (P. 18. 263). Irrigated pastures were limited to areas where the spring and summer rainfall was adequate (P. 18. 258). Other possibilities for irrigation were supplied by rivers, streams and aqueducts (*Dig.* 39. 3. 3. 2). It is clear that dry meadows were considered second best (Cato 8. 1), since their yield was not as great. However, they were not limited climatically and could be put down (*summittere*) even in dry and thin soil (Col. 11. 2. 7). Thus, while it is true that most parts of Italy do not possess the ideal conditions for irrigated meadows, the mistake of assuming that dry meadows were not widespread in the period under consideration should be avoided.

Wherever oxen were kept for ploughing, *prata* were essential (cf. Cato 30; 54; Col. 6. 3. 4–8; 11. 2. 99). Hay was also the normal food for equines (horses, mules, asses: V. 2. 7. 7; Apul., *Metam.* 3. 29), although Columella asserts that chaff is sufficient for an ass (Col. 7. 1. 1). Hay was also fed to sheep (Col. 7. 3. 21); and it was those sheep with especially prized wool which should graze 'in meadows and flat fallow land' ('pratis planisque novalibus'; Col. 7. 2. 3). Pigs should, however, not be allowed into meadows, since they root up the grass (Col. 2. 17. 1).

Conical haystacks are typical of small farms in Italy where working animals are still kept (Pl. IV, 2); Columella's description of the technique and reasons for making them suggests close similarity with the modern type (2. 18. 2–3). On larger farms, however, there would be space to store the hay under cover, which is the best method of keeping it. That Columella and Varro recognized both methods of storage indicates that *prata* were fundamental to the economy of not only the well-equipped arable estate (Col. ibid.; V. 1. 49; 3. 2. 6). As already argued, ploughs and ploughing animals were not restricted to the estate capable of supporting oxen (p. 39).

Meadows could be laid down both for the farm's own needs, and to make a profit from renting out pasture rights (Cato 149), or from selling the hay and then renting out the pasture (V. 1. 21). In the former case the estate's own animals were limited in number and were allowed pasture according to the terms of the contract (Cato 149. 2). The profit to be gained is emphasized by Cato:

> If you have a water supply, pay particular attention to water meadows; if not, have all the dry meadows possible. This is the sort of farm which it is profitable to make anywhere. (9)

There is little doubt that Cato was referring to this system, and not to transhumance as has hitherto been thought, when he is reported as stating that pasturing was the most lucrative branch of agriculture.[14] In a late Republican discussion of Cato's list of profitable crops, it could be stated that some considered meadows should come first, and that the meadows of the Reate basin were famous (V. 1. 7. 10 on Cato 1. 7). Columella notes that many people prefer to own *prata*, *pascua* or woodland rather than vines, and provides an estimate of their return (3. 3. 1–3). It appears, then, that while disagreement existed, the profitability of leasing pasture had been argued from at least the mid-second century B.C. to the mid-first century A.D. This needs to be emphasized and distinguished from the profits gained from large-scale, long-distance transhumance, a phenomenon which has been too overrated for the Roman period by modern scholars (see further p. 125 below).

As an essential and perhaps directly profitable part of the farm, the meadows were carefully tended. Their maintenance must be added to the labour calculations made for the arable farm, and will help to confirm the thesis that slave labour was not incompatible with intensive arable cultivation (cf. pp. 136–40).

---

[14] Col. 6 *pr.* 4–5; Cic., *Off.* 2. 89; P. 18. 29–30; cf. Plut., *Cato* 21. 5.

It has already been mentioned that the meadows should be closed to cattle at certain times of the year. This presupposed fencing or at least careful shepherding. Especially on the larger estates where a considerable number of animals might require pasture, it was necessary to judge carefully the correct ratio of animals to unit of land. Too many or too few would cause loss of profit (V. 2. 1. 24). Stones had to be cleared to expedite the later reaping (Col. 2. 17. 2). Weeding too was essential to avoid deterioration of the pasture (Col. 2. 17. 1). Cattle do not eat weeds and thus they tend to spread unhampered, eventually assuming predominance over the more favoured grasses.

It is clear, however, that meadows were not always maintained in perfect condition. They could deteriorate through neglect or old age, but could be renewed by being ploughed up and by the installation of a rotation (Col. 2. 17. 3–7; P. 18. 259). Turnips or beans (Pliny also includes millet) were sown in the first year as improver crops, followed in the next year by a cereal which, as Columella notes, will yield well after the improver crops, and in the third year the land is fallowed and well worked in order to provide a suitable seed bed for the sowing of a mixed pasture (vetch or clover and grass). This, then, is another type of rotation, clearly a special case, but, given the importance and diffusion of meadows, perhaps not uncommon. The assiduous attention necessary for the newly-restored meadow emphasizes its value: weeds have to be rigorously guarded against, drainage ditches have to be maintained, and the admission of animals will depend on the type of soil—again it is observed that meadows were put down on both heavy and light soils—on whether the meadows are irrigated or dry, or whether manured or not (Col. ibid.).

Mowing was labour intensive. Before sowing occurred the terrain had been cleared from stones and smoothed out with an osier drag. Even the lynchets left by the drag at the borders of the field had to be removed (Col. 2. 17. 4). It is certain, therefore, that the grass was scythed close to the ground. One *iugerum* could be scythed by one man in one day. The grass was then allowed to dry where it had been cut and was occasionally turned over with forks. When dry, it was gathered into sheaves and taken to the farmstead. Any loose hay was raked up, and then the meadow had to be gone over again with *sickles* in order to tidy it, thereby ensuring an even growth of the next crop. The same process would be repeated each time the field was mown (Col. 2. 18; V. 1. 49).

The first cutting was carried out before the cereal harvest. Pliny recommends 1 June (18. 258). The optimum moment is when maximum growth is combined with high nutritive value. Cato stresses that hay should be cut at the correct time— before the seed ripens (53). Cut too late, it was no better as forage than straw, according to Columella. Yet it should not be cut too green, otherwise there will be a danger of rotting or combustion during storage (Col. 2. 18. 1). Since the recommended pasture was a mixture of legumes and grass, the best time would be when the legumes were in flower.

As has been noted above more than once, apparently many (*multi*, Col. 2. 11. 6) farmers grew hay among beans. This could have been the practice of the small farmer, who needed fodder but had insufficient land for a *pratum*. It might equally have been the practice of a farm which had some *prata*, but not enough. What seems certain is that it cannot be understood as an indication of extensive (i.e. not labour-intensive) farming on a large estate. On such an estate it would have been far easier to let go parts of the land under long-fallow, or to put down roughly-tended meadows. Columella, it will be remembered, rejected the idea of such intercultivation as mistaken ingenuity, not because it was careless or labour-saving. For him there was no doubt or difficulty: hay should be grown only in *prata* (2. 11. 7).

## Grass from Short-Fallow

Besides meadows or long-fallow, it appears that the grass which grew on land fallowed for only one year was also carefully utilized as fodder. It has been seen that sheep could be turned into the stubble to feed on gleanings and the grass which grew up immediately after the harvest (V. 1. 53; 2. 2. 12). Such grass would be ploughed up in spring at the first ploughing (V. 1. 27. 2; Col. 2. 4. 1). However, Columella asserts that the best of all foods for sheep is that grass which springs up between the first and second ploughing (7. 3. 20). It might be that he was referring to those sheep with the most profitable wool, which were best grazed 'pratis planisque novalibus' (7. 2. 3). Young lambs, when they first venture from the fold, should be admitted to 'pratis aut novalibus' ('meadows or fallow', 7. 3. 19). In the context, *novalis* probably means land fallowed for one year only. This observation reinforces the argument that on some estates the advantages to be gained from a close connection between arable cultivation and livestock management were both recognized and realized. The land destined to lie fallow for one year was grazed and manured by sheep over the winter, and then again in spring after the first breaking up of the soil. In this way, it was possible to overcome what was only an apparent impasse between shepherd and arable farmer (Col. 6 *pr.* 1; cf. V. 1. 2. 21; 2 *pr.* 5; *Dig.* 33. 7. 8 *pr.*). The manuring of the land and then reduction of it to a fine weed-free bed for the new seeds were the main reasons for the fallow system, which is to be carefully distinguished, as has already been argued, from the aims and needs of dry farming (pp. 23–7).

## TRANSHUMANCE

For the Roman period, transhumance is interpreted as the large-scale, long-distance movement of animals from summer to winter pastures.[15] What is neglected is what is likely to have been the much more common practice of short-distance transhumance; and what is almost completely ignored is the keeping of livestock (other than work animals) on the farm all the year round.[16]

Close contact and tight control are expected between estate and flock owners according to Cato's system. The meadows are to be closed in the spring (when pear trees bloom in late April/early May), obviously to allow growth of hay before the first cutting.[17] Yet it appears that the animals remain until the beginning of

[15] Toynbee, *Hannibal's Legacy* II, 286–95.

[16] M. Pasquinucci, 'La transumanza nell'Italia romana' in E. Gabba and M. Pasquinucci, *Strutture agrarie e allevamento transumante nell'Italia romana (III-I sec. a.C.)* (1979), only once mentions short-distance transhumance (p. 88), and only in Campania does she allow for the possibility of livestock on the farm all year round (p. 146).

[17] Cato 149. 1; cf. V. 1. 37. 5.

June (150. 1), which will mean that they are fed from the cut product, either fresh or stored from the previous year, which is sold to their owner. Contact is then maintained for the following months to allow for division of profits. There can be no doubt that the situation was very similar to that mentioned by Varro:

> If there are meadows on the farm but no sheep [note that Cato kept only working oxen and a 'gelding', 149. 2], the best practice is, after selling the forage, to feed and fold someone else's flock on the farm. (V. 1. 21)

For the months June, July and August (the pastures are open again from September, Cato 149. 1), either very local transhumance to nearby hills or river courses can be assumed, or the livestock concern was on a small enough scale to be completely integrated within the resources of the estate for the whole year. It is thus to be noted that local transhumance signifies a loss of manure to the farm for only three months of the year.

## MANURE[18]

This was the important result of closely combined arable and animal husbandry. Farmyard manure includes not only the dung of farm animals but also their litter, usually straw. 'Straw spread as litter produces a very large quantity of manure' (Col. 6. 3. 1); litter had the essential effect of absorbing the valuable urine which would otherwise be lost. As such it contained nitrogen, potassium and a portion of all the other elements essential for plant growth, which had been present in the original food of the animal and in the straw itself. The other important function of manure which, it should be emphasized, is not shared by chemical fertilizers, is the restoration of humus to the soil. This improves the earth's fertility and texture, rendering heavy, clayey soils more friable and aerated, and giving cohesion and water-retaining power to thinner, sandy soils.

The agronomists had no doubt that manure was efficacious and necessary for the highest yields. Cato places it next to ploughing in importance (61), and Varro makes Agrasius ask: 'How can animals be kept off the land, since they supply manure which enhances its value very greatly?' (1. 2. 21). For Pliny and everyone else it was common knowledge (18. 192). According to Columella, it was the answer to so-called soil exhaustion (2. 1. 7; 2. 13. 3–4). The excellent properties of manure might, of course, have been well known, but Columella implies in his observations on the soil-exhaustion argument what researchers during the *battaglia del grano* discovered: many farmers, particularly small ones, had nothing like sufficient quantities of manure for the best yields.[19]

In fact, the agricultural writers were well aware that not all farmers had sufficient animals to manure their land adequately. After his remark that knowledge of the efficacy of manure was universal, Pliny proceeds to say that if

---

[18] Modern Italian data on manure used in this chapter are from Tassinari, *Manuale*, 141 ff.; Quattrocchi, *Agraria* I, 181 ff.; F. Malacarne, *Il letame e i concimi organici* (1968). Shortage of manure in the historical period is stressed by White, *Roman Farm-* ing, 136 f.; Brunt, Review of *Roman Farming*, 157 f.; Parain, 'The Evolution of Agricultural Technique', 136.

[19] Cf. Manetti, 'Pane e frumento', 319; R. Forlani, *Il frumento sui monti* (1929), 7.

cereals do have to be cultivated without manure, then wheat rather than barley should be sown. Recourse to other fertilizing agents was recommended, such as general compost and farmyard filth including human excrement (Cato 37. 2; Col. 2. 14. 6, 8). This would be the case particularly on the small farm.

Ploughing-under of lupins and beans was also advised. This practice, known as green manuring, besides returning to the soil the nitrogen and other nutrients absorbed by the growing plants, had, like farmyard manure, the important effect of restoring humus and texture; again, as all the agronomists well knew.[20] The fact that such subsidiary methods are still recommended in the modern Italian manuals testifies to the continuing problem of the collection of sufficient amounts of manure.

The ideal situation is to have enough animals on the estate. 'He who has meadowland has animals, he who has animals has manure, he who has manure has bread', as the old Italian proverb puts it. It seems a jingle; more often it was a dirge. Although Columella and the other agricultural writers encouraged those unfortunate farmers who had to cultivate 'land empty of livestock' ('ubi viduus pecudibus ager'), the type of estate on which cereal culture was going to be profitable was 'where herds of four-footed animals were kept' ('ubi greges quadrupedum versantur', Col. 2. 14. 7). Yet it would be a mistake to imagine that only two types of farm existed: that on which there were animals in abundance and that without. Columella was looking at two extremes. Most small farmers would have owned some animals. As today, it would have been more of a question of deciding how to use the limited amount of manure available. Its application may have been in the *hortus* rather than on the grain land.[21]

## Application of Manure

On the larger farms which combined arable culture and animal husbandry, between twenty-four and eighteen loads of manure were recommended for one *iugerum* of grain land. Each 'load' comprised eighty *modii* (Col. 11. 2. 8). The season to apply the manure was sometime before sowing: September for autumn-sown wheat and during the winter for spring wheat (Col. 2. 15. 1; P. 18. 193). Cattle manure should be distributed in piles, although bird manure should be scattered (V. 1. 38. 1). The heavy or light dressings depend on whether the land comprises hill or plain, dry and warm, or wet and cold soils (Col. 2. 15. 2–3). Hills require more manure because the rain washes down a certain proportion of it to the less heavily manured plains.[22] Wet and cold land receive a heavy dressing in accordance with the principle that manure heats the soil. Modern Italian farmers speak in terms of the *caloria* which manure restores to the land (cf. p. 5).

The piles of manure should always be of five *modii*. If the manuring is heavy the piles are placed closer together, for a light application they should be eight feet apart. The manure should be spread (perhaps with a harrow, *crates stercorariae*; see p. 55 n. 49), and then ploughed under as soon as possible, in order to prevent

[20] Cato 37. 2; V. 1. 23. 3; Col. 2. 15. 5; P. 17. 54.

[21] Col. 10. 81–5 seems to describe the small garden cultivator who uses human manure (perhaps from the urban centre) together with the manure of his ass.

[22] Col. 2. 17. 7; cf. *Dig.* 39. 3. 2. 6, where it is noted

that manure washed along with water could obstruct the even flow of the water and thus cause waterlogging of a neighbour's land. While this suggests the danger of manuring sloping ground it also demonstrates the practice.

drying out by the sun and a concomitant loss in strength. Therefore, ideally, the amount spread at any one time should not be more than can be ploughed under in one day (Col. 2. 5. 2). Given the weight (one load weighed 630 kg) and the quantities involved, transport and spreading would have been a protracted and heavy task which must be considered in any calculation of labour times on the arable estate (pp. 137–9).

It appears from Columella's account that only 'lean' (*exilis*) soil was manured (2. 5. 1). This does not necessarily indicate scarcity. Good land, if manured, could well have the undesirable effect of causing cereals to lodge as a result of excessive and imbalanced fertility, as has been discussed on p. 48. This appears to have been well understood.[23] Even if there is a surplus of manure, it is not spread unselectively. It was better to concentrate manure resources mainly on poorer soils, to achieve yields there which approached the level of those reached naturally on rich land. Of course, rich soil would have to be manured every so often, the more so if it were *restibilis* (cf. Col. 2. 10. 6), but in general regular manuring would apply to poor land; and even that need not be manured every year, since most manure, even when well-rotted, releases its energy slowly over one, two or even three years. This might help to explain the first part of Varro's comment: 'We must observe what parts of the land are to be manured, how the manure is to be applied, and the best kind; for there are several varieties' (1. 38. 1). Again, this is not an indication of scarcity as has been thought.[24] Varro is probably referring here to those less fertile soils or those constantly used, which required manuring in any given year. And then there are diverse kinds of manure which vary in their quality and suitability for various crops.

The main sorts of manure that a farm of Varro's type would produce were fowl, human and cattle (V. 1. 38; 1. 13. 4 (slave privies); cf. Cato 36; Col. 2. 14. 1). If a variety of crops with different needs was grown, then separate storage of the diverse manures was necessary. Columella, however, states that on the specialized cereal farm all manures could be kept together (2. 14. 7). This would have done something to cut down on labour costs, although the amounts of manure required for such a farm would have been far greater than for others. Nevertheless, it was always best to keep goat and fowl dung separate in case there was the need for an emergency manuring in the spring before hoeing (Col. 2. 15. 2; cf. V. 1. 38. 1). One of the features of such dung is the speed and energy of its effect, since plants are able to absorb its nitrogen rapidly. The impressive pigeon houses of the great cereal *masserie* of Puglia used to serve the same purpose.[25]

*Quantities*

Columella states that each of the larger animals, including humans, should produce ten loads of manure every thirty days, and the smaller animals one load in the same period (2. 14. 8). This could only have been a rough guide, as the amount of manure will vary considerably with the weight of the animal, its diet and the climate. Moreover, the classification of large and small is imprecise: an ox

[23] *Dig.* 43. 24. 7. 6 notes that should someone distribute a heap of manure on already rich (*pinguis*) land, legal action under *vi aut clam* is possible, since harm has been done to the soil.

[24] Brunt, Review of *Roman Farming*, 157.
[25] Source: S. Zezza and G. Bacile, estate owners in Puglia.

produces much more manure than an ass, yet an ass could be considered a large animal (V. 2. 1. 11). It is clear from Columella and Pliny (who also cites the amounts, although the number of days is not given) that stall-fed animals are meant, in the sense that they are housed and fed at night all year round on the home farm. If the quantities are not achieved, it would be because the animals had been littered badly (P. 18. 194).

Olck considered that Columella's figures of ten loads and one load were far too high for a period of only thirty days. He proposed a simple emendation of the text from thirty to three hundred days, which effectively reduced the estimated amount from each animal to one tenth of Columella's figures. Brunt used the emendation to show that Cato, who kept one hundred sheep on his olive farm, would have been able to dress only sixteen to twenty *iugera*.[26]

To place the argument on securer agricultural, rather than philological grounds, recourse can be made to modern comparisons.

Data used in the following calculations:
   1 load = 80 *modii*; 1 *modius* = 9 litres
   1 cubic metre = 1,000 litres
   1 cubic metre of fresh manure mixed with straw = 400 kg
   1 cubic metre of rotted manure = 850–900 kg
   1 hectare = 4 *iugera*

A. *Manure dressing*

   Italian   40–60 cubic metres per hectare
   Roman   18–24 loads per *iugerum*

Calculation to convert Roman figure into cubic metres per hectare:

$$18 \text{ loads} = \frac{18 \times 80 \times 9 \times 4}{1000} = 51.8 \text{ cubic metres per hectare}$$

$$24 \text{ loads} = \frac{24 \times 80 \times 9 \times 4}{1000} = 69.1 \text{ cubic metres per hectare}$$

It is observed that the Roman quantities are higher than the modern Italian ones but nevertheless similar. White, using contemporary English figures, stated that the ancient amounts were exceeded by 25 per cent (*Roman Farming*, 131). This again emphasizes the need to use *Italian* comparative evidence.

B. *Weight of a load of rotted manure*

1 litre of rotted manure weighs 0.85–0.90 kg. Taking an average of 0.875 kg, one load will weigh:

$$80 \times 9 \times 0.875 = 630 \text{ kg}$$

It is to be noted that, since the weight of rotted manure is *c*.2.2 times that of fresh manure mixed with litter, the number of *modii* of fresh manure required to produce a load of decomposed manure ready for spreading would be 176.

---

[26] Brunt, Review of *Roman Farming*, 157. Olck, in P–W 5. 1761, 'Doch ist das Quantum für 30 Tage viel zu gross, vielmehr erfordert der Sinn *trecenis*' (sc. instead of MSS *tricenis*).

K

C. *Manure obtained from animals*

Italian   Bovine: 36 kg of dry and liquid manure without litter
          Ovine: 3 kg
          (The bovine is a working animal. A stall-fattened animal produces
          twice as much because it is kept all day inside)
Roman     Large animal: 10 loads of manure mixed with litter every 30 days
          (Col. 2. 14. 8)
          Small animal: 1 load

It is to be observed that whereas there is a ratio of 10:1 between large and small animals in the Roman figures, there is a ratio of 12:1 in the modern. (However, the large/small classification can only be approximate; horses excrete less than oxen, pigs more than sheep.)

Roman     Large animals produce $\dfrac{10 \times 80}{30}$ *modii* of manure mixed with litter per day

$$= \frac{10 \times 80 \times 9}{30} \text{litres} = \frac{10 \times 80 \times 9 \times 0.4}{30} \text{kg} = 96 \text{ kg}$$

Italian   Bovine produces 36 kg of manure per day. Combined with agri-
          culturally advised 4 kg of litter $= 40$ kg

The Roman output is 2.4 times that of the modern for a 'large animal' and 2.7 times that of the modern for a 'small animal'. Thus it appears that Columella's estimate is some 2.5 times more than, and Olck's emendation 4 times less than, the modern equivalent. Given that ancient amounts for manure distribution and the ratio of manure production between ox and sheep, as well as ancient agricultural quantities in general (e.g. for sowing amounts, pp. 56–7), are similar to, although somewhat more generous than, modern figures, it is better to accept the higher estimate in this case and retain the manuscript reading.

It is more likely that Columella, when setting an estimated ideal amount for the 'industrious farmer' (*agricola diligens*; cf. 2. 14. 8), erred more on the side of overvaluation than parsimony. Moreover, with the great emphasis placed on abundant and freshly-supplied littering it is probable that ancient manure heaps contained much more material of that sort. Being bulky (besides straw, leaves, ferns and general undergrowth/brushwood were employed),[27] the litter would fill out the *modius* (a volume measurement) more than has been accounted for in the calculations. This could therefore lessen the apparent differences between the modern and ancient figures.

It is important to note from these calculations that a *modius* of fresh manure is very different from a *modius* of rotted manure. As manure rots, it condenses. In order to produce a given volume of well-decomposed manure, more than twice the same volume of fresh manure is required. This observation seriously affects Brunt's calculations which, based already on the unlikely reading of Olck, would be reduced still further. It would mean that Cato, although he had 13 persons, 100 sheep, 6 oxen, 4 asses and an unspecified number of swine, was able to manure only 7–9 *iugera*, less than 4 per cent of the estate. If manure were really that scarce even with so much livestock, we might expect more comment in the sources.

[27] Cf. Cato 37. 2; V. 2. 2. 8; Col. 7. 3. 8.

If Columella's estimates for manure are allowed to stand, and, for the sake of calculation, to his model arable estate of 200 *iugera* (2. 12. 7) are added a *vilicus* and companion, a shepherd and 100 sheep, and 4 asses (all of which remained the whole year on the estate), the manure-producing units (including humans) would be 18 large and 100 small, and the annual output 3,360 *modii*. This would decompose to 1,527 *modii* ready to be spread, sufficient for a light dressing of 85 *iugera* or a heavy dressing of 64 *iugera*, that is, 35 to 42.5 per cent of the estate area.

Thus even on the well-managed arable estate which produced for the market, there was no superabundance of manure. Some allowance might be made for general compost, pig, goat and fowl dung, but even so not more than half of the land could be dressed in any one year. This cannot of course be taken simplistically to fit a biennial rotation pattern where half the land was manured and fallowed, the other half under cultivation in any one year. Instead, the poorer as well as the continually-cropped land might be regularly manured, while good land was dressed every so often. Meadows also would be selectively manured, especially the less fertile and more elevated ones (Col. 2. 17. 7). Thus control of wastage, good storage (see below) and selectivity were practised, to combine the necessity of limited amounts with the virtue of agricultural rationality. This will adequately explain the concern of the agricultural writers about careful use of the available manure on the intensive arable estates they promote and describe.

Of course, animals which grazed in meadows, fallow land, or in recently reaped fields, were a direct source of manure (V. 2. 2. 12). This was the most immediate form of the animal–arable symbiosis and must be considered in addition to the collection and distribution of stable manure. It would thus sensibly increase the calculation of total manure output. Indeed, Pliny refers to one system of careful supervision of this direct method, which is still observed in some areas today and called *stabbiatura*. Pliny speaks of 'fencing in' sheep in the fields (18. 194) and, as so often, knowledge of traditional, modern practice serves to clarify. It is a carefully managed operation of penning the flock in one part of the field after another. The pasture is thus utilized rationally and the manure concentrated.

## Storage

Given the importance of manure, it was necessary to conserve it properly. 'Keep the manure carefully' (Cato 5. 8). Varro advised storage in the farm building complex (1. 13. 4). This would have made collection from yard and stable convenient; presumably some consideration was made for the prevailing winds. The storage place was called a *stercilinum*. Either two *stercilina* should be used, or one divided in two; the first for fresh, the second for rotted manure ready for the field (ibid.). Cato mentions the *stercilinum*, but provides no detail (5. 8). The Loeb translator renders the Varronian term 'pit', but the reference is clearly to heaped manure, since the *sides and top* should be covered to prevent solar desiccation.[28] On the other hand, Columella recommends trenches or pits: 'trench' (*fossa*, 2. 14. 6); 'sunken area' (2. 14. 7); 'with a gentle slope like a

---

[28] Hooper, *Marcus Porcius Cato . . ., Marcus Terentius Varro on Agriculture*, 213.

fishpond' (1. 6. 21). The Columellan system can be seen as an advance in technique compared with Varro's heap, indicative perhaps of the increasing importance of arable cultivation, although both writers reveal careful attention to, and understanding of, the problems of manure conservation.[29]

Careful storage while decomposition takes place allows an augmented fertilizing force (and rapidity of effect) with minimal wastage. It should be ready for spreading within six months. It is still efficacious when a year old if carefully stored, but if kept longer its strength decreases (Col. 2. 14. 9). One important reason for not spreading manure until properly rotten is because when fresh, the grass seeds contained in it are still viable and so would compound the problem that fallowing and careful weeding tries to eliminate. Yet precisely because fresh manure produced grass it could be usefully spread on pasture land: a task for February (Col., ibid.).

---

[29] Two sunken and plastered troughs at the villa of Settefinestre have been ingeniously interpreted as *stercilina*, but are rather too small for such a function. They might rather have served as *labra* for lupins (p. 115 above). E. Regoli, 'La concimaia' in *Sette-finestre. Una villa schiavistica nell'Etruria romana*, ed. A. Carandini (1985) III, 147–9.

# CHAPTER VIII: LABOUR AND THE MARKET

What is argued here is that slaves were not unsuited to cereal and legume cultivation and could, on the contrary, be kept profitably occupied all year round on an estate where cereals and legumes were the main crops. This argument is then followed by some brief comments on the supposed existence and increasing spread during the first century A.D. of extensive as opposed to intensive methods of arable cultivation. It will then be convenient to conclude with some observations on market possibilities. Treatment will of necessity be schematic, since full discussion of what is a highly complex subject is beyond the primarily agricultural scope of this book.

## SLAVE-STAFFED ARABLE ESTATES

The most recent comment on the subject is negative. 'Profit of course lay in labour-intensive crops such as vines rather than in simpler crops like cereals, against which Columella warned his fellow slave-owners'.[1] The reader is then referred to the article 'still worth consulting' by Yeo on the economics of agricultural slavery. In conclusion to his discussion Yeo had remarked:

> . . . oil, wine, sugar, and rice are ideal plantation crops. Grain, on the other hand, having a relatively short growing season and not conveniently cultivated by use of the gang system, can best be made by independent farmers or by tenants. This theory is in practice borne out by the absence of slavery in wheat-raising countries such as Ptolemaic Egypt, by its decline concomitant with increased wheat production in Roman Africa and in the states of Virginia and Missouri, and by the evidence of grain production in only five villas near Pompeii. It may reasonably be inferred that, when the plantation system was operating in high gear, Campania was unable to grow sufficient cereals for her coastal cities, which, like Rome, seem to have imported supplies from abroad . . .
> Nevertheless Roman slaves showed considerable skill and industriousness when employed in making crops proper to a slave economy. It was in raising grain when they showed themselves inefficient, wasteful, and hard to supervise.[2]

To take the last point first, *pace* Yeo, Columella (1. 7. 6–7) warns against the employment of slaves on *distant* cereal estates, not against the employment of slaves in cereal cultivation in general.

> On far distant estates, however, which it is not easy for the owner to visit, it is better for every kind of land to be under free farmers than under slave overseers, but this is particularly true of grain land. To such land a tenant farmer can do no great harm, as he can to plantations of vines and trees, while slaves do it tremendous damage. (Col. 1. 7. 6)

[1] R. P. Duncan-Jones, Review of Kolendo, *L'agri-coltura nell'Italia romana*, *CR* n.s. 32 (1982), 72–3.

[2] C. A Yeo, 'The Economics of Roman and American Slavery', *Finanz Archiv* 13 (1952), 483–4.

The following observations can be made:

(1) This passage does not demonstrate the superiority of free over slave labourers. Columella clearly states that both caused damage on estates not regularly visited by the owner. Tenants did less harm to a cereal estate because they were compelled to work the land to survive and feed their families. Slaves, on the other hand, as part of the 'equipment' of the farm (like oxen), were fed whether they worked or not. They could be sold off if unproductive (cf. Cato 2. 7), but while they remained they did not have to work to survive. This is a fundamental distinction between slave and free labour.[3] In addition it might be that the tenant's rent, whether in kind or cash, was set high enough to encourage production of a surplus and to minimize wastage. Since the subject is a specialized cereal estate, I surmise that the proprietor was concerned to derive profit from local markets.

(2) The passage warns against distant estates, not slaves employed in arable cultivation. All estates, of whatever agricultural emphasis or labour system, do better when regularly supervised by the owner. This applied to slave-staffed arable estates as well.

As for the 'proof' of the theory that slaves were unsuited to cereal cultivation, Yeo's contention that cereals were little cultivated at Pompeii is inaccurate; and the non-employment of slaves in Egypt or Roman Africa was due to the already existing and adequate system of controlled native free labour.[4]

Of course, no one would argue that slaves should not be kept permanently busy for reasons both of economy and security, least of all the Roman agricultural writers. Idle slaves literally eat up profits (Cato 39. 2; cf. Col. 1. 8. 10–11; 11. 1. 26–7; and p. 3 n. 4). Yet Saserna had estimated that thirteen days would be lost out of every forty-five days for reasons of sickness, bad weather or inefficiency due to lack of motivation (V. 1. 18. 2), and Columella allowed forty-five days out of 220 for holidays and rainy weather (2. 12. 9).[5]

Lack of motivation and sickness raise the question of the profitability of slavery as a whole, and cannot be limited to cereal cultivation. Bad weather is beyond control, as anyone who has worked on a farm will understand; under such conditions, ploughing especially would be difficult if not entirely unproductive (cf. Col. 2. 4. 5). As regards labourers, stoppages because of cold and rain could be lessened by the provision of heavy clothing (Col. 11. 1. 21).

Yeo states (p. 468): 'Being all-year crops, olives and vines were admirably adapted to the slave labour regime. They required like sugar, unremitting labour.' This is untrue, at least for olives. Columella was moved to praise the olive as 'first among trees' precisely because it required little cultivation (5. 8. 1). A survey of labour rates near Potenza in Basilicata in the 1920s shows that olives required 74

---

[3] B. Hindess and P. Hirst, *Pre-Capitalist Modes of Production* (1975), 130 ff.

[4] M. I. Finley, *The Ancient Economy* (1973), 70. C. R. Whittaker, 'Rural Labour in Three Roman Provinces' in *Non-Slave Labour in the Greco-Roman World*, ed. P. Garnsey (1980), 77 f.

[5] Duncan-Jones, *Economy of the Roman Empire*, 327–33 gives the best discussion of the labour calculations in the agricultural writers. He suggests that all the information in Col. 2. 12 derived from Saserna, including the estimate for lost days. But note that the ratio of lost time to work is greater in the Varronian citation of Saserna than in the Columellan, 1:3.5 rather than 1:5. It could be, then, that the latter was Columella's own estimate, perhaps based on the less severe climate of Latium compared with Cisalpine Gaul (where Saserna owned land, V. 1. 18. 6).

hours annually per hectare, grain 367, vines 825.[6] Thus it cannot be maintained that monoculture of olives was compatible with slave labour.

Columella implies that viticulture is much more labour-intensive (5. 8. 1–2). Thus Cato's manning ratios (counting only labourers and ploughmen, V. 1. 18. 4) for an oliveyard are one man to thirty *iugera*, compared to the vineyard's one to nine (Cato 10, 11). Columella describes the year's work for the upkeep of olives: (apart from the initial outlay when establishing an oliveyard, 5. 9. 1, 9) it comprises two annual ploughings, two diggings around each tree, trenching around each tree once a year, the removal of suckers on the lower trunk, a manuring every three years, pruning 'every several years', and harvest (for which he provides no details, cf. 12. 52. 2) once every two years (5. 9. 11–15). One man could dig around 80 small, 65 middling or 50 big trees a day (Col. 11. 2. 40); the trenching would take no longer (by analogy with vines, *de arb.* 5. 5). Thus in a year without harvest one *iugerum* might require not much more than three days from the labourer and the same from the ploughmen.[7]

Slaves could not therefore be kept continually busy practising monoculture of olives. One alternative would be to work on another estate when not required in the oliveyard (cf. *Dig.* 33. 7. 12. 8). On Cato's oliveyard there can be little doubt that most of the year's labour was taken up in cereal and legume cultivation. This was probably the usual situation in an oliveyard, where normally half of the land would be under cereals in any one year (Col. 5. 9. 12); only where the soil was too poor (a rare exception) would cereals not be cultivated and the olives as a result planted closer together (Col. 5. 9. 7).

Vines were clearly more labour-intensive, and what manning ratios there are seem roughly to correspond; to Cato's one man to nine *iugera* can be added 1:7 (Col. 3. 3. 8), 1:10 (P. 17. 215), and (just possibly for vines) 1:8 (V. 1. 18. 2—from Saserna).

Apart from estimates of labour for the immense task of establishing a vineyard (for which hired labour would surely be required at least for the *pastinatio*: Col. 11. 2. 17; *de arb.* 1. 5–6; 4. 2 (*pastinatio*); 11. 2. 28; *de arb.* 4. 3 (planting)), one passage provides labour ratios for the operations carried out during the year (Col., *de arb.* 5. 3–5).

*Established Vineyard: Days per* iugerum[8]

| | | | |
|---|---|---|---|
| Loosening of soil | 5 | Digging | 5 |
| Clod-breaking | 3 | Winter pruning | 4 |
| Tying | 6 | Spring pruning[9] | ½ |

Total: 23½ days

---

[6] G. Salinardi, unpublished thesis on the agriculture of Basilicata in the 1920s, submitted to the Faculty of Agronomy at the University of Naples. Salinardi has published a history of his local region, *L'antica terra di Ruoti in Lucania* (1973).

[7] According to the following reasoning: with a 60 foot spacing between trees in a quincunx formation there could be no more than 50 trees to the *iugerum*.

Thus two diggings and one trenching will not take more than three days. From ploughing-ratios (2. 12. 8) the first ploughing takes two days, the second one day.

[8] Not an *arbustum*: *de arb.* 5. 5; vines planted 5 feet apart: *de arb.* 4. 4; thus 1,225 vines: 5. 3. 7.

[9] This takes a boy one day (Col. 11. 2. 44); thus ½ a man-day is estimated: Duncan-Jones, *Economy of the Roman Empire*, 331.

However, this table is clearly defective. The vintage is missing, so are manuring and the time-consuming task of making and setting up stakes. I estimate 7 days for the vintage, ½ day for manuring and up to 4½ days for staking.[10] These further estimates would raise the total to a maximum of some 35½ days of work per *iugerum*.

This would mean a full year's occupation for a vineyard worker on the Plinian manning ratio of 1:10. Cato's 1:9 would also achieve this, especially if a sickness/bad weather allowance is made (p. 134 n. 5). The same can be said for Saserna's rate if his sickness estimate is included. Columella's ratio of 1:7, even with inclusion of his sickness allowance, falls short of a full year, the total arrived at being 321 days.

Yet the calculations made here can only be approximate, since there are several variables admitted by the agricultural writers. For example, depending on the spacing of vines, there can be between 1891 and 325 plants per *iugerum* (Col. 5. 3. 6–9). Or again, stakes might be purchased rather than fabricated on the estate (V. 1. 16. 3). On Cato's vineyard the *salictarius* probably did much of the work of staking or tying, which would lessen the work for the *operarii*. Nevertheless, it seems fair to conclude that monoculture of vines could keep slaves continually busy.[11]

For arable cultivation the agricultural writers provide a variety of labour calculations, some perhaps tralatician, although always with an eye to the agricultural reality, and, in the case of Varro, scepticism of their overall validity.[12] Columella (perhaps deriving material from Saserna) presents calculations based on a model 200-*iugera* estate.[13] Discussion begins with that, and then extra labour ratios are added with the help of comparative evidence.[14]

---

[10] Manuring was apparently carried out once every three years (*de arb.* 5. 4). It was a little more labour-intensive than spreading manure on grain land, which probably took one day per *iugerum* (below), thus I estimate ½ day every three years. For the vintage and staking I refer partially to comparative evidence: Dalmasso, 'Agricoltura Astigiana', 194 f. Columella implies that stakes last five years (4. 17.·2, but this applies strictly to a 'yoke' support; Varro refers to the rotting of stakes, *pali*, 1. 8. 4). One man could make 100 *pali* in a day (Col. 11. 2. 12). If every five years 1,225 stakes had to be made, the yearly average would be 245, thus 2½ days' work. Two further days can be allowed for setting them up in the vineyard.

[11] On the variables as well as the conclusion reached here, Duncan-Jones, *Economy of the Roman Empire*, 331 f. For manning ratios applied to the interpretation of the excavated villa of Settefinestre, D. W. Rathbone, 'The Development of Agriculture in the Ager Cosanus', *JRS* 71 (1981), 12–15. An anthropological study of a specialized vineyard, which provided work all year round, is cited by J. Davis, *The People of the Mediterranean* (1977), 43.

[12] Duncan-Jones, *Economy of the Roman Empire*, 327–33; Varro's scepticism, 1. 18.

[13] Col. 2. 12. 1, 8. The estimate is for *triticum*. Estimates for other grains and legumes are considered below. I use the term 'model estate' in the sense that, since the only staff are two ploughmen and six field labourers, it is not a specimen, fully-contained estate (like Cato's, 10–11) with managerial staff, shepherds, etc. but a working unit which can be multiplied (or divided) to suit one's actual estate. The man to *iugerum* ratio is 1:25.

[14] Labour parallels provided by White, *Roman Farming*, 183, id., 'The Productivity of Labour in Roman Agriculture', *Antiquity* 39 (1965), 102–7, and W. Kaltenstadler, *Arbeitsorganisation und Führungssystem bei den römischen Agrarschriftstellern (Cato, Varro, Columella)*, Quellen u. Forsch. zur Agrargeschichte 30 (1978), 51 are of limited value, since they refer to countries other than Italy. From Italy certain anthropological studies provide statistics to show how little labour is required for wheat. Around Metaponto 1 hectare requires 20 man days (5 days per *iugerum*, 166 days for each of 6 workers on a 200-*iugera* estate). But certain operations are mechanized and all studies concern the poorest areas where farmers have other jobs and spend as little time as possible in the fields. Such material might be useful for comparison with the Roman peasant, but not for the slave-run, intensive arable estate. Davis, *People of the Mediterranean*, 42 f.

*Columella/Saserna: Days per* iugerum

| | |
|---|---|
| Ploughing no. 1 | 2 |
| 2 | 1 |
| 3 | ¾ |
| 4 (at sowing) | ¼ |
| Clod-breaking | 1 |
| Hoeing | 3 |
| Weeding | 1 |
| Reaping | 1½ |
| | 10½ |

The staff of the 200-*iugera* arable unit comprises two ploughmen and their teams, and six field labourers. For a more thorough consideration of the labour estimates, the ploughmen and labourers must be treated separately.

Among all the varied manning ratios supplied by the agronomists for agricultural labour, it is only regarding ploughmen that there is an attempt to reconcile daily work ratios with work on a yearly basis.[15] Columella is at pains to show that the ploughmen will be fully employed all year (2. 12. 7–9).

### Ploughman's Annual Employment

| | |
|---|---|
| Ploughing for main crops | 175 days |
| Ploughing for 3-month crops, haulage, etc. | 115 |
| Bad weather and holidays | 45 |
| Rest after sowing | 30 |
| | 365 days |

After ploughing for the main cereal and legume crops, there will remain some 15 *iugera* (75 *modii*) of three-month crops to be sown, haulage of hay (which indicates the existence of meadows), of forage and manure, and the performance of other 'useful tasks' (perhaps transport of produce to market) (Col. 2. 12. 7–9). The oxen are permitted thirty days' rest after the main sowing period (2. 12. 9), but this need not apply to the ploughmen who, if nothing else, would tend their animals at pasture or gather fodder (cf. Col. 6. 3. 2; and the collection of leaves, P. 18. 314). Presumably too, ploughmen would be responsible for the provision of litter and the cleaning of stalls (cf. Col. 1. 6. 6). But Columella does not explain the staff of six labourers. Could they be kept busy all year?

The 200-*iugera* arable unit of Columella (2. 12. 7–9) I assume to have been divided thus:

50 *iugera* under cereals;

50 *iugera* under legumes;

30 *iugera* under three-month crops (cereals and legumes);

30 *iugera* of dry meadows;

40 *iugera* under fallow.

In this division only the amount of dry meadow is speculative, but seems

---

[15] Duncan-Jones, *Economy of the Roman Empire*, 329.

reasonable given fodder requirements.[16] The manning ratios supplied by Columella 2. 12 and set out above, clearly lack many of the tasks he had earlier referred
to in discussion of arable cultivation. In the following tables these tasks are listed
and estimates of their labour times are based on comparative evidence.[17]

### *Labour Ratios per* iugerum *for Cereal land*

| | |
|---|---|
| Manure (transport and spreading)[18] | 1 day |
| Sowing | ¼ |
| Clod-breaking | 1 |
| Ditch digging/maintenance | 1 |
| Weeding | 1 |
| Hoeing | 3 |
| Reaping[19] | 2 |
| Gleaning[20] | ½ |
| Transport to threshing floor | ½ |
| Threshing and winnowing[21] | 2 |
| Straw (collection from field)[22] | 1 |
| Storage of grain and seed collection | 1 |
| | 14¼ |

The 50 *iugera* of cereal land therefore require some 712 days' labour.

### *Days per* iugerum *for Legumes*

1 *iugerum* of legume land according to the same table would require some 10
days' labour (beans: clod-breaking 1½, hoeing 3½, reaping 1 (Col. 2. 12. 2) and
an estimated 4 for other activities). Thus 50 *iugera* of legumes require 500 days'
labour.[23]

### *Days per* iugerum *for Three-month Crops*

I estimate again 10 days per *iugerum*, since there would be a mixture of
cereals and legumes, some of which would require more, others less, than 10 days.
Thus 30 *iugera* would require 300 days' labour.

---

[16] 1 hectare of the best meadow land can support 1–2 oxen or 5–6 sheep. 30 *iugera* of best meadow land would support 4–8 oxen, or 4 oxen and some 20 sheep. See G. Tibiletti, 'Il possesso dell'*Ager Publicus* e le norme *de Modo Agrorum* sino ai Gracchi', *Athenaeum* n.s. 27 (1949), 9–11.

[17] Comparative evidence: Salinardi, unpublished thesis; Dalmasso, 'Agricoltura Astigiana', 197 f.

[18] Strictly speaking only 100 *iugera* of land might be manured (p. 131). I have allowed a labour time for manure on an extra 60 *iugera* (cereal, legume, meadow and 3-month crops), but this does not significantly affect the argument.

[19] Columella estimated 1½ days for reaping (above); Varro 1 day (1. 50. 3). These estimates are considerably less than those for modern manual reaping. Even allowing for variations in harvesting methods or in terrain, it is difficult to understand how the ancient rate was physically possible. I propose 2 days per *iugerum*. (Salinardi and Dalmasso estimate 10 days per hectare.)

[20] According to Varro (1. 53) this could be collected by the estate's own workforce if labour costs were high. There is no indication that gleaning was a form of charity and performed by women, as was the case in early modern Italy (cf. Testini, *Il frumento*, 45; Rasmussen, 'Harvest in Calabria', 97).

[21] This estimate is made from the comparative evidence. Cf. Duncan-Jones's guess, *Economy of the Roman Empire*, 329.

[22] Col. 11. 2. 54 and pp. 69–71.

[23] A variant for the 200-*iugera* model is 60 *iugera* of grain, 40 of legumes (Col. 11. 2. 46–7). This would make little difference to the estimates offered here.

*Days per* iugerum *for Meadow Land*

| | |
|---|---|
| Manure | 1 |
| Weeding | 1 |
| Cutting (twice) | 2 |
| Haymaking (twice)[24] | 5 |
| Tidying (twice) | 1 |
| | 10 |

30 *iugera* of meadow therefore require 300 days' labour.

*Total Calculation of Days' Labour*

| | |
|---|---|
| Cereals | 700 (approx.) |
| Legumes | 500 |
| Three-month crops | 300 |
| Meadow | 300 |
| | 1800 |

Therefore each of the 6 labourers was employed for 300 days.

To this can perhaps be added 45 days lost through holidays and bad weather, as well as odd jobs which would have included maintenance of farm buildings and fixtures, and fabrication of farm implements; all of which will then account for a full year's employment.[25]

Nevertheless, there is another factor to be taken into account. It is clear from Varro, if not from Columella,[26] that free labourers could be hired at the hay and cereal harvests (V. 1. 17. 2–3). Thus some of the labour days estimated above were consumed by free labourers. Even though it was theoretically possible to harvest with slaves alone, fear of loss through bad weather necessitated speed of work and thus the hiring of extra hands for reaping; threshing could be performed *ad libitum* afterwards, as long as there were facilities for storing the reaped grain. Yet the estate's slaves obviously took part as well in reaping; the frenetic nature of the work does not necessarily correspond to paper calculations but seems to expand, and everyone has a task.

Another consideration is that the various cereal and legume crops do not all ripen at the same time (beans and barley ripen before wheat for example), as has been discussed in earlier chapters. Perhaps only on those estates (rare in my view) which grew only one type of cereal, and where the topography was even throughout, would free labour have been hired on any scale. Although Columella is not explicit in the case of cereals, his remarks on the division of the vineyard into sections according to variety, in order to avoid simultaneity of ripening and thus increased labour expense, could well be pertinent (3. 21. 9–10).

---

[24] 'Haymaking' here means tying into sheaves and stacking. Both Columella (11. 2. 40) and Pliny (18. 262) underestimate sheaving as the comparative evidence indicates. See also Duncan-Jones, *Economy of the Roman Empire*, 332. For the work involved in tending meadows, see pp. 123–4.

[25] I did not include weeding and cleaning of fallow land which may sometimes have been performed by itinerant free labourers: p. 59; cf. following note.

[26] Columella appears to envisage hiring labour on the arable estate only for the clearing of virgin or old fallow ground (2. 2. 12).

Yeo's second main objection remains to be refuted. He argues that grain cultivation necessitated the scattering of the workforce over large areas (he estimates arbitrarily one labourer to every twenty or thirty acres, p. 469), and thus the uneconomical employment of too many other slaves in supervisory positions. This argument shows a lack of practical understanding as well as a failure to read carefully both American and Roman accounts of organized field work. In reality, the labourers were led into the field in a team and, wielding their hoes side by side, gradually worked through the whole estate. Columella (envisaging a large estate, see below) is plain:

> Thus the men will not work by ones or twos because they are not easily supervised when scattered; yet there should be no more than ten together, since, when the group is too large each individual may think that the work does not concern him. (Col. 1. 9. 8)

In conclusion, it appears that intensive arable cultivation could, like viticulture, keep slaves busy all year. Thus the intensive arable estate was economically rational in terms of slave labour. The case for full employment would be further strengthened if it is assumed that some vines and olives were also grown (for subsistence purposes) on the estate which specialized in cereals. Pure monoculture was undoubtedly rare in practice (cf. p. 3 n. 4).

According to Columella's manning ratios, the intensive arable farm required one quarter to one third of the workforce of a vineyard of the same size. Perhaps those who, according to Varro (1. 8. 1), and later Columella (3. 3. 1 ff.), had become disaffected with the capital outlay, waiting period and running costs necessary for the establishment of a vineyard, were unconvinced that the returns from viticulture outdid those from arable farming by a sufficient margin to warrant the much-increased expense in labour.[27]

## EXTENSIVE CEREAL CULTIVATION?

Sergeenko identified two forms of cereal growing in the later part of the first century A.D., which she called intensive and extensive.[28] The extensive system recognized the inherent defect of slavery, namely the slave's lack of motivation. In order, therefore, to reduce the necessity of relying on slaves for manual labour, less intensive methods of cultivation were used. An exponent of the extensive approach was, according to Sergeenko, Cornelius Celsus, who recommended the use of small oxen and light ploughs in order to save on capital outlay (cf. pp. 34 f.) and sought convincing reasons for avoiding the labour-intensive operations of weeding and hoeing (cf. p. 63). Columella, on the other hand, was a supporter of an intensive form of agriculture which relied heavily on manual labour and careful supervision of the slave workforce. His system was bound to collapse.

---

[27] Rostovtzeff, *SEHRE* 1, 98 cites the disillusionment with viticulture which Columella remarks, in order to bear out his hypothesis of decline of vines in Italy due to provincial competition, but omits to notice Varro 1. 8. 1, which does not easily fit his view.

Cf. Aymard, 'Les capitalistes romains', 262 f.

[28] See E. M. Staerman and M. K. Trofimova, *La schiavitù nell'Italia imperiale I–III secolo* (1975), 31 ff. and also p. 1 above.

Kolendo resumes and elaborates the thesis.[29] The wheeled plough, the Gallic reaping machine and the harrow are thought to illustrate the decline of the importance of manual labour and the expansion of extensive methods. This development is in turn connected with the crisis in vine and olive culture in Italy and the change to the 'desolate countryside of the *latifondo* given over to pasturage with the occasional field of grain'.[30]

All this has come a long way from the advice of Celsus. Since he shrank from the expense of heavy equipment and large oxen (Col. 2. 2. 24), it is unlikely that he would have recommended wheeled ploughs or reaping machines. It is surely more likely that Celsus was describing at that point in his work the type of estate where cereal farming was being carried out on a subsistence, not profit, basis. As regards the cultivation of beans, Columella censured Celsus not for avoidance of manual labour but for *falsa diligentia* in attempting to grow two crops on the same land (2. 11. 6). The advice of Celsus that when the grain harvest is good every single seed should be sifted and sorted can only refer to the intensively-managed arable estate (cf. pp. 41 f.), and thus gains the approval of Columella (2. 9. 11). It is surely better to assume that Celsus' writings on agriculture described a variety of arable systems, as did those of Pliny, a fellow encyclopaedist, and thus that extant citations reflect this diversity rather than any consistent point of view.

Despite attempts to the contrary, the Gallic reaper and the wheeled plough cannot be allowed to influence views about labour in Italy. The harrow, however, might have had a wider diffusion, yet Kolendo's argument, which is briefly summarized here, cannot stand on several counts. He argues that the harrow was introduced to replace the more labour-intensive methods of ridging and *sub sulco* cultivation, since with the harrow, the seed need only be scattered broadcast and then harrowed in. Yet while this certainly saved labour, according to Kolendo, it did away with the traditional neat furrows and ridges, thus made hoeing and weeding impossible, and disturbed the psychological state (*sic*) of the Roman cultivator, which in turn led to a decline in the standards of arable farming.[31]

None of this convinces. *Sub sulco* was not a labour-intensive method of sowing (cf. pp. 46–8); harrows had a complicated history of agricultural use in Italy and were not simply 'introduced'; and when and where they were used on the large estate they were integrated with intensive methods. Thus, according to the view expressed in Chapter III, if the harrow saved labour-time, that was in order to allow more land to be *well* cultivated with no extra expense in labour, to respond to the increased demand for cereals and, thereby, to raise profits.

## THE 'SLAVE CRISIS' IN AGRICULTURE

In conclusion something must be said on the so-called *crisi dell'agricoltura schiavistica*, an argument closely connected with the preceding one.[32] On this

[29] Kolendo, *L'agricoltura*, 70, 127 ff. Carandini (who writes the introduction to Kolendo's book) agrees, xl ff.; cf. White, *Agricultural Implements*, 147 f. on the introduction of the harrow in response to a supposed labour shortage.

[30] Carandini in Kolendo, xlii.
[31] Kolendo, 152.
[32] A. Carandini, *L'anatomia della scimmia* (1979), 128 ff. The argument in principle comes from at least as far back as J. E. Cairns, *The Slave Power* (1863), 44.

view, with the growth of large contiguous landholdings in the early Empire,[33] a point was reached where slave staffs became so big that the cost of maintaining a sufficient number of unproductive, supervisory slaves outweighed the profits produced by the slaves who worked. Two solutions were adopted: (1) the number of slaves was reduced and the land turned over to extensive farming; (2) the land was divided up and leased to tenants.

Yet this 'crisis' is difficult to demonstrate from the sources.[34] There are certainly a number of references to large estates and to tenants, but they are not confined to the period of the early or late Empire,[35] and there is no source which refers explicitly to a change to extensive farming.

Two passages from Columella are cited to illustrate this 'crisis'. At 1. 3. 12 he refers polemically (but without geographical precision) to huge estates which were either given over to pastoralism, or were cultivated and manned by a combination of indebted citizens and chained slaves.[36] Yet large pastoral estates can be seen as neither new nor increasing in number, and the reference to the cultivated estates does not demonstrate extensive farming.[37] At 1. 3. 10 Columella refers to 'large amounts of land under long-fallow' ('amplissima veterata'). This could conceivably refer to a system of extensive farming, although it could equally describe the large pastoral estate or an arable estate where parts of the farm were worked intensively, while other areas were left under long-fallow for pasture or because market possibilities did not warrant their being brought under cultivation (see further pp. 120–2).

In the second passage cited (1. 9. 7–8), Columella envisages a large estate with a large number of slaves divided into squads of ten (*decuriae*) for field work.[38] There can be no doubt that this relates to an intensive form of farming, although there is no firm indication of the crops cultivated (at p. 140 above I assumed that it was arable land). It is true that each gang of ten was supervised by one other slave (*monitor*, 1. 9. 7). The supervisors surely did not work as continuously as the labourers, but they might have worked more efficiently, since the reason why they held the positions they did was because they had proved themselves good workers. It cannot be maintained that they were unproductive. The *vilicus*, at the peak of the supervisory pyramid, had many duties to attend to besides supervision of labour in the fields and thus can hardly be termed 'unproductive. But even he

---

[33] A general orthodoxy recently reviewed critically by J. K. Evans, 'Plebs Rustica: The Peasantry of Classical Italy I', *AJAH* 5 (1980), 23 ff.

[34] As Carandini, *L'anatomia*, 130 observes.

[35] Large estates: K. D. White, 'Latifundia', *Bulletin of the Institute of Classical Studies* 14 (1967), 62–79; tenancy: Brunt, 'The Army and the Roman Revolution', *JRS* 52 (1962), 71 f.

[36] 'Chained slaves' is an inference from *ergastula*, since elsewhere (1. 8. 16) he refers to slaves kept in *ergastula* as chained. Chained slaves were not necessarily inferior workers (as implied by P. 18. 36): Col. 1. 9. 4.

[37] Carandini seeks some support for his theory from archaeology (p. 129) but the evidence he cites is too slender in detail to prove his case. He cites, for example, a villa on the Via Gabina in Latium (W. M. Widrig, 'Two Sites on the Ancient via Gabina' in *Roman Villas in Italy*, ed. K. Painter (1980), 119–40).

But this villa expanded in the early Empire and installed oil processing equipment in the second century. While it seems incontrovertible that the villa of Settefinestre ceased wine and oil production at the end of the first or beginning of the second century, the only 'evidence' that the land was given over to extensive arable or pasture is a rotary grain mill found in the abandoned pressing rooms: A. Carandini and T. Tatton-Brown, 'Excavations at the Roman Villa of Settefinestre in Etruria, 1975–9. First Interim Report' in *Roman Villas in Italy*, 16.

[38] It is to be noted that Columella uses the past tense for this labour organization. It was what the *antiqui* did. Thus it cannot be seen as a new development. On the limits of archaeological evidence for such schematic interpretations of slave-run estates, see now M. S. Spurr, 'Slavery and the Economy in Roman Italy', *CR* 35 (1985), 123–31.

should from time to time perform the common work as an exhortation to the others (Col. 11. 1. 17; cf. V. 1. 17. 4).

## THE MARKET

At various points during the foregoing pages reference has been made to the sale of cereals. The ideas underlying such statements can now be briefly clarified. The agronomists emphasize that the intensively-managed villa should have easy access to an urban centre (see below), but it is not until the period following the Social War and into the Augustan age that we can begin to talk about widespread urbanization in Italy.

As archaeology continues to reveal, the 'municipalization' of Italy, after the granting of the Roman franchise (and Latin rights in Cisalpine Gaul), included the physical reconstruction of existing towns, and the construction of new towns, along Roman lines, where there had previously been little organized urban settlement. This urban construction continued with the settlement of veterans and the establishment of *coloniae* by Sulla, Caesar, the triumvirs and, especially, Augustus.[39]

It has been estimated that some quarter of a million veterans were settled in Italy between 88 and 25 B.C., and close study of the sources suggests that peasants, not large landowners, were expropriated to make way for them.[40] This observation is borne out to an important extent by archaeological evidence, which demonstrates that the first century B.C. was the most flourishing period for *villae rusticae*.[41]

It is usually assumed that dispossessed peasants, who did not in their turn join the army, drifted into Rome from all over Italy. But this is inherently most unlikely. Ancient Rome's sphere of attraction was much more limited than that of the modern industrial cities of northern Italy, to which many sons of peasants from the impoverished south have migrated. Failed or expropriated poor farmers of Roman Italy would tend to remain in their local regions, finding work as day labourers where they could, in both town and country. They drifted as far as the new and growing towns in the vicinity. These towns, as their populations increased, provided a market for rural producers.

A study of life in one of the smallest and most backward of modern south Italian towns, Montegrano, 'as poor a place as any in the western world', during the 1950s, showed that a labourer spent only 4 per cent of his earnings that paid for food on wine, and less than 2 per cent on oil. A recent study of grain rations in the ancient world shows that grain foods occupied an even greater share of the Italian lower-class diet in the Roman period.[42]

Differences in wealth and social standing were reflected in Roman times, as

[39] E. Gabba, 'Urbanizzazione e rinnovamenti urbanistici nell'Italia centro-meridionale del I sec. a.C.', *Studi Classici e Orientali* 21 (1972), 73–112; Brunt, *Italian Manpower*, 294 ff.

[40] Brunt, *Italian Manpower*, 343.

[41] Spurr, 'Slavery and the Economy'.

[42] Montegrano: E. C. Banfield, *The Moral Basis of a Backward Society* (1958), 173, Table 10. Roman period: L. Foxhall and H. A. Forbes, 'Σιτομετρεία: the Role of Grain as a Staple Food in Classical Antiquity', *Chiron* 12 (1982), 69.

later, by various grades of bread.[43] This led to an increased range of cereals grown in a town's *territorium*, not a reduction of variety as the orthodox argument would have it. As in earlier periods, robuster, 'inferior' cereals continued to be cultivated, not only as before by the subsistent peasant, but also now by the cereal farmer who produced for the market. Customers would comprise the mass of poor *oppidani*[44] as well as the slaves of those richer members of the urban society who were not directly involved in agriculture. They themselves would be increasingly concerned with the status symbol of 'snowy-white' bread (Juv., *Sat.* 5. 67 ff.). Thus there was a limited market for bread wheats. Such wheats never ousted other cereals but rather contributed to variety. The fodder requirements of specially bred animals for the urban market (*pastio villatica*) will also be recalled.

Thus, as urbanization increased, the agricultural product which provided the securest profit was grain. The market for wine and oil in any one town was much more limited. Thus Italian wine producers relied on a multiplicity of markets within, but especially without Italy, as finds of amphorae from the Ager Cosanus so well demonstrate.[45] As olive and vine cultivation spread in the provinces, overseas markets were increasingly restricted, and the Italian wine trade, as it had been known, was bound to fail. The market for cereals, however, was much more local and, importantly, rarely open to competition from outside.

## TRANSPORT

'It cannot be emphasized too strongly that the first requisite for the improvement of the production of a subsistence economy is the provision of transport.'[46] All the Roman agronomists emphasize that commercial viability is an important aspect of profitable farming. In his first chapter Cato recommends an estate in the vicinity of a flourishing town or near the sea, a navigable river or a well-frequented road. Adequate communication with a market centre is advised by Varro, for this will make the farm profitable (1. 16. 2); he refers to roads and rivers, in that order. Cato's remarks on location should be interpreted with regard to profit. Varro observed that many farmers have something to buy or sell such as grain or wine (ibid.), and his remarks on storage for sale will be remembered. Cato urges the selling of surplus grain (2. 7). Grain accounts (*ratio frumentaria*) are to be checked when the owner visits the estate (2. 5). Varro implies that the market centre is not only a consumer of agricultural produce; it is also a centre for exchange between the rural estates themselves (1. 16. 3). Even villages (*vici*) could provide opportunities for sale and purchase (Pliny the Younger, *Ep.* 2. 17).

Columella also notes the benefits of a navigable river or a coastal location (1. 2. 3), but appears to consider a good road the most important and usual medium of communication. A good road will mean that the owner is prepared to

---

[43] Moritz, *Grain Mills*, 153 f., 177 f. (with a good collection of ancient references, to which add P. 19. 53).

[44] *Oppidani* or *urbani* ('townsmen') for whom there is inscriptional evidence from various Italian towns: *CIL* 9. 2473; 2568; 6257; 2855; further in *ILS* 3 (2), 680 s.v. *plebs*; *plebs urbana*: *CIL* 11. 2650. All these are to be considered town inhabitants not in direct contact with the land.

[45] D. Manacorda, 'The Ager Cosanus and the Production of the Amphorae of Sestius: New Evidence and a Reassessment', *JRS* 68 (1978), 122–31; Spurr, 'Slavery and the Economy'.

[46] Clark and Haswell, *The Economics of Subsistence Agriculture*, 191.

visit the estate more often, that the cost of transport is less, and thus that the profit to be made on the stored produce is greater (1. 3. 3).

This increased emphasis on road transport (if such can be legitimately elicited from the sources) can be seen to reflect the wider Italian vision of Varro and Columella. Most Italian towns would be near neither the sea nor a navigable river. They would have to depend on roads for transport to and from the urban centre. Inscriptional evidence for roads, built by local magistrates or benefactors in *municipia* and their *territoria*, is not uncommon. It would be impossible to prove that such men did so in order to facilitate the transport of their own agricultural produce from country to urban centre, but the likelihood exists.[47] Archaeological surveys in the vicinities of towns refer to road networks but often the evidence is conjectural; despite their solidity of construction Roman roads are notoriously difficult to locate with certainty.[48] One obvious point is that they were not all, or even most, paved. Unless inscriptional evidence specifies (e.g. 'viam silice sternendam', *CIL* 9. 3688), an unsealed surface can be imagined (cf. *Dig.* 43. 11. 1. 2). This would still be an improvement on paths or open country, although, as Pliny the Younger noted, the sandy stretches of some lesser roads could be heavy going for carriages, traversed much more quickly on horseback (*Ep.* 2. 17. 2). Paved roads facilitated wheeled transport but we know that bulky goods, including grain, could be carried by mules (V. 2. 6. 5). One way of utilizing oxen on unsealed roads, or even in open country, was to yoke them to a 'cart without wheels', namely a drag (*trahea*: Varro, *LL* 5. 139).[49]

Much has been written on the high cost of land transport.[50] Calculations are based on the Price Edict of Diocletian and Cato's carrying charges. Yet these referred to *hired*, not privately owned transport. It is unlikely that a landowner hired transport to deliver his agricultural produce to the market. Instead he purchased oxen for the special purpose of hauling wagons. They might go frequently to the nearby village or town even during their breaking-in period (V. 1. 20. 3). Used for hauling jobs around the estate, they would also transport produce and equipment to and from the market centre. Commonly, it can be assumed, the plough oxen were also used for haulage, both internal and external (cf. Col. 2. 21. 5; Cato 62).

On the other hand, we also hear of merchants, but there is no way of knowing how common they were. Frank noted the presence of *mercatores*, who seem to have been 'middlemen' in our sense, at Pompeii, but argued that most growers sold direct to the public.[51] One product, which, like grain, could be stored until the market price was favourable, was honey. Varro describes a small-scale yet highly profitable, honey-producing operation where the owners appear to call in the 'middleman' ('mercatorem admitterent', 3. 16. 11). Then again *mercatores* purchased fruit from suburban orchards (Col. 3. 2. 1). Clearly in these situations

[47] Paving of roads by local magistrates, some examples: Frank, *Economic Survey* v, 96.

[48] The existence of roads is often assumed on insubstantial evidence. For honest remarks on this from the archaeologist's point of view: M. P. Muzzioli, *Cures Sabini*, 44 n. 299.

[49] Not considered by White, *Agricultural Imple-ments*, 154 f. See Pl. IV, 2.

[50] e.g. Duncan-Jones, *Economy of the Roman Empire*, 368; C. A. Yeo, 'Land and Sea Transportation', *TAPhA* 77 (1946), 221–44; A. H. M. Jones, *The Later Roman Empire* II (1964), 841 ff.

[51] *Economic Survey* v, 258.

the middlemen served producers who did not have the necessary land to make the maintenance of haulage animals worthwhile. Such middlemen might also have dealt directly with peasant farmers who found themselves with a surplus. It would be misleading to think that only the large cereal producer was interested in the market. A modern study of a small town in Basilicata observes: 'Peasant farmers have long established relationships with grain merchants to whom they sell whatever grain and pulses they do not keep for seed or food'.[52]

It should no longer be doubted that there was considerable road traffic in agricultural produce, cereals included. In particular, in times of shortage, as Slicher van Bath noted for a later period, 'the traffic in grain increases, because the enhanced prices make it possible to cover the costs of transporting it from greater distances. Never are more carts and shiploads of grain to be seen than in times of need'.[53] Risk of famine was a constant factor in the ancient world. Thus grain prices were rarely stable, and large profits could be made by the cereal producer who could store until prices soared. Of course, like everyone, such a farmer was subject to the vagaries of climate. But selection of soils, of seeds and careful cultivation, could reduce the risks.

[52]  J. Davis, *Land and Family in Pisticci* (1973), 97.
[53]  Slicher van Bath, *The Agrarian History of Western Europe*, 120.

# BIBLIOGRAPHY

The bibliography includes only those works cited more than once in the text.

ACERBO, G. *L'economia dei cereali nell'Italia e nel mondo*. Milan, 1934.

ALMAGIÀ, R. *L'Italia*. 2 vols. Turin, 1959.

AMPOLO, C. 'Le condizione materiali della produzione. Agricoltura e paesaggio agrario'. *Seminario: La formazione della città nel Lazio. Roma, 24-26 giugno 1977. Dialoghi di Archeologia* n.s. 2 (1980), 15-46.

ANDRÉ, J. *Lexique des termes de botanique en latin*. Études et commentaires 23. Paris, 1956.

—— *L'Alimentation et la cuisine à Rome*. 2nd ed. Paris, 1981.

AYKROYD, W. R. AND DOUGHTY, J. *Legumes in Human Nutrition*. F.A.O. Food and Nutrition Series 12. Rome, 1964.

AYMARD, A. 'Les capitalistes romains et la viticulture italienne'. *Annales ESC* 2 (1947), 257-65.

AZIMONTE, E. *Il frumento, come si coltiva o come si dovrebbe coltivare in Italia*. Milan, 1914.

BARKER, G. W. 'Animal Husbandry and Economic Change at Monte Irsi'. In *Monte Irsi, Southern Italy. The Canadian Excavations in the Iron Age and Roman Sites, 1971-1972*, 265-73. Ed. A. Small. B.A.R. Supplementary Series 20. Oxford, 1977.

—— 'The Archaeology of Samnite Settlement in Molise'. *Antiquity* 51 (1977), 20-4.

—— *Prehistoric Farming in Europe*. Cambridge, 1985.

BARKER, G. W., LLOYD, J. AND WEBLEY, D. 'A Classical Landscape in Molise', *PBSR* 46 (1978), 35-51.

BOHRER, V. L. 'On the Relation of Harvest Methods to Early Agriculture in the Near East', *Economic Botany* 26 (1972), 145-54.

BRAUDEL, F. *The Mediterranean and the Mediterranean World in the Age of Philip II*. Trans. S. Reynolds. 2 vols. London, 1972.

BRUNT, P. A. *Italian Manpower 225 B.C.-A.D. 14*. Oxford, 1971.

—— Review of K. D. White, *Roman Farming*, *JRS* 62 (1972), 153-8.

CALLENDER, M. H. *Roman Amphorae*. London, 1965.

CARANDINI, A. *L'anatomia della scimmia. La formazione economica della società prima del capitale*. Turin, 1979.

—— (ed.). *Settefinestre. Una villa schiavistica nell'Etruria romana*. 3 vols. Modena, 1985.

CARTER, J. C., COSTANTINI, L. et al. 'Population and Agriculture: Magna Graecia in the Fourth Century B.C.'. In *The Human Landscape*, 281-312. Ed. C. Malone and S. Stoddart. Papers in Italian Archaeology 4. 1. B.A.R. Int. Series 243. Oxford, 1985.

CASELLI, G. 'Per uno studio tipologico dell'aratro', *Archeologia Medievale* 4 (1977), 281-96.

CASSON, L. 'The Role of the State in Rome's Grain Trade'. In *The Seaborne Commerce of Ancient Rome. Studies in Archaeology and History*. Ed. J. H. D'Arms amd E. C. Kopff. Memoirs of the American Academy in Rome 36 (1980), 21-34.

CASTELLETTI, L. 'Contributo alle ricerche paletnobotaniche in Italia', *Rendiconti dell'Istituto Lombardo di Scienze e Lettere* 106 (1972), 331-74.

—— 'Resti macroscopici di vegetali da Aquileia', *Aquileia Nostra* 53 (1972), 147-68.

CERVESATO, A. *Latina Tellus, la campagna romana*. Rome, 1910.

CHERUBINI, G. 'Le campagne italiane dall' XI al XV secolo'. In *Storia d'Italia* IV, 265-448. Ed. G. Galasso. Turin, 1981.

CINELLI, O. 'La mietitura '. *Giornale Agrario Italiano* l7 no. 5 (1873), 1 ff.

CLARK, C. AND HASWELL, M. *The Economics of Subsistence Agriculture*. 4th ed. Glasgow, 1970.

COLAMONICO, C. *Memoria illustrativa della carta di utilizzazione del suolo della Puglia*. Rome, 1960.

CORNELL, T. J. AND MATTHEWS, J. *Atlas of the Roman World*. Oxford, 1982.

COSTANTINI, L. 'Piante coltivate e piante spontanee a San Giovanni di Ruoti (Potenza)'. In *Lo scavo di San Giovanni di Ruoti ed il periodo tardoantico in Basilicata*, 85-90. Ed. M. Gualtieri et al. Bari, 1983.

DALMASSO, G. 'Problemi economici di agricoltura astigiana', *Annali della Reale Accademia d'Agricoltura di Torino* 53 (1910), 145-288.

DAVIES, R. W. 'The Roman Military Diet', *Britannia* 2 (1971), 122-42.

DAVIS, J. *People of the Mediterranean*. London, 1977.

DE CRESCENZI, P. *Trattato della agricoltura*. 3 vols. Milan, 1805.

DELANO SMITH, C. *Western Mediterranean Europe*. London, 1979.

DELUMEAU, J. *Vie économique et sociale de Rome dans la seconde moitié du XVIème siècle*. Paris, 1959.

DUBY, G. *Rural Economy and Country Life in the Medieval West*. Trans. C. Postan. Columbia, 1976.

DUMONT, R. *Types of Rural Economy*. Trans. D. Magnin. London, 1957.

DUNCAN-JONES, R. P. *The Economy of the Roman Empire: Quantitative Studies*. 2nd ed. Cambridge, 1982.

ENCICLOPEDIA AGRARIA ITALIANA. Rome, 1952–.

EVETT, D. AND RENFREW, J. 'L'agricoltura neolitica italiana: una nota sui cereali', *Rivista di Scienze Preistoriche* 26 (1971), 403-9.

FORNI, G. 'Origini delle strutture agrarie nell'Italia preromana'. In *L'azienda agraria nell'Italia centro-settentrionale dall'antichità ad oggi. Atti del Convegno di Verona, 28-30 nov. 1977*, 13-66. Naples, 1979.

—— 'Il "plaumaratum" (aratro a carrello) di Plinio nel quadro della storia dell'aratrocoltura in Italia'. In *Tecnologia, economia e società nel mondo romano. Atti del Convegno di Como 27-29 settembre 1979*, 89-120. Como, 1980.

—— 'Tipologia e nomenclatura dell'aratro tradizionale'. In *Acta Museorum Italicorum Agriculturae* 6/7, Extract from *Rivista di Storia dell'Agricoltura* 2 (1981), 220-5.

FRANK, T. *An Economic Survey of Ancient Rome*. 5 vols. New York, 1940, repr. New York, 1975.

FRAYN, J. M. *Subsistence Farming in Roman Italy*. London, 1979.

FREDERIKSEN, M. W. 'The Contribution of Archaeology to the Agrarian Problem in the Gracchan Period'. *Dialoghi di Archeologia* 4-5 (1970-1), 330-57.

—— 'Plinio il vecchio e l'agricoltura in età imperiale romana. Gli aspetti tecnici ed economici'. In *Tecnologia, economia e società nel mondo romano. Atti del Convegno di Como 27-29 settembre 1979*, 81-97. Como, 1980.

GABBA, E. AND PASQUINUCCI, M. *Strutture agrarie e allevamento transumante nell'Italia romana (III-I sec. a.C.)*. Biblioteca di Studi Antichi 18. Pisa, 1979.

GRIMALDI, A. *Coltivazioni erbacee*. 6th ed. Bologna, 1979.

GUALTIERI, M. et al. (eds.) *Lo scavo di San Giovanni di Ruoti ed il periodo tardoantico in Basilicata. Atti della Tavola Rotonda, Roma, 4 luglio 1981*. Bari, 1983.

HARLAN, J. R. 'A Wild Wheat Harvest in Turkey', *Archaeology* 20 (1967), 197-200.

HEITLAND, W. E. *Agricola, a Study of Agriculture and Rustic Life in the Graeco-Roman World from the Point of View of Labour*. Cambridge, 1921.

HELBAEK, H. 'Vegetables in the Funeral Meals of Pre-Urban Rome'. In E. Gjerstadt, *Early Rome* II. *Acta Instituti Romani Regni Sueciae* 17 (1956), 287-94.

—— 'Agricoltura preistorica a Luni sul Mignone in Etruria'. In C. E. Oestenberg, *Luni sul Mignone e problemi della preistoria d'Italia. Acta Instituti Romani Regni Sueciae* 25 (1967), 274-82.

HJELMQVIST, H. 'Economic Plants from Monte Irsi'. In *Monte Irsi, Southern Italy. The Canadian Excavations in the Iron Age and Roman Sites, 1971-1972*, 274-82. Ed. A. Small. B.A.R. Supplementary Series 20. Oxford, 1977.

HOOPER, W. D. *Marcus Porcius Cato on Agriculture, Marcus Terentius Varro on Agriculture*. Loeb Library. Revised by H. B. Ash. London, 1967.

HOPFEN, H. J. *Farm Implements for Arid and Tropical Regions*. Rome, 1969.

HOPFEN, H. J. AND BIESALSKI, E. *Small Farm Implements*. Rome, 1953.

JARMAN, H. N. 'The Plant Remains'. In *A Faliscan Town in Southern Etruria. Excavations at Narce 1966-71*, 308-10. Ed. T. W. Potter. London, 1976.

JARMAN, M. R. AND WEBLEY, D. 'Settlement and Land Use in Capitanata, Italy'. In *Palaeoeconomy*, Papers in Economic Prehistory II, 177-225. Ed. E. S. Higgs. Cambridge, 1975.

JASHEMSKI, W. F. *The Gardens of Pompeii, Herculaneum and the Villas destroyed by Vesuvius*. New Rochelle, 1979.

JASNY, N. *The Wheats of Classical Antiquity*. Johns Hopkins University Studies 62. Baltimore, 1944.

JONES, G. D. B. 'Il Tavoliere romano. L'agricoltura romana attraverso l'aerofotografia e lo scavo', *Archeologia Classica* 32 (1980), 85-100.

JONES, M. K. 'I resti vegetali'. In *Settefinestre. Una villa schiavistica nell'Etruria romana* II, 306-9. Ed. A. Carandini. Modena, 1985.

JONES, M. K. AND DIMBLEBY, G. *The Environment of Man: the Iron Age to the Anglo-Saxon Period*. B.A.R. British Series 87. Oxford, 1981.

JONES, P. J. 'Medieval Agrarian Society in its Prime: Italy'. In *Cambridge Economic History of Europe* I. *The Agrarian Life of the Middle Ages*, 340-431. Ed. M. M. Postan. Cambridge, 1966.

KOLENDO, J. *L'agricoltura nell'Italia romana*. Biblioteca di Storia Antica 10. Rome, 1980.

LLOYD, J. L. *The Roman Villa at Matrice: Interim Report*. Sheffield, 1980.

MANETTI, C. 'Pane e frumento', *Minerva dei campi* 16–17 (1931), 303–22.

MANNING, W. H. 'The Piercebridge Plough Group'. In *Prehistoric and Roman Studies*. Ed. G. de G. Sieveking. *The British Museum Quarterly* 35 (1971), 125-36.

MERCER, R. (ed.) *Farming Practice in British Prehistory*. Edinburgh, 1981.

MESSEDAGLIA, L. *Per la storia dell'agricoltura e dell'alimentazione*. Piacenza, 1932.

MONTANARI, I. 'Cereali e legumi nell'alto medioevo nell'Italia del nord, secoli IX-X', *Rivista Storica Italiana* 87 (1975), 439-88.

MORITZ, L. A. *Grain Mills and Flour in Classical Antiquity*. Oxford, 1958.

MUZZIOLI, M.-P. *Cures Sabini*. Forma Italiae, Regio IV, II. Florence, 1980.

NAVAL INTELLIGENCE DIVISION. *Italy*. Geographical Handbook Series, 4 vols. Oxford, 1944-5.

OLIVA, A. *Il frumento nella montagna*. Florence, 1936.

—— 'I frumenti, le leguminose da granella e gli altri semi repertati a Belverde', *Studi Etruschi* 13 (1939), 343-9.

ORTH, 'Hirse'. In Pauly-Wissowa 8. 2, 1950-6.

PAINTER, K. (ed.) *Roman Villas in Italy. Recent Excavations and Research*. British Museum Occasional Paper 24. London, 1980.

PAOLETTI, L. 'Norme pratiche per la semina', *Il Contadino Pisano*. October 1925.

PARAIN, C. 'The Evolution of Agricultural Technique'. In *Cambridge Economic History of Europe* I, 125 ff. Ed. M. M. Postan. Cambridge, 1966.

PASQUI, A. 'La villa Pompeiana della Pisanella presso Boscoreale', *Monumenti Antichi* 7 (1897), 397-554.

PAVOLINI, C. Review of M. A. Cotton, *The Late Republican Villa at Posto, Francolise, Gnomon* 53 (1981), 371-5.

PERCIVAL, J. *The Wheat Plant. A Monograph*. London, 1921.

PETERSON, R. F. *Wheat: Botany, Cultivation, and Utilization*. New York, 1965.

PINTO, G. 'Coltura e produzione dei cereali in Toscana nei secoli XIII-XV'. In *Civiltà ed economia agricola in Toscana nei secoli XIII-XV. Atti dell'VIII Convegno Internazionale del Centro Studi di Storia ed Arte*. Pistoia, 1981.

QUATTROCCHI, A. *Agraria*. 2 vols. 3rd ed. Milan, 1979.

RASMUSSEN, H. 'Grain Harvest and Threshing in Calabria', *Tools and Tillage* 1 (1968-71), 93-104.

RAWSON, E. 'The Introduction of Logical Organization in Roman Prose Literature', *PBSR* 46 (1978), 12-34.

REES, S. *Agricultural Implements in Prehistoric and Roman Britain*. B.A.R. British Series 69. Oxford, 1979.

REYNOLDS, P. J. *Iron Age Farm. The Butser Experiment*. London, 1979.

—— 'Deadstock and Livestock'. In *Farming Practice in British Prehistory*, 97–122. Ed. R. Mercer. Edinburgh, 1981.

RICKMAN, G. *Roman Granaries and Store Buildings*. Cambridge, 1971.

ROSTOVTZEFF, M. *The Social and Economic History of the Roman Empire*. 2nd ed. revised by P. M. Fraser. Oxford, 1957.

SCHEUERMEIER, P. *Il lavoro dei contadini. Cultura materiale e artigianato rurale in Italia e nella Svizzera italiana e retoromanza*. Ed. M. Dean and G. Pedrocco. 2 vols. Milan, 1980.

SERENI, E. *Storia del paesaggio agrario italiano*. Bari, 1961.

SKYDSGAARD, J. E. *Varro the Scholar, Studies in the First Book of Varro's* de re rustica. Copenhagen, 1968.

SLICHER VAN BATH, B. H. *The Agrarian History of Western Europe A.D. 500-1850*. Trans. O. Ordish. London, 1963.

SMALL, A. M. (ed.) *Monte Irsi, Southern Italy. The Canadian Excavations in the Iron Age and Roman Sites 1971-1972*. B.A.R. Supplementary Series 20. Oxford, 1977.

—— 'The Environment of San Giovanni in the Roman Period'. In *Archaeology and Italian Society. Prehistoric, Roman and Medieval Studies*, 203-12. Ed. G. W. Barker and R. Hodges. Papers in Italian Archaeology 2. B.A.R. International Series 102. Oxford, 1981.

SPURR, M. S. 'Slavery and the Economy in Roman Italy'. Review of *Società romana e produzione schiavistica*. 3 vols, ed. A. Giardina, A. Schiavone. *CR* 35 (1985), 123-31.

TASSINARI, G. *Manuale dell'agronomo*. 5th ed. Rome, 1980.

TESTINI, V. *Il frumento: coltura e trebbiatura nella Puglia Barese*. Bari, 1885.

TOYNBEE, A. J. *Hannibal's Legacy. The Hannibalic War's Effect on Roman Life*. 2 vols. London, 1965.

UNITED NATIONS, FOOD AND AGRICULTURAL ORGANIZATION. *Improvement and Production of Maize, Sorghum and Millets*. Rome, 1972.

—— *Manual on the Employment of Draught Animals in Agriculture*. Rome, 1972.

VAN ZEIST, W. 'Aperçu sur la diffusion des végétaux cultivés dans la région méditerranéene'. *Colloque de la Fondation L. Emberger sur la mise en place, l'évolution et la caractérisation de la flore et la végétation circumméditerranéene*. Naturalia Monspeliensia, N. Hors série.

VITA FINZI, C. *The Mediterranean Valleys: Geological Changes in Historical Times.* Cambridge, 1969.

WALKER, D. S. *The Mediterranean Lands.* London, 1960.

WHITE, K. D. 'Wheat Farming in Roman Times', *Antiquity* 37 (1963), 207-12.

—— *Agricultural Implements of the Roman World.* Cambridge, 1967.

—— *Roman Farming.* London, 1970.

—— *Farm Equipment of the Roman World.* Cambridge, 1975.

WHITE, L. *Medieval Technology and Social Change.* Oxford, 1962.

YEO, C. A. 'The Economics of Roman and American Slavery', *Finanz Archiv* 13 (1952), 443-85.

# INDEXES

## I. GENERAL INDEX

## II. INDEX OF PERSONS AND PLACES

## III. INDEX OF SOURCES

### *Literary Texts*

Passages of the principal authors, Cato, Columella, Pliny the Elder, and Varro, are included here only when they are cited fully or partially in the text, or when a particular interpretation depends on them.